The Joy of
Independent Living
for SENIORS®

The Guidebook to Keeping Active and Living Well Into Your 90s and Beyond

Publisher's Note

This book is intended for general information only. It does not constitute medical, legal, or financial advice or practice. The editors of FC&A have taken careful measures to ensure the accuracy and usefulness of the information in this book. While every attempt has been made to assure accuracy, errors may occur and information may change. Addresses, telephone numbers, and internet website addresses were accurate at the time this book was printed. We cannot guarantee the safety or effectiveness of any advice or treatments mentioned. Readers are urged to consult with their professional financial advisors, lawyers, and health care professionals before making any changes.

Any health information in this book is for information only and is not intended to be a medical guide for self-treatment. It does not constitute medical advice and should not be construed as such or used in place of your doctor's medical advice. Readers are urged to consult with their health care professionals before undertaking therapies suggested by the information in this book, keeping in mind that errors in the text may occur as in all publications and that new findings may supersede older information.

The publisher and editors disclaim all liability (including any injuries, damages, or losses) resulting from the use of the information in this book.

So do not fear, for I am with you; do not be dismayed,
for I am your God. I will strengthen you and help you;
I will uphold you with my righteous right hand.

— Isaiah 41:10 (NIV)

Table of contents

Build income for life
Smart strategies to pad your retirement piggy bank 1

Stretch your dollars
Secrets to spending less and getting more .33

Protect your money
Simple ways to sidestep scams and safeguard your savings 89

Age in place
Essential guide to living out your golden years in your own home 129

Evaluate living options
Alternative housing when staying put doesn't make sense.......... 169

Upgrade health coverage
Wise moves to boost benefits without paying more............... 191

Live well
Science-backed tips to tackle your biggest health concerns 247

Index 365

BUILD INCOME FOR LIFE

SMART STRATEGIES TO PAD YOUR RETIREMENT PIGGY BANK

Social Security

When to claim Social Security benefits — it's probably the single most important retirement decision you'll make. After all, 6 in 10 seniors depend on Social Security for at least half their income.

The size of your monthly benefit often hinges on the age — anywhere between 62 and 70 — at which you first file your claim. Which is the right age for you? You'll want to consider the following before deciding.

- How much other retirement income you'll have. Do you have assets to draw from while you delay benefits or do you need the money sooner?

- Whether or not you're eligible for spousal benefits. It might make sense for the higher earner to delay benefits while the lower earner begins collecting early.

- Your employment status. Can you continue working and earn delayed retirement credits?

- How healthy you are and how long you expect to live. The longer you live, the more you'll gain by delaying benefits.

It may be tempting to file for Social Security as soon as you can. But why not first figure out how much more you'd get by waiting a bit longer? Go to *ssa.gov* and click the Retirement Estimator icon for a ballpark figure of how much your check will be if you claim early or delay filing.

5 common Social Security perks many people miss

It pays to play the waiting game. Looking for a simple way to get the most from Social Security? Delay filing for benefits. That's because you can't collect 100 percent of what's due until reaching full retirement age, which is 66 or 67 for most people. And your benefits will increase 8 percent a year until age 70 if you put off collecting even longer.

But what if you need the money before then? By starting benefits at age 62 instead of at full retirement, you're agreeing to lower payments — between 25 percent and 30 percent lower — for the rest of your life.

So let's say you'd receive a full retirement benefit of $1,500 a month at 66. If you claimed Social Security at 62, you'd get just $1,125. But if you waited until 70? You'd take home $1,980 a month. Imagine what you could do with that extra $855 each month.

Kids can change the stakes. Maybe you waited until late in life to have kids. Or perhaps you're a caregiver to a grandchild. In either case, Social Security provides extra funds for eligible retirees raising minors.

Suppose you're 62 years old and in charge of your 8-year-old grandson who qualifies for these benefits. No matter what age you file, your grandson can collect up to half of your full retire-ment benefit — $750 a month if you're due $1,500 monthly at full retirement, for example.

So even if you file at 62, your reduced payment of $1,125 plus the child's benefit would add up to $1,875 a month over the next 10 years — or $225,000. Then when your grandson hits the cutoff point as an adult, you'd have to return to reduced benefits of $1,125.

It's worthwhile to do the math to figure out if you and your fam-ily would come out ahead by filing earlier or later. And remember, Social Security limits how much money your family can get — 150 to 180 percent of your full retirement benefit.

Married people get more bang for the buck. You'll be happy to know that couples who tie the knot get to share more than companionship and household chores. They also get special perks from the Social Security Administration (SSA).

Husbands and wives are entitled to benefits based on their own earnings record or they can opt for up to 50 percent of what their spouse is entitled to at full retirement. For example, let's say your spouse's benefit is $1,000 a month and yours is $2,500 a month. Your partner could get up to $1,250 a month — an extra $250 — by claiming spousal benefits.

You aren't eligible for spousal benefits unless your spouse is already collecting Social Security. Also, the SSA will reduce your spousal benefits if you file before full retirement age.

Look into this loophole for ex-cellent perks. Been married for nearly a decade and headed for divorce court? You might want to stick it out just a bit longer. That's because the SSA looks fondly on former spouses as long as their marriages lasted at least 10 years.

Once you've passed the 10-year mark, you may be able to collect on your ex-spouse's record. How much could you get? Up to half of the full retirement payment if you're still single.

> Social Security benefits grew 2.8 percent in 2019, the largest cost-of-living adjustment (COLA) in seven years. The change boosted the average retiree benefit by $39 a month, or around $468 a year.

What if your ex has passed away? You could be eligible for 100 percent of those benefits if you wait until your full retirement age. There's a catch though — you can't collect if you remarried before turning 60. It's also possible to apply for survivor benefits as early as age 60 — 50 if you're disabled — but you'll wind up with a reduced amount.

Work longer to boost the bottom line. Your Social Security benefit is based on your 35 highest-earning work years. But what happens if you've worked, say, only 34 years? Working an additional year would give you extra spending money. But more importantly, it would also increase your monthly benefit for life by canceling out the zero-income year from the government's calculation of benefits.

But be careful about working while collecting early benefits. The SSA will deduct $1 from your benefits for every $2 you earn over $17,640. That number is raised in the year you retire, when the government will withhold $1 in benefits for every $3 you earn over $46,920.

After that you're home free — no more penalties. Once you reach full retirement age, the SSA will raise the amount of your future benefits to make up for the withholdings.

Oops! Avoid costly claiming mistakes to bag bigger benefits

A recent SSA audit found that 8 in 10 widows and widowers — all eligible for both survivor benefits and their own retirement benefits — did not get the Social Security payments they were entitled to. Why not? SSA employees failed to tell the seniors, as required, of a strategy they could have used to maximize their benefits.

More than 9,000 folks — all age 70 and older — lost out on $132 million in Social Security benefits, according to estimates from the SSA's Office of the Inspector General. Don't want to get caught up in a similar situation? Keep these tips in mind when you apply for benefits.

Surviving spouses have an optimal option. Widows and widowers, unlike many other retirees, are allowed to limit the scope of their application for Social Security benefits. It's called a restricted application, and it permits surviving spouses to claim survivor benefits as early as age 60. In the meantime, their own Social Security payments can keep on growing until full retirement age or later.

You'll have to dot your i's and cross your t's to take advantage of this rule. That's because the SSA will automatically assume you're applying for both benefits at once and will pay you the greater of the two. You can get around the problem by limiting your application to the one benefit you want now.

> A simple mistake in your earnings history could mean the loss of tens of thousands of dollars in life-time benefits. Want to make sure the SSA has all the correct information? Visit *ssa.gov/myaccount* to set up an account and view your earnings statement.

Retroactive payments can prove costly. Suppose you hung in there, waiting until well after full retirement age to collect higher benefits. On the day you apply, an SSA specialist says you're eligible for six months of retroactive payments. Sounds like a great deal, right?

Not so fast. Remember — your Social Security benefits grow by 8 percent each year you wait to claim between your full retirement age and 70. Taking the retroactive benefits means you'll lose six months' worth of delayed retirement credits. All future Social Security payments you — or your surviving spouse — ever receive will be 4 percent less than they could have been.

It might not seem like much, but it adds up. Let's say you can currently claim $1,560 a month. Six months ago you would have gotten 4 percent less — $1,500 a month. If you accept the retroactive payment, all your future benefits will be reduced by $60 a month — or $720 a year.

Be aware, too, that taking a large lump sum as a retroactive payment could hit you in the wallet at tax time.

Maximize monthly payments with a savvy strategy

Failing to understand Social Security's rules can cost you big time, says Jim Blankenship, founder and principal of Blankenship Financial Planning in Illinois. Take the case of his former client, a woman whose health problems caused her to leave work a year before her full retirement age of 66.

"She thought she was doing the right thing," he recounts. "So she called Social Security and told them she wanted to begin her benefits."

They gave her the information, but she didn't apply. Instead she contacted Blankenship, a certified financial planner and enrolled agent, to check out her options.

That's when she learned she was eligible to file a restricted application on her ex-husband's record — an allowance given to people born before Jan. 2, 1954. Doing so would allow her to receive half of her ex's full retirement amount while her own Social Security payments grew 8 percent annually until she turned 70.

All she had to do was wait until her full retirement age to file. So the woman tapped into her retirement savings to help her get through that first year without income and the following four years she received the spousal benefits.

The end result? She'll probably get an extra $100,000 from Social Security over her lifetime, Blankenship says.

The woman got an extra bonus from going this route, he adds. By the time she was 70, her own benefits had grown high enough to avoid having to supplement them with large IRA or 401(k) account withdrawals.

"The end result was that she had nearly zero taxable income," he says.

Retirement gotchas — avoid the tax trap with these tips

Remember 1983? The hit TV show "M.A.S.H." ended its 11-year run, U.S. troops invaded the Caribbean island of Grenada, and it cost just 20 cents to mail a letter. Oh — it was also the year Congress called for taxes on Social Security benefits.

And while prices have increased 150 percent since then, the income threshold for triggering Social Security taxes remains the same. That means an individual filer owes federal taxes on Social Security payments if his combined income is more than $25,000. That total increases to $32,000 a year for a joint filer.

And your combined income — the sum of your adjusted gross income, nontaxable interest, and half of your Social Security payments — determines how much you'll pay in taxes. The following table shows the percentage of Social Security benefits Uncle Sam will tax based on your combined income.

	Percent of benefits taxed		
	0%	**50%**	**85%**
Individual filer combined income	below $25,000	$25,000 to $34,000	above $34,000
Joint filer combined income	below $32,000	$32,000 to $44,000	above $44,000

Want to avoid paying taxes on your Social Security benefits? Here are a couple of strategies to help you on your way.

Consider how your benefits factor in if you're still working. Every dollar you earn at a job while collecting Social Security pushes you closer to going over the income threshold. Choosing to delay taking benefits is probably the simplest method to avoid this. It also means higher payments later.

But what if you've already started receiving benefits? The Social Security Administration allows you to withdraw your application within the first year of claiming. You'll have to pay back all the money, but you can restart your benefits at a higher rate later on.

If you've reached full retirement age, you have another option. You can suspend your benefits and you won't have to pay back any money you've already received. The best part? Your future payments will get delayed retirement credits of 8 percent a year.

Remember to reap Roth rewards. Have you been preparing for retirement by socking away money into traditional IRAs or 401(k) accounts? Don't be surprised to learn withdrawals count toward your combined income.

That's not the case, though, with Roth retirement accounts. You can take out as little — or as much — as you want and it won't factor into the calculations for taxing your Social Security benefits.

Don't yet have a Roth account? You can convert some of the funds from a traditional IRA or 401(k). But be careful about changing over too much money in one year. The conversion is considered income, which could bump you into a higher tax bracket and, if you're collecting Social Security, cause those benefits to be taxed as well.

Senior employment

Would you like fries with that? The next time you pick up your lunch at a fast-food drive-thru, don't be surprised if your server has more wrinkles than pimples. What's up? Turns out casual-dining restaurants and fast-food joints are recruiting new hires in unexpected places like senior centers, churches — wherever older adults hang out. Why? Managers have noticed seniors are usually punctual and friendly, qualities younger workers may lack.

So what's driving retirees back to work? Some need a little budget boost to help make monthly ends meet. Others are worried they'll outlive their retirement savings. But lots of folks just enjoy working and miss it when they retire.

Thinking about jumping back into the job market? You won't be alone. In fact, folks age 55 and older make up the fastest-growing part of the country's labor force. And 1 out of 3 of your retired friends may be thinking about heading back to work, too.

If you're going to stand out in a sea of silver-haired applicants, you'll need to polish up your job-hunting skills. Read on to find out what you can do to pinpoint the post that's right for you.

Throw your retirement into reverse with 4 job-hunting shortcuts

Join a job club. Update your resume, practice interviews, and get advice from employment-seeking folks just like you. Some clubs are formal, run by executive boards and led by career counselors. But beware. This type of club may charge monthly dues.

Other job clubs are more casual, encouraging members to share their job search experiences.

Clubs meet at churches, libraries, community centers, or schools. To find one near you, go to *careeronestop.org* and enter "job club" in the search box. Then click on Job Club Finder.

Check out your library. A treasure-trove for job hunters. Your local library may offer workshops that can help you apply for jobs online, write a cover letter, and sharpen your interview skills. The library is a great place to print copies of your resume, too, but you may have to pay a small fee.

Need to do some job searching online, but don't have internet access at home? Your library probably offers free Wi-Fi. Or you can use one of their computers to get the job done.

Call your alma mater. College grad? Get in touch with your school's career services office. Many colleges and universities offer all kinds of lifetime career help for alumni, from resume reviews to job searching strategies. Some even offer a career advisor network made up of alumni who have volunteered to help answer your employment-related questions. Don't miss out on this great resource.

Search the web. Are you internet savvy? Take a look at these sites, chock-full of jobs both adventurous and conventional.

- Interested in working at a national park? Want to spend some time with would-be astronauts at Space Camp? Zoom on over to *CoolWorks.com* and take a look at the exciting job postings. There's something for everyone.

- If you're in search of more traditional jobs in your hometown, head to *RetirementJobs.com*, a site created to help folks over 50 find age-friendly employers. Enter your ZIP code to see what's available near you.

Grow your cash flow with these budget-boosting side gigs

Jackie loved cooking almost as much as teaching her kindergarten class. Her casseroles and homemade bread were faculty favorites. So when she retired from teaching, she started her own business — a dinner club tailored to teachers who didn't have the time or energy to cook. Within a few months, Jackie had a successful business going, doing something she loves. You can, too. Here are six more ways to increase your cash flow and unfix your fixed income.

Event Planner
Coordinate special events including weddings and retirement parties.

$23 per hour

Youth Coach or Referee
Pass on your love for sports to the younger set.

$10 to $15 per hour

House Sitter
Keeping an eye on someone's home while they travel can leave you in the lap of luxury.

$12 per hour

Tutor
Teach students around the world from the comfort of your home computer.

$14 to $22 per hour

Tour Guide
Show off your hometown by guiding visitors through local museums and landmarks.

$12 per hour

Delivery Driver
Hit the open road and earn a few bucks on the side.

$15 per hour

Hourly rates based on national averages. Actual wages may vary.

Count the costs before you go back to work

Finding a job you love can keep you active and happy throughout retirement. Just be sure to tally the extra expenses of that new job before you punch the time clock.

Heading back to work might drive up the amount you spend on gas, bump up your food bill due to lunches with the office gang, and rattle your budget if you have to spiff up your wardrobe.

If your new gig won't cover all your extra expenses, consider your options. For example, you might take a job close to home so you can save on your commute. You could even work from home and stay in your pj's all day.

And be sure to look into how your new income will affect your taxes and Social Security benefits. For tips on maximizing your benefits, see the *Social Security* chapter.

Be your own boss — startup strategies help you launch a successful business

Find the face of your new boss — in your own mirror. Retirement may be the perfect time to start that business you've always wanted. Just ask Art Koff, the author and aging consultant who founded *RetiredBrains.com*, a resource for boomers, retirees, and people planning for retirement. "There are literally hundreds of entrepreneurial-type jobs that people could look at and say, 'Oh I could do that!'"

So why not you? Here are some tips to get you started down the road to business success.

Find a need you can meet. Koff shared the story of an unemployed man in his late 50s who organized his messy garage at the insistence of his wife. "He cleaned out the garage. He put in shelving and hooks," says Koff. His neighbors were so impressed they asked if he could do the same for them.

So he did — and charged them for the service. "The man now has five or six full-time employees," Koff concludes, "and all they do is clean out garages and improve them with things that don't require a building permit."

Buddy up with an insider. Skip the trial-and-error stuff. Instead, learn about your industry from the experts. Maybe you already know someone who would be willing to mentor you in your new business. If not, check out community colleges and trade groups, or pay a visit to your small business development center.

Invest in top-notch training. Sign up for some courses that will make you an expert in your newly chosen field. You can take classes online and at local colleges or even attend industry conferences. Don't forget to update your marketing and finance skills, too.

Put your money where your dreams are. Are you prepared to back your business with your personal savings? That's how lots of startups get off the ground. Or you could always ask the bank for a loan as long as you have a solid business plan and a stellar credit score. Tapping into a home equity loan might work for you, too.

But heed the experts' warnings — don't fund your startup with credit cards or retirement savings.

Don't expect overnight success. Your new company could take three years or more to find its financial footing. Be prepared to be patient. Have at least six months of fixed living expenses squirreled away, just in case.

Show them your strengths to land that job

Sally's job hunt began when her husband found out his monthly pension was about to be sliced in half. "I left my teaching job years ago to write children's books," she says. "When Tom's pension got cut, I knew my meager income would never be enough to pay the bills. But I had no idea how to find a job."

She asked for help from her adult children. "They set up accounts for me at job sites online, and they told me to network with friends working for magazines and newspapers. But no luck."

Finally, she went old school and checked the local paper. And there it was. An ad for a full-time writer. "I sent in my resume the same day. Then the nail-biting began."

Within a week, Sally was on her way to her first job interview in 35 years. "I was a nervous wreck," she admits. "I know I'm a good writer, but in a job market packed with tech-savvy millennials, why hire a 60-year-old who could barely work her smartphone — let alone a complicated computer?"

During the interview, Sally ditched her self-doubts and focused on the positive instead. "The hiring manager realized I wasn't using this job as a stepping stone to something bigger and better," says Sally. "I convinced her to take a chance on me."

She got the job on the spot. Her advice to other late-in-life job seekers?

"Focus on your strengths. Remember, your work ethic and maturity will make you a valuable employee. Show them what you have to offer."

Reverse mortgages

"My oldest client was 96 years old, and she got a reverse mortgage so she could have 24/7 nursing care in her own home," says reverse mortgage consultant LeeAnn Kearley. "She was under hospice care, which is usually a six-month life expectancy, and she lived another year and a half. I think it's because she got to stay in her house."

If you're over 62, a reverse mortgage could be a smart way to put thousands of dollars in your pocket right now. That's because these loans let you trade home equity for cash payments. And you never have to pay the money back as long as you live in your house.

But these loans aren't for everybody. If you have plans to move in the future or worry that long-term medical issues could keep you from staying at home, think about other options. Here are some other common pitfalls you need to watch out for.

4 reverse mortgage mishaps that could blow the roof off your finances

Sticking other expenses on the back burner might leave you on the street. When you take out a reverse mortgage, you won't have a mortgage payment anymore. But you'll still need to keep up with property taxes, homeowners insurance, and maintenance.

You'll have to repay the loan early if you miss those payments or put off repairs. Make sure you can still afford to stay in your home by counting up all the costs.

Forgot to factor in the upfront fees? Bad calculations could cost you. Mortgages aren't free, and neither are reverse mortgages.

Origination fees, mortgage insurance, and attorney payments all eat into your home equity. That means your payments might wind up being a little bit less than you originally bargained for. Make sure to do your research so you won't be blindsided by fees.

Buying into big promises is a quick way to lose your home. Think signing a few pieces of paper could answer all your money woes? Fast-talking salesmen say they have a solution. But don't rush through the application process.

You need to know the ins and outs of a reverse mortgage before you take the plunge. It's a major financial decision that you shouldn't take lightly. Unfortunately, people who stand to make money off of you don't always tell the whole truth.

> Track down a local government-approved reverse mortgage counselor at *https://entp.hud.gov/idapp/html/hecm_cnslr_look.cfm*. The counselor will go through your specific needs to make sure you make a financial decision that can help you age on your own terms.

Seek out government-approved counselors. They'll steer you in the right direction. And if the loan terms are hard to understand or too good to be true, walk away.

Putting off plans for the future could land you in hot water. Mary and Max wanted to get a reverse mortgage, but Mary hadn't turned 62 yet. They decided to only put Max's name on the loan, and that turned out to be a big mistake. New rules protected Mary from losing the home when her husband died, but she couldn't receive any more payments.

And what if you want to leave your home to your kids? When you're gone, the lender will collect the loan. Your heirs have the option of paying the balance so they can keep the home, but they may not be able to afford it.

Navigate tricky loans with some expert advice

Shopping for a reverse mortgage alone is like trying to drive cross-country without a map. These complicated loans could leave you stranded far from home if you wind up going down the wrong route.

"This is not like your typical mortgage," says LeeAnn Kearley, a reverse mortgage consultant. "It's a specialty program, and there may be things that some traditional loan officers might not even be aware of."

That's why the first step is to seek out a reverse mortgage loan officer you can trust. "Try to work with somebody local," Kearley says. "So many people do it over the phone, but I think you need to talk face to face."

If you can't find anybody nearby that specializes in reverse mortgages, Kearley says you should go through loan counseling before you start applying for loans. "That way when you talk with a loan officer on the phone you'll know how the program works and what questions to ask."

You also need to understand the fees and upfront costs. "And you need to get an amortization schedule so you can see in advance what you'll owe in, say, 10 years," Kearley adds. "Are you still going to be living here? Or are you going to want to move and won't have any equity?" Planning ahead is key, she says.

Searching made simple — how to find the perfect loan

Reverse mortgage shoppers are bound to run into the same dilemma that stumped Goldilocks. You have three choices, but unlike the fairy-tale character you can't test them all. Here's an easy way to narrow down your search.

Looking to make the most of a loan? HECMs give you plenty of options. The Department of Housing and Urban Development's Home Equity Conversion Mortgage (HECM) is by far the most popular type of reverse mortgage. And it's not hard to see why. These loans don't limit how you can spend the cash. Plus you can receive the money as monthly payments, a lump sum, a line of credit, or a combo of monthly checks and a credit line.

HECMs come with a few downsides, though. The upfront costs tend to be higher than traditional home loans, and they cap what you can borrow at $679,650.

Small-sum seekers might want to consider single-purpose loans. Don't need to borrow much? Single-purpose reverse mortgages offered by state, local, and other nonprofit organizations might fit the bill.

They tend to be the cheapest option, but there's a catch. The lenders will determine how you can spend your money. So if you take out a loan to cover the costs of home repairs or property taxes, you can't use the cash for anything else.

If your house is worth a lot, go the jumbo route. Proprietary reverse mortgages let you borrow more home equity than HECMs, but they aren't federally insured. This means they don't charge you mortgage insurance premiums.

To make up for that, lenders often charge higher interest rates. That means these loans aren't always a better deal than HECMs. Shop around to make sure you get your money's worth.

Investments

In the fable "The Ants and the Grasshopper," Aesop warned about whiling away summer days and forgetting to save for the winter. While the ants worked to store food for the lean months, the grasshopper wasted the sunny season. You might have spent your whole career saving up like the ants, but you may still be facing the grasshopper's dilemma.

Experts worry that 15 million households headed by people age 55 to 70 don't have enough squirreled away for retirement. So what can you do when you're facing retirement and you're not sure your savings will last?

If you can't stay financially independent, you'll spend your golden years hunting down odd jobs and taking trips to the food bank. Fortunately, with a little know-how you can keep your nest egg from going rotten.

4 money moves to make your retirement last a lifetime

Use your catch-up contributions to stay ahead of the game. The IRS limits how much you can stow away in your retirement accounts each year. You can contribute $19,000 to your 401(k) plans and $6,000 to your individual retirement accounts (IRAs).

But if you're 50 or older, you're allowed to contribute more. That means you can put an extra $6,000 a year into your 401(k) plans and another $1,000 in IRAs.

Those numbers really add up. When Ellen turned 50, she started putting $6,000 a year into a brand-new IRA. With a 7 percent return on her investment, she saved up $159,262 over the next 15 years. Not too shabby, right? But if she had taken advantage of her catch-up contributions and chipped in another $1,000 a year, she'd have earned a whopping $26,558 more.

Pay your taxes now so you can save later. The best thing about traditional retirement accounts is that they let you put off paying Uncle Sam so your money can can grow tax-deferred until you withdraw it during retirement. But sometimes it's just better to rip that bandage off.

A Roth account lets you invest after-tax dollars, which means you pay taxes upfront so you can withdraw the funds later tax-free. And if your tax bracket is going to be the same or higher in retirement, you can save big.

Just take a look at Sadie's savings. When she was 50, she started paying $6,500 every year into a traditional IRA. With a 7 percent annual return on her investment, she saved $170,014 in 15 years. But because her tax rate didn't change in retirement, a Roth plan would have earned her $4,758 more.

> You can convert money from a traditional account into a Roth, but you'll be taxed on the rollover. An alternative? Open a new Roth account and start sending your savings there. Crunch the numbers to see which option makes sense. Remember, you must have owned your Roth account for at least five years in order to withdraw earnings tax-free during retirement.

Avoid a plunging portfolio by fine-tuning your golden years game plan. When you're young, you feel invincible. Aches and pains are gone in a matter of days. Now, those bruises seem to linger for weeks.

Your investing portfolio isn't too different. Bumps and slips in a young portfolio will work themselves out in time. But those small setbacks can become catastrophes as you near retirement. Risky investments leave you with no chance to make up for lost money when you're older.

Most experts recommend shifting away from a portfolio loaded with high-risk stocks as you approach retirement. Stocks should probably take up less than half of your portfolio by the time you retire. Start gradually moving toward safer options like bonds.

Sweat the small stuff and the savings will add up. A 2 percent ongoing investment fee sounds like a drop in the bucket, but those fees have a bigger impact than you might think.

Let's say you invest $5,000 every year and get a 7 percent rate of return. After 10 years, you'll have earned $73,918. But if you're paying a 2 percent annual fee, you'll only keep $66,034 — that's $7,884 less.

When you're looking into potential investments, make sure you understand how much the fees really cost in the long run.

Retirement drawdown: Protect your portfolio by spending down the right way

"So many people are focused on the accumulation phase of retirement," says Debra Morrison, a fee-only certified financial planner. But before you stop getting a paycheck, she says, you need to think about how you're going to replace it.

It's not as simple as pulling money out of your savings account. Do it wrong and you'll run out of savings too soon or face hefty taxes. "Fortunately, all of that can be mitigated by using the right withdrawal strategies," says Morrison.

So how do you find the right plan for you? You've probably heard of the 4 percent rule. Every year you cash out 4 percent of your portfolio so you get a steady stream of income while keeping your account balance from drying up.

It used to be the gold standard, but experts are starting to shy away from it because it doesn't take into account your asset mix and individual needs. Instead, think of this rule as a building block toward a better strategy.

Simplify your plan with systematic withdrawals. Not a hands-on investor? Think about this variation on the 4 percent rule. Instead of being limited to a flat 4 percent, crunch the numbers to decide how much money you can cash out.

Then set up your retirement accounts to automatically sell some of your investments monthly, quarterly, semiannually, or annually. You'll get a regular income, and you can usually request federal taxes to be automatically withheld, simplifying tax time.

Need help figuring out how long your savings will last? An online calculator can lend a hand. Head over to *calcxml.com*, click "Try Our Calculators," and select "How long will my money last with systematic withdrawals?" Or visit *bankrate.com/calculators/savings* and click "Savings withdrawal calculator."

Keep in mind, market downturns might hurt your plans. Because you're pulling cash out regardless of how well your portfolio is doing, your savings can suffer if you're not careful. Experts say you should rebalance your portfolio every year to make sure you're on track.

Stash your savings by the bucketful to keep the cash coming. The bucket strategy helps protect the money you'll need in the short term while your long-term funds continue to grow. How do you set it up? Divide your assets into three "buckets."

- The first should be made of cash or short-term, low-risk investments. It will cover your living expenses for the next couple of years. So if you think you'll need $3,000 a month and your Social Security check will be $2,000, you'll need $1,000 each month to cover the difference. For two years of living costs, you would squirrel away at least $24,000 in this bucket.

- The second bucket is filled with slightly riskier, moderately growing options designed to cover the next three to 10 years of living expenses. Think bonds and dividend-paying stocks. You should use the earnings from these investments to top off your first bucket.

- Your final bucket can be filled with riskier, more aggressive options like stock. When the market is doing well, you can use this cash to replenish your second bucket.

This strategy requires you to be a bit more involved in your money management. Experts recommend that you frequently check in with your portfolio, rebalancing it to make sure you'll always have money when you need it.

Watch out for this sneaky tax penalty

Traditional IRAs and 401(k) plans are a procrastinator's dream come true. They let you put off paying taxes on retirement savings for years. But you have to pay the piper eventually.

When you turn 70 1/2, the government comes calling for those missed taxes, and you must cash out a portion of your funds. The amount is known as a required minimum distribution (RMD). If you don't take the RMD, you'll pay a 50 percent tax penalty on the amount you should have withdrawn.

But change might be on the horizon. New laws have been proposed that could push back when you must take your first RMD or reduce the amount you have to withdraw. There's no definitive change yet, but keep your ear to the ground.

In the meantime, plan ahead for RMDs so your withdrawals don't bump you into a higher tax bracket. And for more tips, see *RMDs: Sidestep these common mistakes to dodge a taxing penalty* in the *Taxes* chapter.

When is an annuity the wrong move?

In ancient Rome, people would make one large payment into something called an "annua." In exchange they got a yearly stipend for the rest of their lives or a certain period of time. These ancient financial tools are still around today.

Annuities, as they're now called, haven't changed too much over the centuries. You still invest a certain amount upfront in return for future payments. But does this timeless tool line up with your retirement goals?

When should you think about purchasing an annuity? Most experts recommend considering one only after you've hit the limit on your tax-advantaged retirement accounts like 401(k) plans and IRAs.

Steer clear if you want to stay in the driver's seat. Annuities and avid DIYers just don't mix. When you buy one, you're handing the reins of your investments to a big company in exchange for guaranteed income. That means if you're the type of investor who demands a little bit more control, you're out of luck. You won't have much say on how that money is invested.

Need flexibility? Annuities don't let you call the shots on cash flow. You only get a check when your contract says it's time for a payment. But what if you have a medical emergency and need the money now? You may be able to access your investment, but it might come with a high surrender charge.

Save yourself the trouble if you know your savings will last. Annuities are better options for people who are worried about their savings lasting through retirement. You're guaranteed a check no matter how the stock market is doing.

But annuities often come with hefty fees. If your retirement savings will get you through your golden years, you might be better off going with other options.

" Ignore the hype to find investment success

"We're conditioned by the financial services industry to think there's a magic bullet out there," says James, a 64-year-old who's been in the investing game a long time. But, he warns, nobody has all the answers for the perfect investment strategy.

James has built a nice little nest egg over the years, but it took a few tough lessons to become a successful investor. He has learned that following the advice of an investing guru isn't going to make him rich.

"If there really were any financial wizards out there, they would all own Caribbean islands," he says. "They wouldn't be talking to me about how to invest my assets."

But how do you seek out a good advisor when you need one? "I looked for someone who was seasoned," says James, "someone who could show me some track record."

Still, finding a consultant whose strategies matched his goals was a trial-and-error process. His first advisor had a conservative approach and took too little risk. His next advisor also missed the mark. "He made a lot of trades that benefited him more than me."

In the end, James got more involved in the investment process. He put his trust in tools that were ideal for small investors, like index funds and mutual funds. But his biggest takeaways weren't the specific funds he bought and which stocks did well. Instead, he stands by setting realistic goals and taking the time to educate yourself on your options.

"Don't listen to the hype," he says. "Slow and steady is really the best policy."

See through these empty promises to stump scammers

Your age doesn't make you a target for con artists, right? Think again. Experts say scammers cost seniors a whopping $37 billion every year. And one of their biggest targets? Your investments. Watch out for these common lines and you'll spot a scam from a mile away.

"You can get high returns for very low risk." Flashy promises that sound too good to be true probably are. When somebody offers you an investment that is vastly outperforming similar products, chances are it's a trumped-up scheme.

No investments are risk-free. So watch out for anybody who guarantees big returns without warning you of the high risk that is typically linked to high yields.

"You need to act fast because this opportunity could be gone tomorrow." Scammers love to prey on your fears. And who isn't afraid of missing out on easy money? But pleas for quick decisions are best ignored.

Pressuring people into making rash decisions is one of the oldest tricks in the book. You need to take your time and consider investments carefully. Walk away if somebody isn't willing to wait for you to make up your mind.

Life insurance

Living on a fixed income may have you searching for ways to stretch your budget. And skipping that life insurance premium could save you a bundle each month, right? Hold on. Don't pull the plug on that policy just yet.

Your family may need your life insurance money to pay your final expenses. "If you don't want to pass the cost of your final expenses on to your survivors, having life insurance is a smart thing to do," says Steven Weisbart, senior vice president and chief economist of the Insurance Information Institute.

Life insurance can help your family take care of your medical bills, legal expenses like probating a will, and all those other costs you don't want your loved ones to be left with.

And how about the spouse, disabled adult children, or elderly parents you leave behind? "Sometimes older people will have younger dependents, people with disabilities, people with various kinds of limitations, who are not able to sustain themselves financially," says Weisbart. "The death benefits from a life insurance policy would continue to provide some financial support."

But what can you do to make sure preparing for their future doesn't drain your bank account right now? Read on for tips on how to trim your life insurance costs — while still providing for the people you love.

As you get older and face fewer financial obligations, you may not need life insurance. Is your mortgage paid off? Are your children independent? Will your spouse be financially secure if something happens to you? Then you may be able to drop your insurance. Just imagine all the ways you could use that extra money.

Pare down your premiums with 6 money-saving secrets

Take care of your health for a rate reward. Most life insurance companies offer different price levels based on your health and lifestyle. For example, a 65-year-old nonsmoker might pay $443 a month for term insurance while a smoker pays $1,376 — a $933 difference each month. To get the best rate, steer clear of tobacco products, maintain a healthy weight, and exercise regularly.

To shape up your future, pick a company that's fiscally fit. No matter how low the premium, you're not getting a good deal if the company you sign on with is financially shaky. To find out if an insurance company is reliable, research their standings with a few independent ratings agencies. Go to *iii.org* and type in "ratings agency contact information" in the search bar. Choose the first option for the website, address, and phone number of each agency.

Shop around for the best buy. You've heard it many times before, but it's worth repeating. If you want a good deal, you need to compare prices. You may save hundreds of dollars in annual premiums, even among the most well-known companies. See how your favorites stack up by getting quotes from sites like *lifeinsurance.net*, *policygenius.com*, or *accuquote.com*.

> Life insurance companies can check your driving record before they insure you. If you've been cited for speeding or reckless driving, they may decide you're not a good risk — and that means you'll pay more. Kept your record clean for the past decade? You're cruising down the road to lower premiums.

Not comfortable sealing the deal online? Buy a popular business or money magazine and flip through the insurance ads. To get details about their policies, just call the phone number printed on the page.

Pay less to get more. Some companies offer discounts for certain insurance amounts. For example, you could actually pay a lower premium for a $250,000 policy than you would for a $200,000 policy if the company applies a discount at the higher amount. To find out if you're getting the best price, talk to your insurance agent, or do a thorough search on the company's website.

Save time and money with a renewal guarantee. Once your policy's term ends, a renewal guarantee lets you start a new term without going through another health exam. You can expect to pay a higher premium based on your current age. But if your health has declined, you might have to pay much more for a brand-new policy — or you might not be able to get coverage at all.

Want to score super discounts? Join the club. Some organizations for seniors, like the Association of Mature American Citizens and the American Seniors Association, offer deals on life insurance for their members. And don't forget to tap the discount clubs, like Costco and BJ's, to see how their premiums measure up.

Insider trick saves you hundreds every year

Ever heard the expression, "timing is everything"? Turns out it holds true, even when it comes to paying for your life insurance. Picking the perfect time to pay can save you big bucks on your premiums.

Pay once — and save a bundle in interest. When it's time to pay your premium, you usually get to choose — should you pay once a year, once a quarter, or once a month? Of course, sending in that check once a month gets you the lowest payment. But is it the best deal? Not necessarily.

According to Dr. Steven Weisbart, senior vice president of the Insurance Information Institute, the interest rate you're charged for your monthly payments can be higher than you think, costing you more money. His advice? The least expensive way to pay is annually.

But how to make that big yearly payment? "Plan for it. Put some money away in a savings account," Weisbart advises. "And when the time comes, pull it out and use it to pay the premium. That would probably be the cheapest way to go."

Watch your savings stack up with the yearly discount.
Processing just one payment a year cuts down on administrative costs for your insurance company, which is why they may offer discounts if you pay your premiums annually. These discounts often range from 2 to 8 percent. And that can mean big savings for you.

For example, the average annual premium on a 20-year term life insurance policy for a 60-year-old nonsmoker is about $2,900. An 8 percent discount would save a solid $232. Check with your insurance agent to see what discounts your carrier offers.

That's life: What to do when your policy runs out

So time's up on your term life policy. You size up your financial situation and decide you still need coverage. But what are your options?

Apply for a new policy. If you're under 70 and still in good health, buying a new term life policy is most likely your least expensive option. But you'll probably be required to take a medical exam to prove you're still fit as a fiddle.

Extend your coverage. Are you over the age of 70? Health problems make it difficult for you to qualify for a new policy? Check with your agent to see if you can keep your current policy in force by continuing to pay your premiums. But expect the cost to go up significantly every year.

Opt for whole life. With whole life insurance, you don't have to worry about your policy reaching an end point. And your premiums usually stay the same for your entire life. On the downside, a policy like this can cost you six to 10 times as much as comparable term life insurance.

Bottom line? Check with a trusted financial advisor before you sign on any policy's dotted line.

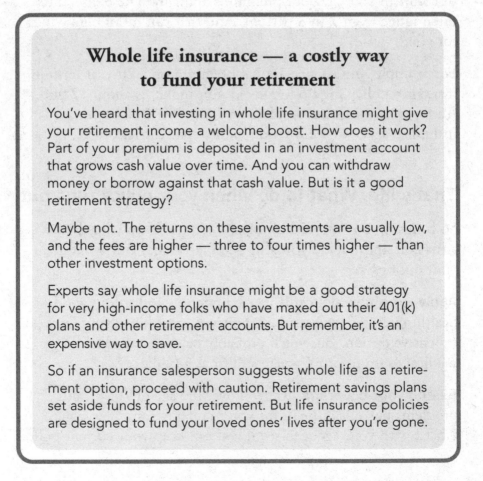

Whole life insurance — a costly way to fund your retirement

You've heard that investing in whole life insurance might give your retirement income a welcome boost. How does it work? Part of your premium is deposited in an investment account that grows cash value over time. And you can withdraw money or borrow against that cash value. But is it a good retirement strategy?

Maybe not. The returns on these investments are usually low, and the fees are higher — three to four times higher — than other investment options.

Experts say whole life insurance might be a good strategy for very high-income folks who have maxed out their 401(k) plans and other retirement accounts. But remember, it's an expensive way to save.

So if an insurance salesperson suggests whole life as a retirement option, proceed with caution. Retirement savings plans set aside funds for your retirement. But life insurance policies are designed to fund your loved ones' lives after you're gone.

STRETCH YOUR DOLLARS

SECRETS TO
SPENDING LESS AND
GETTING MORE

Groceries

You won't find any cracked eggs on Trevor Deforest's watch. As winner of the National Grocers Association Best Bagger Championship — along with the $10,000 prize — he knows just how to bag your groceries so you get everything home safe and sound.

No smashed bread or bruised fruit. No running back to the store to buy replacements. And since the average American household spends more than $4,300 on groceries each year, Trevor's expert bagging is one thing every shopper can appreciate.

But even before you get to the bag boy at the end of the checkout lane, you'll find plenty of ways to stretch your grocery budget. From old-school coupon clipping to cutting-edge phone apps, this chapter is chock-full of ideas to help you keep plenty of green in your pocket. Just what you need to stay financially secure well into your future.

5 savvy strategies to slash your food bill by $1,000 every year

Check out store brands for a stellar price cut. That's the word from Sheila Johnson, a front-end manager for a well-known national grocery chain. "Often the manufacturer of the name-brand item produces the generic brand you see in the store. Same recipe, same ingredients, different packaging," explains Johnson.

For example, the generic brand of peanut butter crackers sells for $1.99 at Johnson's store. The name-brand crackers cost $2.79 — 80 cents more for the same taste.

Other products you might want to compare? Johnson says shoppers should consider buying store-brand bottled water and generic milk instead of national brands.

Bottom line? According to Consumer Reports, generic brands often cost 15 to 30 percent less than those name-brand products. Just think. If you switch to store brands for just a quarter of the groceries you buy, you could save an average of $327 every year.

Cook like a "Chopped" champion to get the most for your money. Are you impressed by the delicious meals those TV contestants put together out of random ingredients? You can cook that way, too. Don't throw away the perfectly good food in your fridge. Get creative instead. Use what you already have, and you'll pay less every month for groceries.

According to a survey sponsored by the American Chemistry Council, folks say they throw away $640 worth of food every year. The U.S. government, on the other hand, suggests the figure is closer to $900. That means this money-saving tip could save you $53 to $75 each month. Simply cut down on the waste by shopping in your pantry for tasty dinner ingredients — instead of heading out to the grocery store.

> Dinnertime! What deliciousness can you cook up with your uneaten chicken, apple juice, and fresh chives before you have to toss them? Head to sites like *myfridgefood.com* and *supercook.com* where you can check off the ingredients you have on hand to find a recipe. And voilà — apple juice chicken is on the menu tonight. Yum. Waste not, want not.

Save more when you choose paper over plastic. And it's not about how you bag your groceries. It's about how you pay. Studies show that you spend more — and buy more junk food on impulse — when you use a debit or credit card at checkout. It's called the pain of payment. It hurts a lot more to pull out hard-earned cash to pay for those vice items than it does to swipe a card.

And besides, paying with cash helps you stay within your budget. Want to cut down your average weekly grocery bill from $84 to $74? That's easy. Go to the store with only $74 in your wallet, and leave the plastic at home. Do this each week, and you'll save an extra $520 every year.

Make a list to sidestep budget-breaking impulse buys. While you're out, you decide to make a stop at the grocery store. Spur of the moment decision. Once inside, the temptations begin. Sure that candy looks delicious, and the new tabloid is calling to you from the checkout lane. But resist the impulse to buy.

One study from the University of Pennsylvania shows that an unplanned trip to the grocery store can increase impulse buying by 23 percent. What does that mean in cold hard cash? Just one unplanned weekly shopping trip could tack on an extra $19 to your grocery bill. Make a list before you shop. And stick to the plan, Stan.

Surprise! Buying in bulk may not be the best deal. The warehouse store may be a great place to stock up on items for your next family get-together or holiday party. But have you ever bought the enormous bag of tortilla chips or pretzels at the warehouse store — just to throw half of the snacks away because they got stale? You're not alone.

In a study conducted by Ohio State University, more than half the people surveyed said they waste more food when they buy in bulk or overstock their pantries during sales. It's like throwing money in the trash can, along with the rest of those cheap chips you bought.

Clip art: Save with coupon tricks from the pros

"I never pay for toothpaste," says John Vernon, director of Atlanta's Jesus Place Inner City Mission. Because his job calls for supplying hundreds of folks with food and hygiene items each month, John knows how to use coupons to get the best deals.

"There are so many wonderful sales and coupons for toothpaste that you can usually get it for pennies — or even free," he says. Ready to become a voucher virtuoso? John has a few tips for you.

Start at the source. "You can find coupons in newspapers or in free flyers from libraries and grocery stores," says John. "You can also print coupons from the internet." Just check out the offerings at sites like *coupons.com* or *couponmom.com*. You can sort the deals by categories based on the product type, brand, and store to make searching easier.

Become a preferred shopper. Don't forget to sign up for preferred shopper memberships, loyalty cards, and rewards programs. As John points out, "In some cases, you're only eligible for special sale prices if you use the store membership card."

Get organized. Staying organized is the key to coupon success. John arranges his coupons in envelopes according to their dates, but some people prefer to use a binder with baseball card holders. Others group them according to the aisles of the stores they'll be visiting. "Find a system that works for you. You can lose a lot of value by not being able to find your coupon at checkout."

Ask these magic questions to unlock unbelievable deals

The manager at your local grocery store wants your business so badly he'll give you great grocery deals — if you ask for them.

Request a rain check. If the store runs out of a sale item, ask the manager for a rain check — a voucher that lets you buy the same product for the sale price at a later date. That's how it works at the grocery store Sheila Johnson manages. "If something is mentioned in the sales ad, and we run out, we'll issue a rain check for that item if the customer requests one."

Ask for a substitute. "We will also make a substitution," explains Johnson. "If we're running a sale on our store-brand chicken, for example, and we sell out, we'll give our customers a rain check for that product. But if they ask, we'll also sell them the name-brand chicken at the advertised sale price."

Beware grocery gaffs that steal your cash

Go ahead. Give yourself a pat on the back. You're definitely a savvy shopper. You remembered to bring your coupons. You took advantage of the store's cost-cutting deals. You even signed up for the store's app.

And now you can't wait to see that rock-bottom total on your receipt — a reward for all your hard work and planning. But the super-shopper total you expected turns out to be a budget-busting shocker. How could you have spent that much money? Take a good look in your cart for these sneaky savings snatchers.

Pass by the pricey pre-cut produce. Sure those store-cut celery sticks make a quick and easy addition to your party veggie tray.

But the convenience comes with a price. At one market, a 3-ounce bag of celery sticks costs $2.99, while a stalk of celery has the do-it-yourself price of $1.29. A savings of $1.70? Yes, please.

Skip the snack-sized treats. Take pretzels, for example. A 9-ounce box of individual servings will run you almost $4.00. That's about 44 cents per ounce. A big 16-ounce bag of the same brand of pretzels will cost about $3.69. That's 23 cents per ounce. Just add your own snack bags for a tasty do-it-yourself bargain.

Housewares can wear a hole in your budget. Mugs, plates, and platters. Kitchen gadgets and shiny cookware. To secure your savings, leave those snazzy serving pieces on the shelf.

For example, you've seen that fancy frying pan advertised on TV. And there it is on your grocery store shelf. But is $29.99 the best deal? Nope. Get the same pan online for $22.49, a savings of $7.50.

Don't pay extra, extra to read all about it. Before you buy your favorite magazine at the grocery store, take a look at the news-stand price on the cover. You might be in for a pricey surprise.

For example, did you know a copy of Time magazine at the supermarket could cost around $5.99? That's $311.48 if you buy a copy each week. Instead, buy a subscription for a full year — that's 52 issues — for $30. Just 58 cents a copy. Check online for the subscription prices of your favorite magazines and save a bundle.

Celebrate good times — on the cheap. Head over to your local dollar store for party supplies like plates, streamers, napkins — all the things you need for a successful bash. And at just $1 for each item, you can afford to party like there's no tomorrow.

While you're there, stock up on greeting cards, too. The Dollar Tree, for example, is known for its two-for-$1 selection of cards. And that's a deal worth celebrating.

Good health on your shelf
Stock your pantry for pennies

Many seniors don't get enough protein and immune-boosting fruits and vegetables in their diets, says registered dietician Paula Vandelicht. Her advice? Pile up on nutrient-rich, low-cost fare. These flavorful foods cost pennies per serving.

EGGS
10¢ per large egg

KIDNEY BEANS
15¢ per 1/2 cup

MOZZARELLA STRING CHEESE
24¢ per stick

NONFAT GREEK YOGURT
74¢ per 1/2 cup

WHOLE WHEAT PASTA
6¢ per 1/2 cup

WHOLE GRAIN BREAD
9¢ per slice

FROZEN BLUEBERRIES
62¢ per 1/2 cup

CANNED TOMATOES
13¢ per 1/2 cup

FROZEN BROCCOLI
12¢ per 1/2 cup

FROZEN SPINACH
14¢ per 1/2 cup

Go app happy: Make the most of the penny-pinching power of your phone

When you head to the grocery store, don't leave your phone behind. It could be your most important cost-cutting tool. Save more at your store with these free apps, available for iPhone or Android.

- **Favado.** Never miss a great deal again. This app lists each item that's on sale at your favorite supermarkets, including Kroger, Publix, Walmart, and 65,000 more stores across the country. Choose the store, choose the item, and save.

- **Grocery Pal.** No more coupon clipping. With this app you can select coupons online and add them right to your store's loyalty card. You automatically save when you swipe the loyalty card at checkout.

- **Flipp.** This app matches the deals you see in local flyers with coupons for the brands you buy. Simply add the loyalty cards from your favorite stores. Load the coupon deals to your card and you're ready to save at checkout.

- **Ibotta.** Get paid for shopping. Use your phone to browse through rebate offers at your favorite stores. Then purchase items, snap a pic of your receipt, and watch the money roll into your Ibotta account.

- **SavingStar.** This app gives you cash back with a healthy twist. In addition to other rebates and rewards, you get money back on fresh produce with the Healthy Offer of the Week program. To get started, link your store cards with the app. Then select the rebates you want to use, present your store card at checkout, and enjoy your savings.

- **Checkout 51.** Thursday may become your favorite day to shop. That's when 20 brand-new offers go live on this app. Browse through the savings, add your favs to your list, and shop. Take a picture of your receipt with the app's built-in camera. When your savings hit $20, cash out and watch for your check in the mail.

> ## Don't let scanner slip-ups steal your savings
>
> Lara couldn't believe her eyes when she spotted the deal online. Get $10 off a $30 purchase of her pup's favorite dog food. She printed her coupon and rushed to the market to cash in. But when she got home and checked her receipt, she realized she'd been charged full price.
>
> She returned to the store and got the money she was owed. "If I hadn't checked the receipt," she said, "I would have been out that $10, just because the scanner wasn't pro-grammed for the coupon."
>
> Lara has also had trouble with items scanning at the wrong price. Her advice? "Make sure you watch the price that comes up as the item is scanned. And double-check your receipt." To keep you as a loyal customer, your store may even give you the item for free.

Nutrition in a box: Meals on demand may fit the bill

"Eating well is vital at any age, but as you get older, your daily food choices can make an important difference in your health," says Richard J. Hodes, M.D., director of the National Institute on Aging. "Good nutrition is one component of an overall strategy to stay healthy."

In fact, a balanced menu of healthy foods may help prevent heart disease, type 2 diabetes, and bone loss. But when you can't get to the grocery store, how can you eat well — without breaking the bank?

Try this "free-wheeling" deal for a delicious meal. Meals on Wheels programs, located across the country, provide nutritious meals for older adults, generally age 60 plus, who are homebound or unable to shop and cook.

Costs will vary depending on your income and local program's payment policy. Fees are often based on a sliding scale, from no charge to full price. Some programs even take food stamps. Go to *mealsonwheelsamerica.org* to find a location near you.

Enjoy a tasty dinner delivered to your doorstep. Looking for a company that lets you choose your own prepared meal? Try a convenient and delicious meal delivery service. Your choices are delivered right to your door, prepped and ready to go into the microwave or oven.

The price tag will hinge on the service you choose. Fresh n' Lean options, for example, range from $9 to $15 per meal, while entrees from the more budget-minded Mom's Meals go for $6.99 plus shipping. Mom's Meals is also a Medicaid meal provider. If you qualify, Medicaid will help offset the cost of your meals.

Channel your inner chef with a meal delivery kit. Now you're cooking with gas. If preparing a meal in your own kitchen is not a problem for you, but getting to the store is a chore, a meal delivery kit might be the answer.

Consumer Reports rated HelloFresh and Green Chef as their favorite meal delivery kits, but Plated, Blue Apron, and Purple Carrot also scored high marks. Go online to choose the meals you'd like to try. You'll receive the necessary ingredients — you may need to use cooking oil or spices you have on hand — along with instructions for prepping your food. Most meal kits include nutrition information, too. Gluten-free, vegan, and other special meal plans are usually available.

Like ready-to-heat meals, the kits may come with a little sticker shock. Expect to pay upwards of $10 per meal. But you'll save money on gas going to and from the store, and you won't be tempted by those impulse buys.

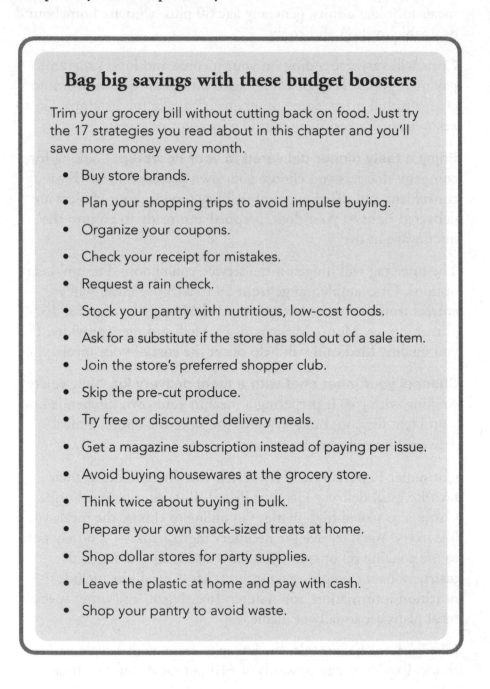

Bag big savings with these budget boosters

Trim your grocery bill without cutting back on food. Just try the 17 strategies you read about in this chapter and you'll save more money every month.

- Buy store brands.
- Plan your shopping trips to avoid impulse buying.
- Organize your coupons.
- Check your receipt for mistakes.
- Request a rain check.
- Stock your pantry with nutritious, low-cost foods.
- Ask for a substitute if the store has sold out of a sale item.
- Join the store's preferred shopper club.
- Skip the pre-cut produce.
- Try free or discounted delivery meals.
- Get a magazine subscription instead of paying per issue.
- Avoid buying housewares at the grocery store.
- Think twice about buying in bulk.
- Prepare your own snack-sized treats at home.
- Shop dollar stores for party supplies.
- Leave the plastic at home and pay with cash.
- Shop your pantry to avoid waste.

Car costs

Some 3 million and counting. That's the mileage Irvin Gordon has racked up on his Volvo P1800 since 1966, when he bought the brand-new, cherry-red car for $4,150. The secret to Gordon's super-high mileage — enough to have taken him to the moon and back six times — is simple. A strong dedication to maintenance and repair.

"I just follow the owner's manual and do what it says to do, and if something is broken I try to take care of it right away," Gordon, a retired science teacher from Long Island, says in a documentary.

Nobody knows the exact amount Gordon has spent over the years on things like oil changes, battery replacements, and brake jobs. But driving a car doesn't come cheap.

The American Automobile Association (AAA) pegs the average cost of owning and operating a new vehicle at $8,849 per year. Among the largest expenses? Depreciation — the value your car loses after driving it off the lot — along with things like gas, insurance, and maintenance and repairs.

Steering clear of unnecessary expenses and roadster rip-offs will help you stay in the driver's seat. Here's how to do it.

Put the brakes on maintenance and repair costs with these 5 tips

Stick to a game plan and skip pricey problems over the long haul. The most important thing you can do to keep your car on the road? Change your oil and oil filter on a regular basis.

Otherwise bits of metal and dirt that end up in the oil will wear down the engine. Replace dirty air and fuel filters, too, to keep your engine humming along.

And don't forget about replacing coolant, brake, transmission, and power steering fluid. Unsure if your car needs any work? Follow your vehicle's recommended maintenance schedule — it's in the owner's manual.

"It's the best way to keep your repair costs as low as possible," says Tony Molla, vice president of the Automotive Service Association in North Richland Hills, Texas. "That way you catch small problems before they become big headaches."

Don't spin your wheels on tire care. Check your tire pressure once a month when the tires are cold. Underinflated tires can be dangerous, and they tend to wear out more quickly and drag down gas mileage.

Are the treads shallow and worn? It might be time for a trip to a warehouse store like Costco, Sam's Club, or BJ's Wholesale Club. They'll sell you the tires and mount them for you, too.

The best part? Installation also covers the costs of balancing and rotation, things you'd often have to pay extra for at other locations. And it includes flat repair at no charge.

Learn the nuts and bolts of a repair job before you hand over the cash. It happens all the time. You take your car in for a simple oil change and are told you need a wheel alignment or new brake pads. How do you know it's really necessary? Many times such problems are visible, so ask the mechanic to show you the part of the car that needs fixing.

Also ask the technician if a repair needs to be done immediately or if it can wait. Have him prioritize mechanical issues so you can focus on the most urgent ones first.

Of course, some repairs — like getting your brakes fixed — need to be done immediately. And don't ignore manufacturer recall notices, no matter how minor they seem. Recalls are only issued over serious matters that affect your car's performance or your safety. While it may be a nuisance to take time out of your schedule for the repairs, you won't be charged and will gain peace of mind.

A little TLC now saves a lot down the line. Keeping your car's exterior clean does more than make it look good. It keeps things like road salt, tree sap, and dead bugs from ruining the paint. Take the time while washing your car to look for cracks or corrosion. Be sure to note any unusual smells or fluid leaks.

And don't forget about regular checkups. "If you're in retirement, you should have your vehicle looked at by a professional technician at least twice a year — in the spring and fall," Molla advises. "They'll catch things like frayed fan belts and damaged hoses that could leave you stranded somewhere."

So your car is in the shop, and you need a rental. Don't feel like calling around for rates? With just a few keystrokes and clicks of the mouse, you can narrow in on the best deals at rate comparison sites like *autoslash.com*, *cheapcarrental.com*, and *kayak.com*.

Why pay when you can get services for free? Few things strike fear into the hearts of car owners like the glow of the check engine light. It could be caused by something as simple as a loose gas cap. On the other hand, a far more serious problem could be in the works.

Fortunately, some auto service chains — including Advance Auto Parts, Pep Boys, and O'Reilly Auto Parts — will diagnose the problem for free. Many such stores will also install wiper blades, test your battery and alternator, and lend you tools without charging you a nickel.

Budget breaker: Plan for repairs to fortify your finances

Roughly 1 in 3 drivers in the U.S. wouldn't be able to pay for an unexpected auto repair without going into debt, according to the American Automobile Association (AAA). That's why the organization recommends you set aside at least $50 a month for the upkeep of your car. Consider the following when deciding how much you'll need to save.

- The odometer. Expenses tend to increase dramatically between the 25,000- and 100,000-mile mark, then rise less dramatically.

- The type of auto. Luxury brands like BMW and Mercedes-Benz will likely cost more to maintain than economy models.

- Your driving behavior. Aggressive driving, like braking with a heavy foot and speeding, wears down your vehicle more quickly. Brake gently — you won't have to change your brake pads as often, potentially saving you more than $600 over the life of your car.

Rising insurance rates? Drive down high premiums to get back on track

Auto insurance rates have skyrocketed over the last several years, with premiums hitting a national average of $1,427 a year. What's driving the increase? Turns out, lots of things.

Damaging storms and wildfires over the last couple of years have sparked an increase in claims, and lower gas prices have put more cars — and distracted drivers — on the road. Then there's the rising cost of repairing new safety features — think backup cameras and blind spot detection monitors — installed in newer vehicles.

Fortunately, insurance premiums don't have to break the bank. Pay attention to these pointers if you're looking to pay less.

Maximize discounts to minimize costs. Your insurance company won't lower your premiums unless you give them a reason to. Ask your insurer about these discounts and more to see how much you can lower your bill.

- Mainly using the car to drive to the store and back? That can save you between 5 and 15 percent on your premium if you drive less than 7,500 miles a year — an extra $214 in your pocket if you pay the national average.

- You also may be eligible for a multi-car discount if more than one vehicle is on your policy. That could save you between 10 and 25 percent — or up to $357 a year.

- Belong to any organizations? You may qualify for an affiliate group discount. They're awarded to members of many alumni, business, and professional associations, including Mensa and the Automobile Association of America (AAA).

The right strategy will get you more savings. Unfortunately, clipping coupons from the Sunday paper won't get you very far when it comes to auto insurance. But coming up with a game plan can help keep costs from spiraling out of control.

- You can save up to 10 percent — or nearly $143 — a year by insuring your home and auto with the same company.

- If your car is more than 10 years old or is valued at less than 10 times your premium, repairs could cost more than your ride is worth. If that's the case, you might consider dropping your collision coverage. Doing so could cut your costs by 40 percent and put an extra $571 in the bank.

- Filing a claim could raise your insurance premium more than 40 percent if you're at fault. If you're in a small accident and only your car is involved — let's say you backed into a pole and are unhurt — you might be better off paying for repairs out of pocket.

A good credit report works in your favor. Here's one more reason to pay your bills on time and maintain a solid FICO score. Insurance companies may look at your credit rating to create their own credit-based insurance score. Why? They believe this score, along with factors like your driving and claims history, will help predict the chances you'll file a claim in the future. And that determines how much they'll charge you.

One study found the average difference in rates between people with good and fair credit was 17 percent. And between drivers with good and bad credit? A whopping 67 percent difference. That means maintaining good credit could save you hundreds every year.

So be sure to monitor your credit report for errors, and keep an eye on your spending habits. Also steer clear of types of credit that might ding your score, including credit cards from department stores and credit accounts from your local tire dealer, auto parts store, or service station.

"

Bypass repairman rip-offs to rev up your savings

Looking for a mechanic to do right by you and your car? It's worth the search. After all, leaving your auto with the wrong person could mean fixes that fall apart, days — if not weeks — without your vehicle, and hundreds of dollars in unnecessary repairs.

So how do you find a mechanic you can trust? Follow the advice of Tony Molla, vice president of the Automotive Service Association (ASA), a nonprofit organization that helps improve the practices of auto shops nationwide.

- Ask friends and neighbors for a recommendation.

- Drive by the shop to see if it looks professional.

- Go online for customer reviews.

- Check if the shop is accredited and in good standing with the Better Business Bureau.

- Find out if the mechanics are certified by the National Institute for Automotive Service Excellence.

- See if the garage belongs to an organization, such as ASA, that follows a code of ethics.

If all that checks out, Molla says, drop your auto off for a test run.

"Bring your car in for a small job, like an oil change or safety inspection," he recommends. It will give you the opportunity to see how well you get treated.

Talk to the owner about his business, Molla advises. Taking an interest will help build a relationship. That can be important down the road when you might need repairs. "Nobody takes advantage of customers they like," he says.

And how do you spot a shady business? "Go with your gut," Molla suggests. "If you ask the same question three times and still don't understand the answer, thank them for their time and go somewhere else."

"

Tank goodness: Save over $800 a year at the gas pump

Don't like Mondays? You could be missing out on big savings, according to a recent GasBuddy study that found nearly half the states offer their lowest fuel prices at the start of the workweek. And the day when gas prices are generally the highest? Friday. Want to fill up on more cost-saving tricks? Read on for additional ways to save.

	Potential Annual Savings*
Don't waste money on premium gas if your car doesn't need it. Switch to regular and you could save 50¢ a gallon.	**$306**
Stop speeding up quickly and slamming on the brakes. Steady driving will boost your gas mileage.	**$171**
Remove your cargo box to lower wind resistance and raise your fuel economy.	**$147**
Use money-saving apps like GasBuddy and Gas Guru to find the cheapest fuel in your area. A difference of just 15¢ a gallon adds up.	**$92**
Keep your engine properly tuned and save 11¢ on every gallon of gas.	**$67**
Use the recommended motor oil to save up to 6¢ per gallon of gas.	**$37**
Instead of idling several minutes each day, turn off the engine to save gas.	**$31**
Slow down. Each 5 mph you drive over 50 mph adds 20¢ per gallon to the price you paid at the pump. Cruise at 50 instead of 55 for a quarter of the miles you drive to rev up the savings.	**$31**

*Savings based on gas price of $2.81 per gallon, gas mileage of 22 mpg, and 13,476 miles driven per year.

TOTAL POTENTIAL SAVINGS **$882**

Clothing

How much should you spend on new threads and upkeep for your getup? Experts say 5 percent of your budget is about right. But that's not much if you're retired and on a fixed income. In fact, it comes to around $70 a month if you're living on the average Social Security benefit.

But there's good news. You can still look like a million bucks without breaking the bank.

- Go shopping in your closet and take note of what you have. You may find a forgotten pair of pumps and a classic-cut blouse that pair together for an elegant ensemble.

- Sell the clothes you haven't worn in over a year to a consignment shop, on eBay, or at a vintage store. Or host a small party where you and your friends swap clothes you no longer wear.

- Make a list of what you need and a budget of how much you can spend. Then invest in quality pieces that don't go out of style. After all, a little black dress or pair of well-made slacks will provide much more service than, say, a fringed caftan or harem pants.

Read on for more tips on building a wardrobe that fits your lifestyle — and your wallet.

4 shopping secrets that let you dress for less

Shop consignment for chic on the cheap. Looking for an Ann Taylor blouse or Burberry trench coat but don't want to pay top dollar? Consider stopping by a consignment shop for brand-name clothes at bargain-basement prices.

So how much can you save on, say, a pair of Ray-Ban sunglasses that originally sold for $200? Well, items on consignment often arrive on the sales floor at 50 percent off — so around $100 or so. The shop owner will cut the price further — to $75 and less — if the glasses sit on the shelf too long.

Want to find a locale in your area? Enter the terms "consignment shops near me" into your search engine.

Embrace thrifty thrills to get the most bang for your buck. Seeking even steeper savings? Try a thrift store like Goodwill or Value Village, where you'll get around 75 percent off retail prices on secondhand clothes. Be aware, though, you're more likely to find casual wear than cutting-edge fashion.

Just be sure to look over any potential purchases for stains and missing buttons. You might have to dig a little, but you'll often unearth great deals.

"I once found a pair of leather walking shoes for $2.98," says longtime thrifter Charlene. "I don't think anybody ever wore them. They were in perfect condition when I got them and have lasted for years."

Here's a helpful hint — find out which day your local thrift store restocks its shelves. This way you'll get dibs on new arrivals.

Score big when you know the details on retail. Get brand-name items for less at discount stores like Ross, T.J. Maxx, and Marshalls. They sell overstocked items, which allows them to offer bottom-of-the-barrel prices.

Shopping at the mall? Remember that retailers showcase higher-priced clothes at the front of the store and hide the sales and clearance items near the fitting rooms in the back. You'll also get a lot more bang for your buck by buying apparel out of season.

Think September for swimsuits and shorts, and February for winter coats and gloves.

And ask about senior discounts. Kohl's, for example, offers a 15 percent discount to people 60 and up on Wednesdays. And Stein Mart gives discounts on the first Monday of the month if you're at least 55.

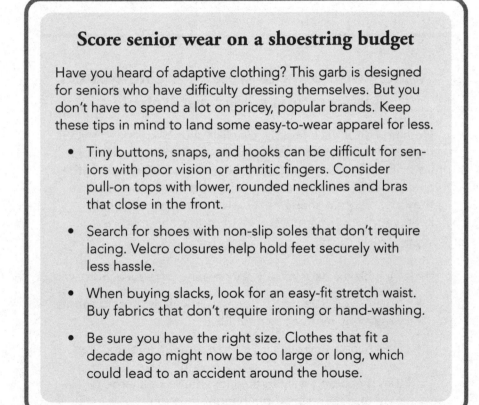

Score senior wear on a shoestring budget

Have you heard of adaptive clothing? This garb is designed for seniors who have difficulty dressing themselves. But you don't have to spend a lot on pricey, popular brands. Keep these tips in mind to land some easy-to-wear apparel for less.

- Tiny buttons, snaps, and hooks can be difficult for seniors with poor vision or arthritic fingers. Consider pull-on tops with lower, rounded necklines and bras that close in the front.

- Search for shoes with non-slip soles that don't require lacing. Velcro closures help hold feet securely with less hassle.

- When buying slacks, look for an easy-fit stretch waist. Buy fabrics that don't require ironing or hand-washing.

- Be sure you have the right size. Clothes that fit a decade ago might now be too large or long, which could lead to an accident around the house.

Go virtual to find real money. Before you buy that new sweater set — whether online or at a brick-and-mortar store — search for coupons and other promotional offers at *RetailMeNot.com* or *BeFrugal.com*. Or just Google the name of the retailer and "promo code" for instant savings.

You can also sign up for emails from department stores you shop at regularly. Then check your inbox for coupon codes to use on future purchases.

Online retailers, meanwhile, hate it when computer users leave their virtual shopping carts at checkout. Stores often send a follow-up email — along with a coupon code — to prod online customers into completing the forgotten sale. Why not play along? Abandon your cart deliberately to get the same discount.

Winter wise: How to store your cold-weather clothes to make your wardrobe last

Nothing keeps Jack Frost at bay like chunky knits and thick flannel. But come springtime, you've got to make way for light linens and airy cottons. The most important part of the changeover? Properly storing your cold-weather clothes so they'll be in great shape next year. These steps will help keep your winter garments free of moths and mildew.

- Wash or dry clean your clothes.

- Take plastic bags off any dry cleaning to reduce moisture.

- Brush overcoats out of doors, particularly around seams where tiny moth eggs might live.

- Hang coats and suits on sturdy hangers in a zippered, fabric garment bag. Don't have one? Make a garment bag by cutting a slit in the closed end of a large pillow-case and then slipping a hanger through.

- Fold sweaters and scarves into tightly sealed plastic containers.

- Store clothes in a cool, dry, and well-ventilated spot.

Thrifty techniques for creating the style you crave

Recently retired? Then you may be flying by the seat of your pants when it comes to your wardrobe. After all, the clothes you wore in your professional life might not fit into your new routine. Fortunately, you can transition to a fashionable new style without losing your shirt. All you need is a strategy.

Look at your lifestyle to narrow down options. Think about how you'll spend the majority of your time in retirement. Will you go to museums and the theater? Or are you more of an outdoorsy type who likes hiking and gardening? Perhaps you plan on moving to a warmer climate or doing volunteer work with the public.

Decide which activities you'll focus on. Create your wardrobe with this in mind, devoting more of your budget to the style of clothes you'll need and wear most.

Consider your personality before buying. Think about what you liked from your work attire and include similar items in your more casual retirement wardrobe. Someone who, for example, enjoyed wearing suits might feel comfortable pairing a button-down shirt and blazer with jeans. If that's the case, you can probably mix some of your old garments with the new.

Looking for a totally different style? Study the outfits worn by your fashion heroes to get a sense of what might work for you. Opt for clothes you enjoy wearing.

Quality basics provide a put-together look. You'll get a lot more out of your closet if you purchase several classic pieces in neutral colors. A good foundation for women includes dark-wash jeans, dress pants in a lightweight wool blend, a tailored blouse and blazer, a white T-shirt, and a quality handbag. Men should look for a suit and sports coat, a polo and dress shirt, dark jeans, dress pants, and a pullover sweater.

Purchase well-made items. Be on the lookout for natural-fiber clothes with metal zippers, strong stitching, and spare buttons. Remember the cost-per-wear rule. The more you wear something, the better the return on your investment.

Accessories take you from dull to dazzling. Got the basics of your wardrobe covered? Then it's time to add splashes of color with neckties, handkerchiefs, hats, scarves, and belts. Chunky bracelets, for example, are a great way to bring a bit of fun and flair to your outfit — with a price point that's easy on the wallet.

The best part? Trendy, less expensive accessories update the look of your clothes — and help you get a lot more mileage out of them.

Button down high clothing costs with some TLC

Despite having a net worth of $87 billion, the investment wizard Warren Buffett is a man of modest taste. He's lived in the same Nebraska home since 1958 and spends his free time playing bridge. Buffett, still going strong at 88, appears to take the same approach when it comes to his wardrobe.

"Whether we're talking about socks or stocks, I like buying quality merchandise when it is marked down," he has told shareholders in his company, Berkshire Hathaway.

Another way to stretch your dollars and still look snazzy? Delay having to replace your favorite garments. Here's how.

Wise washing keeps your clothes top-notch. It turns out that less is more when it comes to detergent. Why is that? Extra suds can discolor your clothes and damage your washing machine. What else can you do to keep from putting too much wear and tear on your garments?

- Don't go overboard with laundering your jeans. Wear them at least three or four times before turning them inside out and washing in cold water. It helps prevent fading and protects rivets and seams.

- Unbutton shirts before tossing them in the machine to keep buttons from pulling loose. And make sure zippers are closed. Otherwise they might snag other garments.

- Wash delicate lingerie and swimsuits by hand and air dry. Swimsuits should be washed after each use to prevent chlorine and saltwater from damaging fibers and elastic.

- Wear suits and dress pants and skirts multiple times before taking them to the dry cleaner.

Well-cared-for clothes mean big savings. You've heard the old saying — an ounce of prevention is worth a pound of cure. It holds true for clothes as well. Follow these tips to keep your wardrobe looking fresh as a daisy for years to come.

- Fold your fine knits and store them on a shelf to prevent stretching.

- Wear old T-shirts under sweaters to absorb perspiration. You won't have to wash the sweaters as often, reducing the risk of shrinkage and pilling.

- Stitch loose buttons before they pop off and are lost forever.

- Treat stains promptly so they don't set in. To learn how to remove the toughest ones, go online to *cleaninginstitute.org/laundry* and choose Stain Removal Chart from the sidebar.

- Keep your shoes looking new by waterproofing, brushing, and polishing when they look dull. Your local cobbler can replace uneven heels and worn soles.

- Wipe the outside of your leather handbag once or twice a year with the proper cleaner, then apply a moisturizer to avoid cracks. When storing, stuff with bubble wrap so the bag keeps its shape.

Consignment boutiques: Where you'll find recycled style for a song

Mimi Crawford began shopping at consignment stores while in college. Her reason was quite simple. "All the girls wore high-fashion clothes," she says. "I didn't want to pay the price tag, but I still wanted to look nice." It didn't take long for Mimi to get lots of positive feedback on her purchases.

She hasn't looked back since. Now a successful business-woman, Mimi still visits consignment shops near her Atlanta-area home. You'd be surprised at the great bargains out there, she says.

"I once paid $70 for a winter white, wool blend Carolina Herrera shift dress that would have cost more than $2,000 at Neiman Marcus," Mimi recalls. But, she explains, it's not the designer label she was after.

"It's more about the quality of the dress," Mimi says. "It's a really well-made classic that will last a decade or two."

That purchase was a one-time consignment splurge. Mimi says she normally spends a lot less — between $10 and $20 per visit.

Then, when she gets home, she either washes the gently worn clothes or has them dry cleaned.

Mimi suggests stopping by a consignment store at least once every three months. The best time, she advises, is when the owner adjusts the clothing stock to reflect the change in season.

She admits there are downsides to consignment shopping. Many of the stores won't accepts returns, she warns. And they tend to cater to smaller-sized customers.

So what keeps her going back? "It's the thrill of the hunt and then finding a really good deal," she explains.

Utilities

Are your utility bills creeping up now that you're retired? If so, you're not alone. Many retirees notice that their electricity, gas, and water tabs skyrocket after they hang up their briefcases.

The source of your ballooning bills? It's you. You're not spending your days at the office, so you use up more energy at home. Experts estimate that the average homeowner over 65 spends $3,730 on utilities each year. Fortunately, a few simple tweaks can slash that sum without zapping the comforts of home.

4 home hacks save you hundreds on heating and cooling costs

Get a smart thermostat to avoid dumb mistakes. Too hot one minute and too cold the next? Your solution may be to adjust your thermostat frequently. But studies show those little temperature tweaks really ramp up your power bills. Save money by making smart adjustments instead.

Experts say changing the thermostat 10 degrees from your normal setting for eight hours a day can save you 10 percent on your energy bill. For instance, try running the AC less during those summer nights, and keep your heat lower during the

Own a heat pump instead of a central heating system or furnace? Think twice before toying with the temperature or buying a programmable thermostat. Yo-yoing the heat up and down actually keeps the pump from working efficiently. And that means your bills will be higher. Instead, keep your home at a steady, moderate temp.

winter days. How much could this shave off your heating and cooling bills? About $179 each year.

Don't want the hassle of messing with your thermostat? Look into a programmable one. These gadgets let you schedule temperature changes to maximize your savings automatically.

Use your windows wisely to keep money in your pocket. A third of your home's heat escapes through your windows. Are you neglecting your first line of defense? Most homeowners don't adjust their shades and curtains, but if you use them properly, you can save some serious cash.

On sunny winter days, open up your curtains and let the natural light warm your house. Then do the opposite in the summer. Pull down the blinds on windows that get direct sunlight to keep your air conditioner from working overtime.

Buy why stop there? If you invest in insulated cellular shades — those designed with honeycomb-shaped pockets — you can reduce your home's heat loss by as much as 40 percent. That works out to a 20 percent discount. Couple that with your thermostat savings, and you can slash your heating bill by up to 30 percent.

Cheap solution stops sneaky drafts. This simple 25-cent fix can help lower your heating and cooling bills. All you have to do is line the inside of your outlet and switch plate covers with little foam gaskets that insulate your home from air leaks.

Hidden behind those covers are electrical boxes that protect and conceal your wires. When these boxes are located in exterior walls, they are practically holes to the outside world.

Fortunately, you can pick up inexpensive foam gaskets at your local hardware store and pop them behind your plate covers. They block out drafts and keep you in control of your climate.

Crush cooling costs by fixing your filters. Your air conditioner works by pumping warm air from your home over evaporator coils that absorb heat and cool the air. It then sends frosty gusts back into your home.

An air filter blocks dust, pollen, and other debris from hitching a ride to the coils. But if this screen gets clogged, it blocks airflow and can allow dirt to make its way to the coils. And that means your unit has to work extra hard to cool you down.

Experts estimate that regular filter changes can save you up to 15 percent a year on your power bill. That's about $17 you can put back in your pocket each month.

Score over $4,500 worth of energy-saving home improvements for free

Want to save more than $280 a year on your energy bill? The Weatherization Assistance Program may be able to help, regardless of whether you rent or own or live in an apartment, house, or mobile home. Here's how it works.

- Go online to *nascsp.org/about/state-contacts* to find your state program and see if you qualify. Low-income seniors over 60 often get priority.

- Once you're approved, local experts will inspect your home and determine the most cost-effective way to make your space more energy efficient.

- Next, the crews get to work. Upgrades might include sealing off air leaks, installing insulation, and repairing ducts.

Draft defense: Stop your savings from vanishing into thin air

You wouldn't dare go to bed on a chilly winter night without a thick, warm blanket. But chances are, your house doesn't have the same protection. The North American Insulation Manufacturers Association estimates 9 out of 10 homes are not sufficiently insulated. That means your warm air is escaping in the winter. And your cool air is getting out in the summer.

The worst part? It's taking hundreds of your hard-earned dollars along with it. But according to the Department of Energy, you can save up to $166 on heating and cooling costs each year if you simply seal up air leaks. Here are some often-missed spots you need to secure.

Seal your garage and hang onto cash. Do you have an unheated garage? Think of it as a portal to the outside world.

Your first step is to seal small air leaks with caulk and bigger ones with foam sealant. This blocks car exhaust and other airborne pollutants — think gardening supplies, paints, and solvents — from finding their way into your home.

Then install the same insulation you'd use for an exterior wall between the living spaces and your garage. That advice applies to the floors of rooms above a garage, too.

An arctic attic could add hundreds to your annual energy bill. Heat rises, which means your warm air is trying to escape through the roof. If you don't have enough insulation to trap it inside, your heating costs will skyrocket. For example, if you live in the Northeast, poor insulation in your attic could tack an extra $600 a year onto your bills.

How do you tell if your attic insulation is up to snuff? It should have an R-value — a measure of resistance to heat transfer — of at least 30. But if you live in a cooler climate, that number could even be higher. The rating also varies depending on the thickness and type of material.

Contact a local building supplier or an insulation contractor to find out if your house is properly equipped for your area. Or go online for more information at *energy.gov/energysaver/ weatherize/insulation*.

High heating and cooling costs? The blame might be with your vents. Air ducts are supposed to help warm and cool your house. So it might surprise you to find out they could actually be doing the opposite.

Experts say your air ducts can cost you hundreds of dollars if they allow heated air to seep into unheated spaces. Put a stop to this money drainer by sealing up air leaks and insulating your ducts.

Utility-switch swindles — don't get bewitched by these power plays

Ring. Ring. A telemarketer promises you a 20 percent discount on your next utility bill. All you have to do is switch over to a new gas provider. But get hooked by his line and your savings will sink.

Chances are this offer is temporary. After you're signed on with a long-term contract, your energy costs will shoot up. And the worst part is you're saddled with high cancellation fees, so it's impossible to get out unscathed.

Some companies will also contact you and claim they just want to gauge your interest in switching. Don't give them your account or billing information though. They may switch you over to their company without your go-ahead. This illegal practice is called slamming.

Websites like *powersetter.com*, *chooseenergy.com*, and *power2switch.com*, as well as websites specific to your state, will compare energy rates for you. Contact your state Public Utility Commission to learn about your options.

And remember, a legitimate company will allow you to lock in a specific rate for a specific amount of time — usually a year.

> # Power down your payments with these senior specials
>
> Say watt? You're not taking advantage of the senior discounts offered by your utility company? If you're having trouble keeping the lights on, don't despair. You might qualify for a price cut.
>
> Take it from Bill Edge, the public information officer for the Georgia Public Service Commission. "A senior citizen could save almost $30 a month on their electric, gas, and telephone bills in the state of Georgia if they qualify," Edge says.
>
> Georgia's requirements? You must be at least 65 years old, the utility bill has to be in your name and at your current address, and you can't make more than $24,280 a year.
>
> You have options regardless of what state you live in, but the benefits vary depending on local laws and your utility providers. Reach out to energy companies or your local government to find out what discounts they provide.
>
> Edge also adds that programs designed for low-income families are good for seniors, too. He specifically points out the Low Income Home Energy Assistance Program. While it doesn't target seniors, it often gives priority to people over 60.
>
> "You can apply through your local community action agency," Edge says. "And receive up to $300 toward your utility bills."

Shrink your electric bill with washday wisdom

The ancient Romans put a lot of effort into doing laundry. They trampled on their dirty robes in tubs, rinsed them in a complex series of basins, hung them to dry, brushed the nap with hedgehog skins, treated them with sulfur to whiten, then flattened them out in screw presses.

Hard to complain when all you have to do is chuck your clothes into the washer and go about your day, right? But this convenience comes with a price — literally. Modern machines can add hefty numbers to your power bill.

Keep it cool to crush your cleaning costs. The energy it takes to warm up water for a load of laundry accounts for almost 90 percent of the power your washer uses. Simply wash everything in cold water to save a cool $40 a year.

Consult the clock to stop your dryer from working overtime. It's tempting to throw your clothes in the dryer and just forget about them. But if you over-dry your clothes, you waste dozens of dollars. In fact, letting your dryer run for an extra 15 minutes after your clothes are done can tack on $34 a year to your power bill.

See if your dryer has a moisture-sensing setting that automatically shuts off the heat when your clothes are ready. Otherwise, estimate your dry time and check in frequently toward the end of the cycle.

Try this no-tech solution to dry up bloated bills. One of the easiest ways to save on your clothing costs is also one of the oldest tricks in the book. Line dry your clothes on nice, sunny days to buff up your budget.

If you line dry just one load once a week, you could save over $20 a year. Plus line drying is gentler on your clothes so they last longer. Looking for more ways to save big bucks by keeping your wardrobe in tiptop shape? See *Button down high clothing costs with some TLC* in the *Clothing* chapter.

Curb your kitchen costs by almost $200

You know that $20 you saved on groceries by clipping coupons? It just went up in smoke on your dirty stovetop. Those burner pans aren't only for catching drips and grease. They reflect heat back at your pots and pans. So when they are grimy and blackened, your stove has to work harder. And that means your power bills suffer. Scrub them up until they shine, and then start saving with these other kitchen hacks.

Just-right tools cut the price of food prep. Did you know using the wrong size pan for your stove could cost you $36 a year? Cooking with a pan 2 inches too small for your burner lets 40 percent of the heat escape, taking your hard-earned money with it. So make sure your pots and pans match your burner sizes.

And while you're at it, check the bottoms of your cookware. Warped surfaces keep pots from touching the electric burner coils, which can slow cook times and amp up your bills.

Spare fridges swipe hundreds from your wallet. One out of every 4 American homes has more than one refrigerator. Do you really need all that storage space? Getting rid of an unnecessary appliance could save you up to $140 a year.

If you are determined to hold on to that second fridge, at least keep it stocked. Experts say it needs to be about three-fourths full to work at peak efficiency.

Freeze energy hogs to save a bundle. Automatic ice makers hike your refrigerator's energy usage by up to 20 percent. But taking 30 seconds to switch your ice maker off could save you $18 a year. Most turn off with the flip of a switch or the lift of a shut-off arm.

Then go old school and use ice trays. And if you need more freezer room, it's usually easy to remove the automatic ice maker entirely.

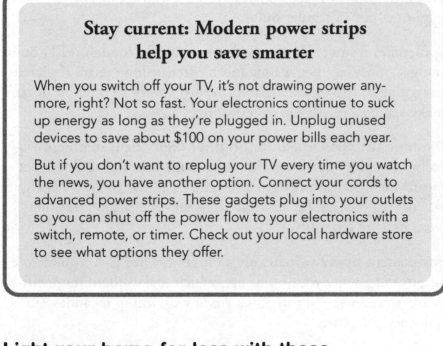

Stay current: Modern power strips help you save smarter

When you switch off your TV, it's not drawing power anymore, right? Not so fast. Your electronics continue to suck up energy as long as they're plugged in. Unplug unused devices to save about $100 on your power bills each year.

But if you don't want to replug your TV every time you watch the news, you have another option. Connect your cords to advanced power strips. These gadgets plug into your outlets so you can shut off the power flow to your electronics with a switch, remote, or timer. Check out your local hardware store to see what options they offer.

Light your home for less with these simple switches

The lightbulb shares a spot in history books with revolutionary inventions like the automobile and the telephone. But you're not driving around in a Model T or making calls with Alexander

Graham Bell's original design. So why are you still using old-school lightbulbs in your house? Not only are they dated, but they're energy hogs, too. Make a couple of updates and you'll save over $100 a year on your power bill.

Spark your savings with LED bulbs. While incandescent bulbs are cheaper to buy, they cost more in the long run. Switching over to Energy Star LED lights can save you about $75 a year.

And even though these bulbs are more expensive initially, they last longer than your old incandescent lamps. LEDs may be good for more than 10 years, compared to the average of one year you might get out of regular bulbs.

Sometimes it's not smart to make that switch, though. LED bulbs can get pricey, so they're only more efficient long term. If you're just going to flip on the light in the attic every so often, it doesn't make sense to splash the cash on pricey lights.

Dimmer switches make for brighter bills. Light dimmers originally worked by diverting electricity from your lightbulbs. That meant the lights didn't burn as brightly because the extra energy was turned to heat. So not only were they inefficient, but they were also fire hazards.

Fortunately, newer switches are a lot safer. They also regulate the amount of energy your bulbs use, which makes them more efficient. You can save up to $30 a year by dimming incandescent bulbs to half power.

A word of warning — lighting plays a big part in reducing falls and injuries. Don't dim your lights if it makes it difficult to spot furniture, stairs, and other objects around the house.

12 simple ways to cut your water bill

	Potential Yearly Savings*
Fix running toilets. A leaking toilet tank could waste 200 gallons of water every day.	**$365**
Swap sprinklers for a drip irrigation system. Watering plants at the root could save 30,000 gallons a year.	**$150**
Install a WaterSense toilet. Inefficient toilets can waste over 35 gallons a day. Look for the WaterSense label, a marker of efficiency.	**$65**
Swap baths for showers. Save about 32 gallons every time you choose to shower instead of soak.	**$58**
Add aerators to your faucets. These little gadgets reduce the amount of water used every time you turn the tap.	**$49**
Shorten your showers. Trim your shower time from 10 minutes to 5 minutes. Start by turning off the water while you lather up.	**$46**
Do laundry less often. Washing 2 loads a week instead of 4 will curb costs.	**$22**
Repair leaky faucets. A faucet that drips once every second wastes about 10 gallons in a day.	**$18**
Switch to WaterSense shower heads. Efficient, low-flow models save about 56 gallons per week.	**$15**
Use the dishwasher. Load up an energy-efficient dishwasher a few times a week instead of washing dishes by hand after each meal.	**$8**
Don't let the water run. Turn off the faucet while brushing your teeth or shaving to save over 90 gallons every month.	**$5**
Visit the car wash. Instead of washing your ride in the driveway every other week, go to a facility that uses recycled water.	**$3**
Total savings	**$804**

*Savings based on $0.005 per gallon average and 2-person household.

Cable, phone, and internet

You pay about $70 a month for your cellphone and landline. Don't forget to add another $60 for internet. And $100 for cable. Before you know it, you're spending over $2,700 a year. But are you getting your money's worth?

First, figure out whether bundling your cable, phone, and internet services together is going to help you save or drain your budget. These all-inclusive packages claim to be convenient and cost-effective. After all, getting your services from the same company means you only have one bill to keep track of. And sometimes you can find great bargains.

But bundling isn't a money-saver if you don't use everything you pay for — like that high-speed internet you don't need or those premium channels you don't watch.

If you determine bundling isn't for you, shop for different providers to see if you can get better deals when you buy services a la carte. But as you cherry-pick your services, avoid doubling up. For example, do you need a cable subscription when you already watch your favorite shows on Netflix? Are you using your landline and cellphone or could you drop one?

Sorting through all your options can be tricky, but the simple tips in this chapter can help you save hundreds every year — without losing your marbles.

Put a modern twist on an old phone to hook hundreds

Is your landline bill draining your budget? You're in good company. "AT&T was going to charge us $10 a month plus junk fees if we bundled it with their other products," says David, a longtime landline user. That meant he needed a cable and internet subscription just to get that price. But if he wanted only landline service? That cost over $30 a month.

He started researching cheaper options and stumbled across Ooma, a phone service that makes calls over the internet. Because he lives in an area with great internet service, making the switch was a no-brainer. He went online and tracked down an inexpensive used Ooma Telo device, which let him hook up his old handsets to the internet and keep his old landline number.

"We receive crystal-clear phone service for $0 a month for any call made to any phone in North America," David says.

And he didn't have to compromise on safety. For a few dollars a month, he gets an E911 feature that ensures local emergency services know exactly where his phones are calling from.

All in all, David pays $60 a year for nearly unlimited landline access. "That's much better than the annual $480 the traditional telecom company was trying to charge us," he says.

4 good calls help you dial down phone fees

Senior discounts ring up big bargains. Do you use 4 gigabytes of data every month? Are you maxing out your minutes? Should you spring for 4G coverage or the top-tier unlimited plan? Got all that? No? Cellphone contracts can be expensive and confusing. But some companies offer simple plans tailor-made for seniors.

- You can have a smartphone and a straightforward plan. T-Mobile and Sprint, for example, offer packages for folks 55 and up that have all the bells and whistles, like unlimited talk, text, and data.

- If you don't need all the newest features, budget-friendly basic options might be your best bet. Companies like Jitterbug and Republic Wireless offer cheap plans with just texting and calling.

Buy used to get cutting-edge phones for yesterday's prices. New phones are expensive. The latest, greatest gadgets can cost well over $1,000 if you buy them new. But why spend all that money when you can get the same tech for a fraction of the price? Websites like *gazelle.com*, *ebay.com*, and *amazon.com* sell gently used phones for a big discount.

Before you buy, get the serial number from the seller. You need to check with your carrier to make sure the phone will work with your cell network. And they will confirm that the device hasn't been flagged as stolen or missing.

Your old phone could feel new with a little TLC. You love your old phone, but after years of use it has started to slow down. An upgrade is out of the question, and you can't find anyone who sells that model anymore. Fortunately, you can breathe some new life into your cellphone with a few easy tweaks.

- Smartphone users should delete old, unused apps. They waste space and can cut your phone's performance.

- Clean out old pictures and voicemails. If you don't want to lose your photos, upload them to your computer. You'll save space without sacrificing precious memories.

- Replace the battery. An old battery will bog down your phone. Changing it could be a simple task, depending on what kind of cellphone you have. If you can't do it yourself, a computer repair shop should be able to handle the task for a small fee.

Update old tech for stellar savings. Your landline is expensive, but what if you don't want to rely entirely on your cellphone? After all, it won't offer the quickest response time if you call 911 and are unable to tell the operator exactly where you live.

Voice over Internet Protocol (VoIP) phones, on the other hand, come with Enhanced 911 (E911) features, which means they automatically provide emergency responders with your callback number and, in most cases, your address. VoIP phones make calls using the internet. They look like landlines, but cost about $45 less each month.

Disable your cable — cut the cord to save over $1,000 a year

Some folks spend $150 a month on cable. But with a little know-how, you can pay that — or less — just once and get plenty of channels forever — including some that aren't even on cable.

Over-the-air alternatives breathe new life into your budget. When you were a kid, your family didn't pay hundreds of dollars for cable TV. All you needed to do was get those bunny ears just right and you could catch local broadcasts for free. Today updated antennas let you watch high-definition channels for the same time-honored price tag.

- Indoor antennas are great if you live close to the TV towers, and if nearby buildings and trees don't block your signal. They generally range from $10 to $80.

- Outdoor options are more powerful. These models could cost up to $300, but you can find them for less than $50.

Head over to websites like *tvfool.com* and *www.antennaweb.org* to see what stations are available in your area and what kind of antenna you might need. Just type in your address or ZIP code to get started.

Start streaming to fend off high cable fees. Want to go beyond your local broadcast channels? Streaming might be your best bet. This technology delivers content, like movies and TV shows, over the internet. But that doesn't mean you can only stream on your laptop or computer. The right tech will let you watch online-only shows on your home TV.

- Smart TVs. The latest, greatest tech means smart TVs can hook right up to your internet, allowing you to view entertainment galore on streaming apps from services like Netflix and Tubi.

- Streaming sticks and boxes. Already have a perfectly good regular TV? Streaming devices act as a middleman for your tube and internet. You plug them into your TV to access apps and watch your favorite shows, movies, and more. And prices start at just $30.

Some streaming services come with a monthly fee. But if you know where to look, you can get by without paying a penny.

Waive streaming fees to find your favorites for free

Paid streaming services like Netflix and Hulu offer you thousands of hours of TV and movies. But can't you get hours of entertainment for free? Why yes, yes you can. Here's how.

Find free TV without splashing the cash on premium channels. Streaming services could cost $10 a month — more if you go for the commercial-free or ultra-high-definition options. But you'll shell out zero cash on these free services.

- Sony Crackle. Access a rotating selection of popular movies, TV shows, and original content.

- Tubi. Browse a huge library of movies and TV shows. It's supported with ads instead of subscription fees.

- Comet. Sci-fi fans can get their fix from this service that offers movies and TV series, from cult classics to undiscovered gems.

> Want to switch to streaming without missing the latest episodes of your favorite shows? Most on-air TV shows aren't available on streaming services until after the season is over. But some networks, like ABC and NBC, let you stream recent episodes for free. Just search for the network app on your streaming device.

- Hoopla. If your local library supports this streaming app, you can check out movies, TV shows, and audiobooks from the comfort of your couch.

Stay up to date without paying through the nose. One of the main reasons people don't cut the cord is they don't want to lose out on live content. But you don't have to miss the nightly news when you swap your cable box for a streaming stick.

- Some TV networks offer apps for streaming live news feeds, on-demand video clips, and other content from the day. You might have to watch ads, but that's a small price to pay for free TV.

- See what free apps are available through your streaming device. Pluto TV, for example, lets you tune in to live news stories, while NewsON offers live and on-demand broadcasts from local stations.

- You can also check out your local news station's website for live streams or replays.

Ring up big discounts with a single phone call

Are your cable and internet costs creeping up? Is your phone bill more expensive than it was last year? Don't just deal with it — find a better deal. Here's where to call.

It's not the main customer service department. Believe it or not, you should head straight to cancellations. The employees working here are often allowed to give bigger discounts in order to keep your business. But they might not always offer the best deals upfront. You'll need to have a few tricks up your sleeve if you want to get the lowest prices.

- Be polite. The representatives in call centers spend long days dealing with angry customers. Being friendly might help you get a better discount. As the old saying goes, you catch more flies with honey than vinegar.

- Know your contract. Sometimes cable and internet companies sneak early termination fees into your agreement. Read over your paperwork so you'll be ready if the representative mentions any contract charges.

- Come prepared with the competitor's prices. If you claim you can get a better deal elsewhere, have the numbers to back it up. These bargaining chips could help you strike a deal with your current provider.

- Ask for a new-customer discount. Companies often offer big discounts to reel in new customers, but that doesn't mean the devoted regulars are out of luck.

- Get it all in writing. You need a record of any deals representatives offer. Otherwise you can't count on the billing department to honor them.

Should you pay a pro to strike a bargain?

You have two choices when you're ready to negotiate your bill. Do the grunt work yourself or enlist the help of an expert. Bill negotiating services claim they'll lower your costs — for a price. But are these services worth it?

Maybe — if you hate talking on the phone so much that you'd pay someone to do it for you. Reputable companies often charge half of the amount they save you over the first year. So if they get a $50 discount over the next 12 months, you'll owe them $25. And you won't pay a dime if they fail.

These companies don't have special bargaining powers, though. Plus they usually ask for your private account information so they can negotiate on your behalf.

If you're willing to take the time, you can get the same deal yourself. Skip these services if you have privacy concerns or want to maximize your savings.

Reel in these deals to crush your internet costs

"I predict the Internet will soon go spectacularly supernova and in 1996 catastrophically collapse," wrote Robert Metcalfe, one of the pioneering minds behind the internet. Years later, he was forced to eat his words — literally. In a keynote speech, Metcalfe blended a copy of the article into a smoothie to make up for his failed prediction.

And how very wrong he was. These days you can't escape the internet. But you can cut down on the costs. Here's how.

Drum up senior deals and save $600 a year. Senior discounts could save you up to $50 a month on internet costs. But if you don't know where to look, you could miss out.

First, check out the Lifeline program from the Federal Communications Commission (FCC). It offers eligible seniors up to $9.25 a month toward their phone and internet bills. Go to *lifelinesupport.org* to see if you qualify.

> Internet companies often charge $15 a month for a modem and a router which let you connect to the internet. But you can buy your own from your local electronics store for about $100. That means you'd save $80 in rental fees after just one year.

Internet providers offer great deals, too. Comcast's Internet Essentials, for example, is only $10 a month for eligible seniors over 62. AT&T's Access program offers similar discounts for certain customers who participate in the Supplemental Nutritional Assistance Program (SNAP) or receive Supplemental Security Income (SSI).

These deals vary depending on your location and carrier. Reach out to your internet company and research other providers in your area to see what options you have.

Slash your speed to save big. You don't need a Lamborghini to drive to the corner market. Likewise, you don't need top-tier internet speeds to stream movies at home. So why are you paying for the premium package?

Internet companies pitch lightning fast internet hookups because they're also the most expensive packages. You might see ads promising blistering speeds of over 70 megabits per second (Mbps). Unless you want to watch several high-definition videos at the same time while downloading files on multiple devices, you can go for something cheaper.

Experts say dropping your speed could save you $35 or more a month, depending on your carrier. Speeds of 10 to 20 Mbps are more than enough to stream movies, check your email, and surf the net without a hitch.

Entertainment and hobbies

Anna Mary Robertson Moses enjoyed creating colorful needlepoint pictures of local farm life for her friends and family. But that stopped at age 78 when arthritis made stitching difficult. So she turned to painting, a new hobby that led to fame, fortune, and her well-known nickname — Grandma Moses. Your favorite pastime might not garner as much glory, but it can improve your life.

- Recent studies show that having a hobby lowers stress, improves quality of life, and may even help you live longer.

- And all those tasks you need to do to stay independent, like bathing, dressing, and feeding yourself? Researchers say hobbies can help your ability to perform those activities of daily living by keeping your brain and body active. Like the saying goes — use it or lose it.

Grandma Moses enjoyed painting, but if that's not your style, you can reap plenty of health benefits by choosing an activity that suits your interests — like gardening, writing, or playing a musical instrument. Even a good game of Scrabble might help keep you sharp.

And your hobby doesn't have to cost an arm and a leg. Grandma Moses, for example, saved money on paint supplies by creating several pictures at the same time using a similar sunny palette of yellow and green for each. Pretty thrifty. Read on to learn how you too can have a big time on a teeny budget.

Don't miss out on your library's free-for-all

"A library outranks any other one thing a community can do to benefit its people. It is a never-failing spring in the desert," said Andrew Carnegie, the 19th-century business-man who donated his sizable fortune to fund more than 1,600 libraries across the country.

And when you take a look at all today's libraries have to offer, you'll see the truth behind his words. Just ask Amy Mapel, director of the Carnegie Library in Newnan, Georgia.

Get fit — and have fun — for free. "Free exercise pro-grams like Exercise is Medicine and Gentle Yoga are our most popular," says Mapel. But craft classes, like crochet and beading, are favorites, too. "We pay for all the supplies. Patrons come in, make the project, and go home with some-thing they've created."

Master the web without spending a dime. Researchers know learning new skills — like navigating the internet — can help keep you mentally sharp. "We offer computer classes for folks who have never really figured out what Instagram is," says Mapel. And to make sure those pics you post on social media are perfect, her library offers free pho-tography classes.

Connect with friends to chase away the blues. The social interaction with other senior adults can be just as important as learning new things. "People who have lost a spouse and are floundering have come to these programs and found a great group of friends," says Mapel. "It's so heartwarming to know that we have provided a place for them to make connections."

Find out more about programs offered at your local "spring in the desert." Call your community library or check it out online.

5 super sources for 'fun'ding your free time

Discover freebies aplenty at your local library. Marian the librarian wouldn't recognize the place. CDs, DVDs, audiobooks, computers, magazines, Wi-Fi. You'll find them all at the library — for free.

Would you like to visit an art museum in town, or maybe drop by the local zoo? Check with your library to see if they offer free passes. Of course, if you really just want to read, you can always go old school and check out a new best-seller.

Shop online to net rock-bottom deals. Popular websites like *craigslist.org* and *ebay.com* are known for their great bargains. Maybe you're a fitness fanatic, looking for an exercise bike. A brand-new indoor cycling bike could run you $434 online. But on Craigslist? You could pick up the same bike, gently used, for $275. Score.

Or perhaps you're hoping to hit the links with some cutting-edge clubs. A new fairway wood might cost upwards of $200 at your local sporting goods store, but you might find the same club — preowned, of course — for less than $150 on eBay.

Rack up thrifty picks at bargain stores. Are you a whiz in the kitchen? Love to spend your free time boning up on all the new cooking gear and gadgets? Buying them brand-new can take a big bite out of your budget.

For a great deal on cookware, check out your local thrift stores. One bargain hunter bragged about finding a used popular cooking pot for about one-third of its $100 online price. With bargains like that, you'll soon be cooking up a savory storm.

Tap into "app"lause-worthy savings on the go. Let your fingers do the walking on your smartphone for colossal savings on entertainment and activities. One of the best-known apps, Groupon, offers discounts of up to 70 percent off restaurants, travel, local events, and more. Check out all the offers in your area by going to *groupon.com* or downloading the app.

And don't forget to look online for deals at your favorite restaurant. Is Krispy Kreme your go-to stop for morning coffee and a quick breakfast? Get a free doughnut just for signing up for their rewards program online or downloading the app.

Track down budget buys at yard sales. Your favorite form of entertainment is spending the day with your grandkids, so you're always on the hunt for inexpensive toys and games. From Barbies to Legos, yard sales offer a variety of bargain-priced entertainment.

For example, a build-your-own model roller coaster set could run you $200 online. But at a yard sale, a thrifty shopper snagged one for just $20. Now that's a bargain worth bragging about.

On the house: Bring the internet into play for cheap indoor fun

Rain, rain, go away. Come again another day. As a child, you couldn't wait to get outside to play ball or climb trees. Now that you're older, your favorite pastimes may include indoor activities like watching movies or enjoying a good book.

And since you're certainly wiser, too, you'll appreciate these tips that will keep you entertained for free. Come rain or shine. All you need is an internet connection.

Research your family history for no charge. Interested in finding out more about your ancestors? Go online to *familysearch.org* to access the largest collection of free genealogical records in the world.

Need more help? You'll find free genealogy sites listed at *family historydaily.com*. Just type "50 free sites" in the search box and you'll be climbing that family tree in no time.

Complimentary books to stock your home library. Become a book reviewer and read for free. Just go to *readerviews.com* and click on "become a reviewer." You'll be asked to fill in an application and select the types of books you'd like to read. Submit your review within four weeks of receiving the book, and it's yours to keep. Your grandkids can become reviewers, too, and build their own collection of kids books.

Enjoy a good audiobook every now and then? They're even better when they're free. Find classics you'll love at *openculture.com/ freeaudiobooks*. And while you're there, take a look at the site's collection of free e-books. Just click "eBooks" on the menu bar, and settle in for a great read.

Search these sites for reel enjoyment. Download or stream your favorite flicks — for free. The Internet Archive at *archive.org* touts more than 20,000 full-length feature films, documentaries, and more in its extensive library.

And if you're a fan of movies dating from the turn of the century up to the 1960s, you need to take a look at Free Classic Movies. Just go to *free-classic-movies.com* and scroll through the extensive list of films available to you at no charge.

For more ways to watch TV shows and movies for zero bucks, see *Waive streaming fees to find your favorites for free* in the *Cable, phone, and internet* chapter. Now get that popcorn popping.

Science-backed hobbies that boost your health
(and how to do them for free)

Gardening

Increases vitamin D, a nutrient important for strong bones, and lowers your risk of dementia by 36%.

Contact local garden centers, colleges, or gardening clubs for free classes.

Dancing

Lowers your risk of dementia and improves your balance.

Find free dance classes at your local library or senior center.

Expressive Writing

Reduces stress and even shortens the time it takes for wounds to heal.

Your local library may offer free writing workshops, or check online for free classes from top universities.

Playing and Listening to Music

Lowers your stress level, improves your memory, and boosts your immune system.

Sign up for free college classes, or listen to your favorite tunes through free online services like Pandora or Spotify.

Learning a Second Language

Delays symptoms of brain aging and Alzheimer's disease.

Start your language lessons for free at sites like *duolingo.com*, or check out your local library for free classes.

Taking Care of a Pet

Decreases loneliness and lowers your cholesterol and blood pressure.

If you're 60 or older, visit *petsfortheelderly.org* to find a new companion and get help paying for pre-adoption exams and other fees.

Turn yard sale deals into downright steals with these pro tricks

Yard sales can yield a bounty of inexpensive hobby supplies. But you've got to know where, when, and how to shop.

- Do your homework the night before. Scan local papers or use sites like *garagesalestracker.com* or *yardsale search.com* to find the best sales near you. Once you're there, use the eBay app to check and compare prices.

- Timing is everything. Shop early and beat the crowd for the best selection of big-ticket items like TVs and stereos. But for discounts on CDs, DVDs, and books, you may want to hold off until after 11 a.m. Sellers may be more willing to bargain later in the day.

- Come prepared to negotiate. Stock up on small bills if you plan to haggle. Sellers are more likely to agree to your offer if they see cold hard cash in your hand.

Get more — and pay less — when you explore the great outdoors

Runner Herbert Berman, age 81, can hold his own in the fast lane. In fact, his gold-medal-winning time in the 5K race at the Georgia Golden Olympics was enough to win him a spot in the National Senior Games, an Olympic-style competition for folks over 50.

Now maybe you're not track-and-field ready, but you still have plenty of opportunities to enjoy the great outdoors. And here's how to do them for free.

- Born to run. Whether you've been pounding the pavement for years or you're a newbie heading to your first race, a running group may be just the thing to kick-start your journey. Running with a group helps keep you safe and motivated. Check out your local sporting goods stores or search online for local running clubs to find free training sessions near you.

- Land the big one. In many states, anglers can fish without a license for one day — or even a weekend — during National Fishing and Boating Week. Find out about the next free fishing days in your area by going to *takemefishing.org*. Just type "free fishing" in the search box.

- Float your boat — safely. Need a safety refresher course before you get your boat out on the water? Go to *boatus.org/free* for a no-charge online boat safety course designed especially for your state.

> Looking for a deal on spacious skies and purple mountain majesties? An America the Beautiful pass, sold by the National Park Service, covers entrance fees at national parks and wildlife refuges from sea to shining sea. For folks 62 and over, an annual pass runs $20. A lifetime pass is bargain-priced at $80. Fruited plains included.

- Take a hike. From stocking your backpack to choosing your campsite, the American Hiking Society at *american hiking.org* has free tips for making your next hike the best ever as well as resources for finding trails near you. You can also go to *traillink.com* to discover over 30,000 miles of hiking trails — both near and far — ready and waiting for you to explore.

- Spin your wheels. Is cycling more your speed? For free classes on bike safety, mountain biking, even bikepacking — that's backpacking by bicycle — visit a nearby bike shop or pedal on over to your local Recreational Equipment, Inc. (REI) store for a schedule of free events near you.

PROTECT YOUR MONEY

SIMPLE WAYS TO SIDESTEP
SCAMS AND SAFEGUARD
YOUR SAVINGS

Identity theft

Your personal information is more vulnerable than ever. Last year, identity theft cost Americans more than $16 billion. That amount of money could buy 17 homes for every homeless person in the country. To keep your bank accounts and credit cards safe from scammers, follow these top tips.

- Freeze your credit to block fraudsters from opening an account in your name.

- Check your credit reports at least once a year for accounts that aren't yours.

- Set fraud alerts on your bank accounts to help you spot unauthorized activity.

- Cover the number pad on the ATM whenever you punch in your PIN.

- Use strong passwords online and on your computer to stay safe from hackers.

- Keep your computer software up to date to avoid security breaches.

But what if it's not just your money scammers are after? Crooks have their sights set on new targets — your health records. Medical identity thieves use your information to get prescriptions and treatments, file insurance claims, and obtain medical goods or services — all on your dime. This con hits you with more than a big bill, though.

- Fraudulent information on your medical records confuses doctors, which means you could get the wrong treatments.

- You might also miss out on medical care entirely if swindlers have already submitted claims for services you need.

Fortunately, you can take steps to avoid becoming a victim.

9 smart tricks to stop medical ID thieves in their tracks

Guard your cards to stave off scammers. You're pretty careful about protecting your checkbook. But do you give the same consideration to your health insurance information? Your ID cards contain sensitive data, so keep them away from prying eyes.

Contact your health insurance company immediately if your card is lost or stolen. If you have Medicare, call Social Security at 800-722-1213 to get a replacement card.

Keep your insurance information on a need-to-know basis. You wouldn't read your Social Security number out loud to a crowded room, would you? So why would you do the same with your health insurance information at, say, the doctor's office?

Stay mindful of who you let see or hear your insurance number. As a general rule, anyone who isn't a medical professional should stay in the dark.

Watch out for the high price of free offers. A salesman calls you up and promises a free hearing aid. All you have to do is give him your Medicare number. Sounds like a good deal, right?

Wrong. Offers like this are scams designed to steal your medical identity. Don't give out your insurance information to callers, regardless of how good the deal appears. If an offer seems suspicious, call 800-MEDICARE to double-check that you're dealing with an approved provider.

Better browsing can protect your info. You might not think twice before typing in your insurance number online. That's a huge mistake. Fake webpages or unsecured sites leave your details vulnerable, which could end up costing you hundreds of dollars.

Only enter your data into websites you trust. Look for a little lock icon on the top bar of your web browser. Also make sure the official URL begins with "https." Both are signs that the website encrypts your info, which helps protect it from hackers.

Stay up to date on your medical docs to catch thieves. Scan over all the bills and statements you get from your doctor's office. If you see charges for medicine, treatments, or other services you don't remember, you could be a victim of identity theft. Reach out to your insurance company's fraud department immediately.

You should also periodically review your medical records and alert your provider if you find errors. To get a copy, submit a written request to your provider and ask about required fees. If they don't send your records to you within 30 days, go to *hhs.gov/ocr* to file a complaint.

Service notices help you fight fraud. You should receive a Medicare Summary Notice (MSN) or an Explanation of Benefits (EOB) after a service is provided. Examine the docs carefully for signs of ID theft, like unfamiliar treatments or prescriptions.

Early warnings give you an edge. Sign up for fraud alerts from your health insurance company. You'll receive text messages or emails that notify you about activity on your accounts.

Shred your papers to protect your identity. One man's trash is another man's treasure. That's a motto that some identity thieves live by — literally. They'll root through your garbage hoping to find old papers with Medicare numbers or personal details. Run your documents through a shredder before you throw them out.

Don't let old medicine come back to haunt you. Believe it or not, your pill bottles say a lot about you. And some thieves will do anything to get their hands on your old prescription labels.

When your medicine runs out, don't just toss the bottles in the trash. Tear off the labels or black out all your information first.

Senior Medicare Patrols help you fight fraud

Raise your hand if you find Medicare confusing. Raise your hand if you're wary of scams and fraud. Raise your hand if you rely on Medicare anyway. Out of hands? Then you're like most of the 58 million Medicare beneficiaries searching for a little help. Find it with Senior Medicare Patrols (SMPs).

These volunteer organizations help you prevent, spot, and report health care fraud. From group presentations that teach you how to avoid getting fleeced by scammers to one-on-one counseling where volunteers review your Medicare Summary Notices for accuracy, SMP services help you protect what's yours. And the best part? It won't cost a penny.

To reach out to a local SMP, go online to *smpresource.org* and click Find Help in Your State.

Retirement wreckers — duck these scams that will leave you broke

Could the number of candles on your cake put a bull's-eye on your back? Experts say seniors are more likely to fall victim to scammers than any other age group. Keep an eye out for these three cons that will break the bank and your heart.

Give government impostors the slip to shore up your savings. Ring. Ring. A voice on the other line claims to be a Medicare representative calling about a problem with your benefits. They'll help you get it sorted out, but you need to verify your identity first.

The so-called government official on the other line is actually a crook. And as soon as you read out your Medicare number you fall into his trap. You're not alone, either. Impostor scams like this cost Americans a whopping $328 million last year.

Never give out your personal information over the phone unless you're the one who made the call and it's to someone you trust. The government won't dial you to deal with account trouble. They prefer to use the post office to reach out.

Pick out phony prizes to ward off thieves. Not many things are as exciting as a surprise gift. So when a letter turns up that says you've won a million dollars, who wouldn't be happy?

But there's a catch. You need to wire your benefactor money to cover taxes and fees before you claim your winnings. A few days after you take a trip to the bank, however, the shoe drops. It's a phony prize and the money you wired is gone.

So what can you do? First off, never give anyone money to claim winnings. That's a surefire sign it's a scam. Next, report the scammers to officials by calling 1-877-382-4357 or going online to *ftc.gov/complaint*.

Don't let serial scammers prey on your emotions. Sometimes schemers will use the personal details of your loved ones to try to dupe you into sending them cash.

Recently, thieves started swindling seniors with a con called the Grandparent Scam. Here's what happens. You get a call from somebody who claims to be your grandchild in distress. They may say legal troubles

You can't keep up with every single scam. That's why identity theft expert Carrie Kerskie says to look for these red flags to spot a con — inflexible demands, a sense of urgency, and severe consequences. For example, a scammer might say your only option is to pay them in gift cards right now or your bank account will be shut down.

landed them in prison and they need fast cash to post bail. This scam is so effective that 1 out of every 4 seniors who get this call reach into their pockets to pay up.

If you do get a call asking for emergency funds, don't panic. Take a deep breath and gather all the details before you do anything. Try calling your grandkids back at a number you trust. Or get in touch with another relative who can shed light on the situation.

> ## " Log in to lock out internet impostors
>
> "The greatest generation grew up in a time where you didn't have to lock your doors," says Carrie Kerskie, president of Griffon Force, a company that helps clients combat and counter identity theft. But the world isn't as straightforward anymore. Scammers and swindlers are everywhere. And one of their favorite places to lurk is the internet.
>
> You might think you'll be safe from identity thieves if you stay off the internet. "But that couldn't be further from the truth," Kerskie says. "If you're not online, you actually have a greater risk of becoming a victim."
>
> That's because everyone from your bank to your utility company to the IRS uses online accounts. "And if you don't create accounts for yourself, you leave them wide open for a bad guy to come in and do it on your behalf," Kerskie says.
>
> So if you're not online, go ahead and set up these accounts with strong passwords. Not internet savvy? No worries.
>
> "Work with someone who does use technology, like a trusted friend or a family member, to create the online accounts with their email address," she says. "If there are any problems or if someone tries to access the accounts, that person will be notified via email." "

Take these steps to ward off modern-day grave robbers

A stolen identity is bad enough, but the idea of somebody impersonating your recently deceased loved ones is downright disgusting. Sadly, it happens all too often. Con artists read obituaries to find details they can use to open credit cards, apply for loans, and get tax refunds. Here's how you can protect your loved ones' identities.

- When the official death certificate becomes available, request at least 12 copies. You will need these as proof that your loved one has died.

- Thieves scan obituaries looking for information they can use to create an identity. Don't give it to them. Keep your loved one's birthdate and mother's maiden name a secret.

- Cancel the deceased person's driver's license.

- Unless you notify the credit bureaus Equifax, Experian, and TransUnion, they will not be aware of the death. Send them copies of the death certificate, and ask them to place a deceased alert on the person's credit reports.

- A surviving spouse or executor of the state may request free copies of the deceased's credit report. Get one periodically and look for suspicious activity.

- Inform the Social Security Administration of your loved one's death. Be prepared to forward them a copy of the death certificate.

- Give copies of the death certificate to financial institutions, mortgage companies, insurance agencies, and the Department of Veterans Affairs if the person served in the military.

- Always make copies of all of your correspondence.

Credit monitoring: All bark and no bite?

Professional credit monitoring services sound sweet. They'll keep an eye on your credit so you don't have to. But you might want to think twice before shelling out big bucks on these programs.

They offer detection, but don't give much in the way of protection. Because these services won't notify you until after thieves use your info, they won't prevent identity theft. At most you can catch it early.

And at $10 to $25 a month, the benefits might not keep up with the cost. After all, you're not legally liable for accounts set up by credit thieves. And even if you're late to report stolen credit cards, you're not responsible for charges after the first $50.

Fend off fraudsters taking aim at the military

People used to give up sugar, grow victory gardens, and collect scrap metal to support the military overseas. But today men and women in uniform are under fire on the home front. At ease. You can combat crooks who target veterans by learning how to protect your privacy.

Don't let your identity go AWOL. Veterans are twice as likely as civilians to have their identities stolen. That's because online security breaches left military data vulnerable to hackers a few years ago.

Plus, every time you need to prove you served, you have to show sensitive documents. But do you even think twice about sharing your info?

Be mindful of who you give your personal details to. And consider applying for a Veterans Identification Card at *va.gov* for a safer, more convenient way to show proof of service. "With the card, Veterans with honorable service to our nation will no longer need to carry around their paper DD-214s to obtain Veteran discounts and other services," says Dr. David J. Shulkin, secretary of the Department of Veterans Affairs (VA).

The VA also offers a free program called More Than a Number designed to help you learn how to avoid identity theft. Find more online at *va.gov/identitytheft*. Or call the VA at 1-855-578-5492 if you suspect your identity has been stolen.

Steer clear of these scams targeting veterans. Some swindlers are after more than just military IDs. They'll go after anything from your pension to charitable donations.

- The process of filing a claim to get your benefits or disability pay can be complicated, but dodge anyone who offers help for a price. Make sure you're working with credible attorneys, claims agents, or other organizations by checking them out at *va.gov/ogc/apps/accreditation*.

- Other grifters might take aim at your pension with lump-sum scams. They offer you a cash advance in exchange for your checks down the line. But if you crunch the numbers you'll see the math doesn't work in your favor.

  Say someone offers you $50,000 for your $1,997 monthly payments over the next five years. Sounds like a nice payout, but if you do the math you'll see that five years of monthly checks adds up to $120,000, which means you lose out on $70,000.

- Don't get duped by phony charities. Scammers often pretend to represent foundations that help your fellow veterans. So while you think you're helping people get back on their feet, you're actually funding a crook's Jamaican cruise.

  To avoid getting fleeced, don't give money to charities without doing your research. Check out their ratings at websites like *give.org* or *charitywatch.org*. And double-check the name. Scammers use made-up organizations that sound similar to well-known charities and hope you won't spot the difference.

Watch out for these telltale signs of ID fraud

Identity thieves aren't as obvious as common crooks who smash in your windows and steal your jewelry — you may not even realize you've been victimized. Look for these red flags to put a stop to their pilfering ASAP.

Bank alerts

Your bank, credit card company, or other financial institution warns of unusual activity.

Extra accounts

Unauthorized accounts show up on your credit report.

Missing money

Funds disappear from bank accounts, or you see purchases you never made.

Tax troubles

The IRS claims you've already filed a report when you submit your tax returns.

Phantom bills

You get bills for accounts you never opened.

Collection calls

Debt collectors pester you about debts that aren't yours.

Plummeting scores

Your credit score drops even though your spending habits haven't changed.

Denied benefits

The government turns you down for benefits you're entitled to.

Prescription problems

Your pharmacy won't fill an Rx because it interacts with unauthorized meds obtained in your name.

Simple strategies to take back your identity

You checked your bank statement this morning and noticed that $25 was withdrawn from an ATM two states away. The only explanation? Identity theft. Now that you've caught the crooks red-handed, what do you do?

Call quickly to recoup your cash. Recovering your losses often has an expiration date. If you report a missing debit card within two business days of learning about the theft, for example, you only owe up to $50. If you report it within 60 days, you'll lose up to $500. Any longer than that and you have to eat all the costs.

Wave a red flag to warn credit companies. Fraud alerts notify businesses that they need additional verification before opening an account in your name. That means they will take extra steps to make sure you're actually who you say you are. You only have to place a fraud alert at one of the three credit bureaus, and it will contact the others. The alert lasts a year.

Double-check to make sure you're not missing major mischief. If your data was exposed, thieves could still be doing unseen damage. Order your credit reports and scan for any accounts you don't remember or suspicious charges. To get a free copy of your report from each of the bureaus once a year, visit *AnnualCreditReport.com* or call 1-877-322-8228.

Consider a credit freeze to ice out thieves. Freezing your credit guarantees nobody can open new accounts without your personal PIN. If you need to apply for a loan, get a new credit card, or do anything else that requires a credit check, you need to plan ahead. Simply contact the credit bureaus to temporarily lift the freeze, allowing some time for them to process your request.

Freeze out credit thieves to keep your ID safe

Want to stop scammers from accessing your credit information and opening new accounts? You'll have to choose between a credit lock and a freeze. Both will protect your information, but they come with a few key differences.

Locks let you switch credit access on and off in an instant with your phone or computer. Unfreezing your credit may take longer — up to an hour if you make the request online or by phone, or three business days if through mail.

The downside to locks? They might come with a cost. Some credit bureaus charge $10 to $25 a month for packages that include credit lock. Plus when you sign up, you might waive your rights to join a class-action lawsuit.

Freezes used to come with fees, too. But new federal laws mean they're free. So why pay for protection you can get without shelling out a cent?

Financial abuse

It's called the crime of the 21st century — the financial abuse of older Americans. Nobody knows for sure exactly how much scammers and thieves steal from seniors each year — it's said to be in the billions — but fleecing them out of their hard-earned savings is more common than you'd think. In fact, nearly 1 in 6 Americans age 65 and up say they've been taken advantage of financially.

The aftereffects, meanwhile, can be devastating. Some folks have lost their life savings, causing them to become dependent on family, friends, or government programs. A human toll exists as well, with victims wracked by fear, shame, guilt, and anger. Financial fraud can lead to depression and anxiety, even premature death.

Why target seniors? They're more likely to have savings and a regular stream of income. Retirees are also more accessible than someone working a 9-to-5 job, and tend to be more trusting than younger generations.

Plus older adults are more likely to be isolated. They may have lost a spouse or have health problems or dementia — all factors that make them particularly vulnerable to financial fraud.

Con artists have lots of ways of making contact.

- Television or radio. Look out for ads with big promises, like quick-weight-loss schemes, and products that have large shipping and handling fees.

- Mass mailings. You'll get a letter inviting you to a free lunch investment seminar. Or it may say you've won the lottery.

- Phone. Impostors pretend to be IRS agents seeking unpaid taxes or a troubled grandchild in need of money.

- Computer. You'll get an official-looking email or pop-up message designed to trick you into clicking it. It's a ruse to get your personal data.

At times the con is much more personal. In some cases, door-to-door salesmen overcharge for home repairs and yard work. In others, fraudsters pose as financial advisors to get access to retirement savings. Hard to imagine, but sometimes caregivers, family, and friends steal money or misuse legal documents.

Don't let yourself or a loved one get caught in this terrible trap. Read on for tips on recognizing potential fraud and how best to prevent such predatory behavior.

Easy action plan to guard your 4 main sources of wealth

Electronic banking means fewer mishaps. Studies show that the ability to manage complex financial tasks often gets more difficult with age. So why not tap a trusted loved one to help you manage your expenses?

Combining several bank accounts is a good place to start. You both will keep much better track of your finances.

"An elderly person should not have more than one checking and savings account and no more than two or three credit cards," suggests Carolyn McClanahan, director of financial planning at Life Planning Partners in Jacksonville, Florida.

> A new federal law seeks to protect you from senior financial abuse. Dubbed the Senior Safe Act, the law protects banks and financial advisors from being sued after reporting suspected fraud to law enforcement. It also encourages the training of employees to identify possible cases of abuse.

Next, ask about setting up automatic bill payments and alerts. This way, you won't have to worry about writing checks for recurring expenses like your phone and utility bill — or having someone else do it for you. As an added bonus, your bank will send you a text message if it notices unusual account activity.

Research counts when it comes to investments. Some studies say financial abuse is the No. 1 crime of abuse against people over 65. And your investment portfolio is a major target. Here's how to protect yourself from criminals who prey on seniors.

- Check out the disciplinary history of an investment professional for free at *investor.gov.*

- Avoid pitches promising unrealistic rates of return.

- Don't be rushed or pressured into handing over your money.

- Be wary of unsolicited offers and offshore investments.

Remember, smart investors do their own independent research and consult with family and friends before handing over any money. If a deal sounds too good to be true, it is.

Beware of strangers interested in your estate plans. Undue influence. It's when someone close to an older, isolated person — possibly a new "best friend" or caregiver — exploits a retiree for financial gain. In some cases, the vulnerable senior ends up including this person in his will, trust, and other estate planning documents.

Sometimes, McClanahan warns, caregivers will emotionally blackmail the dependent seniors. "They'll say something like, 'If you don't do this, I won't be able to take care of you anymore.'"

The best way to keep this from happening? Stay connected with family and friends. "You need to develop a community," advises McClanahan, "because depending on just one or two people puts you at a bigger risk."

Stay on your guard during the Thanksgiving and Christmas holidays — the season when seniors are particularly vulnerable to financial abuse. Why this time of year? More visitors tend to come in and out of your house. And con artists believe it's when you're more likely to make a "charitable" donation.

Check your credit to stop thieves. Did you know that anyone can steal pre-approved credit card offers from your trash, change the address, and apply for a new credit card under your name? Keep yourself safe from casual acquaintances — like a dishonest handyman or home health worker — by shredding any offers before tossing.

You can find out if any accounts have been opened in your name by ordering a free credit report from Equifax, Experian, or TransUnion at *AnnualCreditReport.com*. In the meantime, check your credit card statements each month for suspicious charges.

You also might consider placing a freeze on your credit — it will make it a lot harder for con artists to assume your identity and get a card. And the best part? It's also free.

For more strategies to help you avoid having your identity stolen, see the *Identity theft* chapter.

1st step to saving a senior from suspected abuse

Have a feeling something isn't right? Maybe your elderly neighbor is trying to collect lottery winnings by wiring thousands of dollars in "legal processing fees" to a Nigerian government official. Or maybe he's got new "friends" controlling his finances.

If you suspect financial abuse, contact your local office of Adult Protective Services (APS). APS will check out the situation and determine whether the person needs any assistance or services. The organization can also refer cases to law enforcement for investigation and prosecution.

Remember, though, that seniors always have the right to decline services.

Contact the National Adult Protective Services Association at *napsa-now.org/report* or call 202-370-6292 for help in finding your local agency.

Are you a victim? What to do and who to call

Joe, who gave up driving at 81, was grateful when his new neighbor offered to run errands for him. All went well for a couple of months, so Joe gave the woman a debit card to buy his groceries. But soon after, the bank called Joe to tell him his account was over-drawn — by $750. She had stolen the money to pay off a debt.

Sadly, similar stories of financial abuse happen all too often. Think you've been a victim? Here are some things to do.

- Tell someone you trust about your situation.

- Close any financial accounts affected by the scam.

- Contact your bank and credit companies.

- Place a fraud alert with the three major credit bureaus.

- Freeze your credit.

- Call law enforcement and make a report.

- Talk to a lawyer about your options.

If you need help navigating through the system, contact one of the following agencies. They provide resources to seniors who have been financially abused.

Organization	Contact details
The National Center for Victims of Crime	victimsofcrime.org
National Center on Elder Abuse	ncea.acl.gov
Consumer Financial Protection Bureau	consumerfinance.gov
Federal Trade Commission	ftc.gov
Better Business Bureau	bbb.org/scam-stopper
U.S. Securities and Exchange Commission	sec.gov/complaint/select.shtml
Financial Industry Regulatory Authority	finra.org/investors/investor-complaint-center
The U.S. Department of Justice	justice.gov/elderjustice

Protect yourself from fraudsters in your home

Most seniors want to live independently while staying connected to the people they love. Sometimes, that means hiring someone to help with chores like shopping, cooking, and housekeeping. Finding the right person can provide companionship and welcome relief.

On the other hand, employing the wrong person could lead to disaster. That's because some in-home caregivers try to take financial advantage of older adults. Take the following steps to ensure this doesn't happen to you.

Screen candidates to weed out a bad match. Don't feel pressured to hire someone just because you need help right now. Instead, rely on family or friends until you find the right person. Evaluate candidates by doing a criminal background check and looking at their social media accounts. If you see any red flags, move on.

Remember, it's better to be safe than sorry. If you're not comfortable with an applicant but don't know why, trust your gut and find someone else. Be particularly wary about hiring a friend or caregiver with a drug problem or in need of financial help.

Shield your finances to avoid trouble. Your relationship with in-home help is a professional one. That means not letting your employee open your mail, pay your bills, or manage any of your accounts. Nor should you lend money or personal property to your caregiver or let him use your debit or credit card to make purchases. Instead, send him to the store with enough cash to cover the bill and ask for a receipt.

Of course, you'll also want to protect your estate. Don't appoint anyone working for you as your agent under a power of attorney. And never let a caregiver sweet talk you into changing your will or making him a beneficiary of your retirement account.

Secure your valuables for ease of mind. You've heard the old saying that an ounce of prevention is worth a pound of cure. Either remove cherished items from your home or secure them in a lock box or safe. If you choose the latter, consider aiming a security camera in the area so you'll know if anyone tries to gain access.

But theft isn't limited to things like jewelry and stamp collections. Consider using a locked filing cabinet to store private documents, including retirement account, credit card, and bank statements.

For more information on finding and hiring a quality caregiver, see the *In-home care* chapter.

Choosing a caregiver: How to ensure you're in safe hands

Having a stranger working in your home can be risky business. That's why some people turn to an agency for help in finding someone trained and experienced in caregiving. But don't ink a deal with just any agency. Ask the following before signing on the bottom line.

- Do you conduct background checks and drug tests on your employees?

- Are your workers bonded? (If so, you're more likely to receive compensation if the caregiver steals from you.)

- How do you determine if the client and caregiver will be a good match?

- What training and certification do you require your caregivers to have?

- Can you supply references from previous clients?

- How does your agency supervise the quality of care provided?

"Watch for warning signs: Don't let your loved one fall victim

Is your elderly mother using her credit card more than usual? Perhaps she's just decided to live it up a little. On the other hand, unusual credit card activity could be a sign of something more sinister — financial abuse.

"You should be concerned if all of a sudden the person starts charging up a lot of stuff or becomes secretive about his finances," says Carolyn McClanahan, director of financial planning at Life Planning Partners in Jacksonville, Florida.

McClanahan, who began her career as a physician, warns that the appearance of a new best "friend" might also be a cause for concern. Be on the lookout, too, she says, if your loved one complains about missing credit cards.

McClanahan says all seniors are at risk of being defrauded. The most vulnerable, she says, tend to be isolated. "They're lonely, so they'll trust anybody who is friendly to them," she says.

Others are overconfident in their ability to spot someone trying to take advantage of them. Or they base their feelings about other people on gut instinct rather than facts.

Sadly, she says, scam artists prey on older adults with dementia. After all, it's easier to swindle someone who has difficulty balancing a checkbook or reading a bank statement.

So how can you protect the senior in your life from scammers and predators?

"The best way to prevent fraud and abuse is to plan early before there's a problem," she advises. "If you have one little iota of concern about your loved one, you need to open a conversation right then and there."

Taxes

"The hardest thing in the world to understand is the income tax," said renowned physicist Albert Einstein. It's not surprising then that taxpayers reportedly needed an average of 15 hours — nearly two full workdays — to complete the old Form 1040 used to file their federal income tax returns.

The recent redesign of Form 1040, reducing it from 79 lines to just 23, wasn't expected to help much. In fact, the revamped form comes with a whopping 117 pages of instructions.

Does the thought of having to plow through all that paperwork make your heart skip a beat? Then read on for simple tips on avoiding costly filing mistakes and keeping more of your money.

Save big tax dollars by avoiding these top 4 filing goofs made by seniors

Failing to take deductions and credits. Turn 65 this year? You can increase your standard federal deduction by $1,600 if you're single and $2,600 if both you and your spouse are 65 or older. That simple addition will lower your taxable income by $13,800 if you're single. And for married couples filing jointly? A whopping $27,000.

Along with the extra deduction, you may be eligible for the Credit for the Elderly or Disabled, which reduces your tax liability dollar for dollar. You must be 65 or older or have a permanent disability for which you are receiving taxable benefits. The credit — ranging between $3,750 and $7,500 — comes with strict income limits. To see if you qualify, use the online Interactive Tax Assistant at *irs.gov/help/ita*.

Not realizing Social Security can be taxed. Seniors living solely off Social Security can generally avoid paying taxes on those benefits. That's not often the case, though, if you supplement your payments with, say, a part-time job or retirement savings. In fact, if you're single and have a combined income of more than $25,000 a year — that amount rises to $32,000 for a married couple filing jointly — you must pay taxes on your Social Security earnings.

On how much? Between 50 and 85 percent of your benefits. To figure out your combined income, add your adjusted gross income and nontaxable interest to half of your annual Social Security payments.

For strategies to help you avoid paying taxes on your benefits, see *Retirement gotchas — avoid the tax trap with these tips* in the *Social Security* chapter.

Miscalculating the tax on dividends. Depending on dividend-producing stock to supplement your retirement nest egg? You're in luck when it comes to paying taxes. That's because qualified dividends fall under capital gains tax rates that are lower than the rates paid on ordinary income.

You'll pay nothing, for example, on your qualified dividends if your adjusted gross income is less than $38,600 a year. Take home more than that? The rate increases to 15 or 20 percent — still less than the 22 to 37 percent tax rate that higher earners pay on ordinary income.

Dividends are generally considered "qualified" if they are from a domestic or qualified foreign corporation and you have held the stock for a longer period of time. Review your shares to see if you're eligible for the lower tax rate.

Neglecting to give your return a once-over. Mistakes on your tax return — a misspelled name, for example, or inaccurate Social Security number — could end up costing you big. At the very least, it might mean a delay in your refund. You can avoid many common errors by filing electronically and looking out for these oversights.

- forgetting to sign your forms

- making math mistakes

- entering bank routing numbers incorrectly

- missing the tax deadline

- choosing an incorrect filing status

- not including earnings from a side job

Not worth its SALT? Revamp puts limits on this deduction

The good news? You can still deduct state and local taxes (SALT) when you itemize on your federal return. The bad news? It might not be worth it.

That's because the Tax Cuts and Jobs Act of 2017 capped the SALT deduction at $10,000. On the other hand, the standard deduction is $12,200 for single filers and $24,400 for married couples filing jointly.

So let's say you live in a high-tax state like Connecticut. You paid $6,000 in property taxes and $5,650 in state income tax. That adds up to $11,650, but because of the reduced SALT deduction, you can only deduct $10,000 when you itemize.

As a joint filer, your standard deduction is $24,400, which means you need more than that in itemized deductions to make itemizing worthwhile. If you don't have at least $14,400 in other itemized deductions — say, health care expenses or mortgage interest — you won't be able to take advantage of the SALT deduction.

High property taxes got you down? A deferral may be the answer

The average American household pays $2,197 in property taxes each year. Sure, it may not seem like a lot to some. But for a senior on a fixed income, getting hit with a bill that size could mean the difference between staying put and having to sell.

Fortunately, you may never have to pay property taxes again — as long as you own your own home. In fact, seniors throughout half the nation are eligible through some two dozen statewide deferral programs that allow older adults to delay paying real estate taxes. How do they work?

In a nutshell, you borrow the amount you'd otherwise owe in taxes. To ensure repayment, the state typically files a lien on the property.

Then when you sell the residence or pass away, the back taxes, plus interest, become due. Where does the money come from? Your equity in the home or, in the event of a death, from your estate.

Of course, different restrictions apply. In California, for example, you must be at least 62 years old, take home no more than $35,500 a year, and have at least 40 percent equity in your home. In Illinois, you must be at least 65 and have no more than $55,000 in annual income. Individuals who have reverse mortgages are not eligible in either state.

Want to find out if your state offers real estate tax deferrals? Contact your local appraisal office or your state's Department of Revenue.

RMDs: Sidestep these common mistakes to dodge a taxing penalty

What do former Vice President Al Gore, singer James Taylor, and journalist Bryant Gumbel have in common? They were each born in 1948. And that means they have to begin drawing down funds from their qualified retirement accounts — or else.

That's because the IRS requires you to begin taking required minimum distributions (RMDs) from IRAs and 401(k) accounts in the year you turn 70 1/2. Ignore the rule and you'll face a steep tax penalty. How much? Fifty percent of the amount you were supposed to have withdrawn.

Read on for high-priced errors seniors often make when hitting this retirement milestone — and how to avoid them.

Misunderstanding the rules for IRAs and 401(k) accounts.
To figure out how much you have to withdraw from these savings, add up your prior year-end balance and divide it by the government's life-expectancy factor for your age. For help with the calculations, refer to the worksheet at *irs.gov/pub/irs-tege/ uniform_rmd_wksht.pdf.*

You must calculate the RMD separately for each IRA that you own, but the IRS will let you withdraw the total amount from either a single IRA or from a combination of them. Fortunately, you don't have to take RMDs from Roth IRAs if you're the original owner.

> Need free tax advice? The Tax Counseling for the Elderly program provides tax help to people age 60 and older, specializing in questions about pensions and retirement issues. To find a location near you, go to *irs.treasury.gov/freetaxprep* or call 800-906-9887.

Have more than one 401(k)? You've got to calculate your RMDs separately and withdraw that exact amount from each Roth and traditional 401(k) plan.

Forgetting that working affects your RMDs. Looking for an exception to RMD rules? You can delay taking payments from your 401(k) if you're still working at the company sponsoring the plan. But you'll have to withdraw RMDs from any 401(k) accounts sponsored by previous employers.

Those rules, however, don't apply to traditional IRAs. You'll have to begin taking RMDs at 70 1/2, whether you're working or not.

Withdrawing your RMD from your spouse's IRA. Remember — there's no such thing as a joint IRA or 401(k). That means you must calculate your RMD based on your age and account totals and withdraw that amount from your own IRAs or 401(k) accounts. Taking your RMD from your spouse's account will lead to trouble — the 50 percent penalty imposed by the IRS, along with potentially higher taxes.

Not taking your RMD at all. And what if you forget to take your RMD? Don't pretend it never happened. The IRS can waive the 50 percent penalty if the shortfall is due to a reasonable error.

> Considering moving for a new job? It might be more expensive than you think. That's because you're no longer able to deduct the cost of job-related moving expenses unless you're an active-duty member of the military. The change in the law is effective until tax year 2025.

Here's what you do. Calculate how much you should have withdrawn and remove it from your retirement account. Then file tax Form 5329 and attach a letter explaining what happened, why it happened, and the steps you took to fix the error.

Scams and swindles: Spot the rip-offs that target your refunds

Tax season — the first few months of the year when the majority of Americans gather up the financial paperwork they need to complete their tax returns. Turns out, though, it's also a busy time of year for another group — the financial fraudsters who prey on them.

How do they do it? Often the con artists phone victims and threaten to arrest or deport them unless they pay a bogus tax bill. They'll even alter caller ID numbers to make it look like the IRS is calling — hoping you don't know that the IRS doesn't reach out by phone.

And that's not the only way they try to hoodwink taxpayers. Don't want to fall victim to tax-time hucksters? Read on to recognize these common scams.

"Ghost" tax preparers. Don't lose your shirt to dishonest preparers promising you a big refund. They'll fill out your tax return for a price and then fail to sign it — a move that means the crook remains under the radar of the IRS and your tax return appears self-prepared. Look out for shady tax preparers who do the following:

- require payment in cash and won't provide a receipt.

- claim fake deductions or tax credits to get a larger refund.

- direct refunds into their own bank accounts.

The IRS advises you to review your tax return carefully and check that your routing and bank account number on the completed return are correct.

Fake charity donation requests. It's awful but true. Criminals set up fake charities in the wake of a natural disaster and then ask you for donations by phone or in person. Or they use emails to lure you to a fake website that appears to belong to a legitimate charity.

In another version of the con, the thieves contact disaster victims and, claiming to be from the IRS, seek personal information under the pretext of needing it to file a casualty loss claim. Follow these tips to avoid getting swindled.

- Don't give out personal financial information, including your Social Security number.

- Be wary of charities with names that resemble famous organizations.

- If a charity claims to be tax exempt, check it out at apps.irs.gov/app/eos.

The "tax refund" scam. In this scheme, crooks steal your personal information from legitimate tax preparers and file fake tax returns. This tricks the IRS into depositing a refund into your bank account. Then the hooligans, pretending to be collection agency officials working for the IRS, call your attention to the "error" and tell you to forward the funds to them. What if this happens to you?

- Contact your bank and have it return the refund to the IRS. Find out if you need to close your account.

- Call the IRS at 800-829-1040 to explain why the direct deposit is being returned.

Learn the ABCs of the new IRS debt collection program

Did you know the IRS has hired four private collection agencies — CBE Group, ConServe, Performant, and Pioneer — to recoup overdue taxes on its behalf? Here's how you can tell the difference between these legitimate debt collectors and scammers trying to steal your money.

- The IRS will notify you by mail that it is assigning your debt to one of the collection agencies. The contracted collector will also send you a letter before calling.

- The debt collectors will only call about a tax debt you've had for several years. You will have already heard from the IRS about the debt.

- IRS debt collectors will never ask for payment via a debit card or wire transfer. They will direct you to pay the U.S. Treasury.

Not sure if you owe the IRS money? Go to *irs.gov/payments/view-your-tax-account* to check your account balance.

IRS knocking at your door? Here's what to do if you can't pay your bill

Maybe the kids are grown and you can't claim them as dependents anymore. Or you paid off your home and lost your mortgage interest deduction. Whatever the reason, you get some bad news at tax time — you owe the IRS money.

But what happens if you don't have enough to cover the bill?

File your tax return anyway, the IRS advises. You'll still owe the debt, but at least you won't be penalized for filing late. Then figure out how much you can afford to set aside each month. Here are some of the payment plans offered by the IRS.

- The 120-day program. It's a short-term option for paying off the full amount within three months. Since the IRS doesn't consider it a formal payment plan, you don't have to pay a user fee. However, be aware that interest and penalties accrue until the debt is paid off.

- The longer-term installment agreement. A $149 user fee applies, but it can be reduced to $31 if you make your payments via direct debit.

- An offer in compromise, where you and the IRS agree to settle the debt for less than the full amount. Going this route requires an application and fees, and restrictions apply.

- A temporary suspension, where your outstanding balance is put on hold. This occurs only if the IRS determines that you can't pay both your taxes and reasonable living expenses. The debt doesn't go away, and interest and penalties apply during the suspension.

Contact the IRS at 800-829-1040 to discuss the payment plan that's right for you.

Caring for the caregiver: Make the most of these tax breaks

Nearly $7,000. That's the average amount caregivers spend out of pocket each year on their loved ones. And where do family members get the money? They dip into savings, cut back on personal spending, and set aside less for their own retirement. Some even take out loans to help make ends meet.

Are you looking after an aging family member? Don't jeopardize your own financial security in the process. Instead, take advantage of some of these tax breaks.

Head of household status. Taxpayers who qualify as head of household get a higher standard deduction than single filers — $18,350 instead of just $12,200. And they get wider tax brackets, meaning more of their income is taxed at lower rates. You may qualify for this benefit if you're single and pay more than half of your dependent parent's household expenses, even if that parent doesn't live with you.

Dependent care credit. This tax break applies if you paid someone to look after your spouse or dependent parent so you could work or look for a job. It generally covers up to 35 percent of $3,000 worth of costs for things like home health nurses or adult daycare.

So if you owe $2,000 in taxes and get the maximum credit of $1,050, you'll owe Uncle Sam just $950 at tax time.

Credit for other dependents. Recent changes to the federal tax code have expanded a $500 credit to include adult dependents. The bonus is meant to assist those looking after disabled or senior family members. And if you're taking care of a friend? Someone not related to you can qualify as a dependent if he lives with you.

"

Bypass premium prices on the bridge to Medicare

What if you had to retire at, say, age 62? On the one hand, you'd be old enough to collect Social Security benefits. On the other, you'd be three years too young for Medicare health insurance.

Seniors in this boat often turn to the marketplace established under the Affordable Care Act (ACA) for insurance coverage, says Robert Burgess, a retired certified public accountant who helps run the United Way of Southwest Michigan's Volunteer Income Tax Assistance program. Some rely on ACA advanced premium tax credits — government subsidies that offset the cost of premiums — to foot the bill.

Problems begin, Burgess says, when the new retirees cash out their 401(k) or 403(b) accounts — either to cover expenses in retirement or because the plans require it. All that extra money, counted as income, can make them ineligible for the credits.

"At tax time, the individual may have to pay back some or even all of the advanced premium tax credits they received during the year," he warns. "This could result in a penalty of thousands of dollars owed at tax time."

A smarter alternative? Roll over your 401(k) or 403(b) accounts into an IRA or other qualified plan if you expect to receive ACA tax credits. That way the money won't count as income.

Burgess also has advice for low-income seniors who don't have to file federal taxes — you might want to do it anyway. That's because the IRS will notify you if someone has already filed a return in your name — a sure sign that your identity has been stolen.

"Consider whether protecting yourself from identity theft is worth the hassle of annual federal income tax filing," Burgess advises.

"

Estate planning

Preparing for your family's future is an important part of growing older. So it may surprise you to learn that 6 out of 10 Americans haven't drawn up estate planning documents such as a will or trust. The main reason they give? They just haven't gotten around to it.

Of course, nobody wants to think about their own mortality. But without proper documentation, costly decisions about your property and funeral arrangements may be made without your input.

Take the case of Pablo Picasso, who died without a will. At age 91, he left behind thousands of pieces of art, five houses, gold, cash, and stocks and bonds. It took six years to divide his estate, a time of bitter squabbling among his heirs. The cost? Some $30 million.

Remember — you don't have to be as rich as the Rockefellers to need a will. Tally up your assets — things like your car, house, bank account, life insurance policy, investments, and retirement savings. You might just discover you're worth more than you thought.

5 time-tested tactics to secure your estate

Draw up a will to head off problems. Intestate — it means dying without a will. It's a situation that creates a slew of complications for those left behind, including delays and expenses in settling your estate. Furthermore, your wishes may not be honored. That topaz ring you promised your niece? It will go to your closest relatives — spouse, children, or siblings — who may have very different ideas about the rightful owner.

That's why a will is one of the most important documents you need to protect your estate. It's where you name a guardian for children, dependents, and pets, as well as an executor who will distribute your cash, property, and treasured objects according to your wishes.

But a will might not be enough. Consider setting up a revocable trust — either in addition to or instead of a will — if you want your heirs to avoid the cost and hassle of probate. Beneficiaries in a trust, unlike those in a will, receive their inheritance without having to go through the courts.

A trust is a good way to go if you want someone to manage the inheritance you leave to a young grandchild. Otherwise, he'll receive all the funds upon turning age 18 — perhaps not the best time in life to manage a lot of cash.

Be prepared for emergencies with a durable power of attorney. This document gives someone else the power to act on your behalf, both financially and legally, in case you can't make decisions. That could mean withdrawing money from the bank, tapping into retirement accounts, and selling property. Experts agree you should have a high level of trust in the person you choose.

You should also consider the age of the individual, says Georgia State University Law Professor Mary F. Radford. A husband and wife in their 60s could be effective agents for each other, but that might not be a good idea if the couple is in their 90s, she says. In that case, a child or younger sibling would probably be a better fit.

Update beneficiaries to keep your wishes on track. Check that you have beneficiaries on your retirement, bank, and investment accounts, along with any health savings accounts and insurance policies.

And don't forget to review your choices every couple of years. Circumstances change, after all. Let's say you get divorced. If your ex is still listed as the beneficiary on your IRA, he'll get all the money in the account in the event of your passing.

You should also name contingent beneficiaries. This means if the primary beneficiary dies before you, the account will go to the secondary person after your death.

Informed loved ones mean fewer headaches later. Be sure to tell those closest to you the location of your beneficiary designation papers and estate planning documents. A fire-resistant, waterproof safe in your home would be best, but make sure someone you trust has the lock combination.

Remember to share with them where you keep the following vital documents.

- your Social Security card, along with birth and marriage certificates

- contact information for your tax preparer and financial institutions and advisors

- deeds to property and cemetery plots

- vehicle titles and registration

"Pay on death" funeral accounts bring peace of mind. Tell your family about the type of funeral you want and ask them what would be meaningful and practical for them, suggests Joshua Slocum, executive director of the Funeral Consumers Alliance, a nonprofit agency that monitors the funeral industry.

But be wary about prepaying for the service, he says. That's because states have different regulations when it comes to pre-arranged funerals, which can cause problems if you want to cancel your contract in less consumer-friendly states like Florida, Hawaii, and Alabama.

His advice? Put the funds for your funeral in a "pay on death" account. "That money stays there and nobody skims a sales commission," Slocum says. "It's available to your survivors to pay the funeral home, whichever one they choose and no matter where you are."

Pick a pro for guidance on senior issues

Can't decide if you need both a will and a trust? Or maybe you're having trouble figuring out the best way to leave money to charity. It might be time to call an elder law attorney, someone who specializes in the needs of seniors.

Along with estate planning, these professionals assist older adults with things like tax planning, long-term care options, and getting the most from Medicare and Social Security.

So how do you find someone to help you? The National Elder Law Foundation at *nelf.org* and the National Academy of Elder Law Attorneys at *naela.org* are good places to start.

But before signing on the dotted line, find out which areas of elder law the attorney focuses on. Ask how fees will be calculated — either a flat rate or by the hour — along with how you should prepare for the first meeting.

Your will: Quick fixes for top mistakes

When actor Heath Ledger died in 2008, his will left everything to his parents and sisters. The problem? Ledger signed the will before the birth of his daughter. That left the child, age 2 at the time of his death, with nothing.

Fortunately, the story had a happy ending. Ledger's family opted to donate the entire estate to the little girl.

Of course, such situations often don't turn out that way. Out-of-date documents can lead to major trouble — including family fights and lawsuits. Avoid these mistakes when drawing up your will.

Including personal information. Access to your online financial accounts is one of the most important pieces of information you can give the executor of your will. After all, how else will he be able to wrap up your estate?

But never include your usernames, passwords, PINs, and related accounts in your will. A will becomes a public document when it's filed with the local probate court. Your heirs will be much better off if you leave your executor a list detailing your personal information.

Failing to include a residuary clause. Just a few short sentences can make a huge difference in how your will is handled. That's why it's so important to include a residuary clause. This action names a beneficiary for any remaining assets after items specifically mentioned have been distributed. An example of the clause? "I give the residue of my estate to my sister, Monica."

The clause covers property acquired after your will was written. Say you bought a car just weeks before passing on. You didn't have time to name a beneficiary in your will. Without a residuary clause, the car will pass to heirs based on the intestate laws of your

Ever heard of this old wives' tale? Leave $1 in your will to a relative you want to disinherit. That way he can't say you forgot him and contest the will. Bad idea. It means your executor will have to track the person down. Instead, include a sentence saying the person's absence was intentional.

state. Residuary clauses also handle assets not distributed due to the death of a beneficiary.

Using your will to change beneficiaries. Did you know beneficiary designations override the wishes you make in your will? That means you can't dethrone your ne'er-do-well sister's place as your life insurance beneficiary by writing it into your will. A will has no power over assets with a named beneficiary. Don't try to give away these six things in your will — it won't have any effect.

- retirement plans
- payable-on-death accounts
- living trust assets
- life insurance policies
- investment bonds
- joint ownership property

How to choose the right executor

Choosing the executor for your will can be a tricky business. This person will be responsible for wrapping up your obligations, including paying bills, maintaining property until the estate is settled, and distributing assets to your heirs.

Many people choose spouses, children, or siblings to take over the task. Here are a few things to consider before asking someone to sign on for the role.

- How well does he manage his own finances? Most likely, he'll manage yours the same way.

- Does he have plans to move away? It can be difficult to do the job from a distant location.

- How well does he know your heirs? Settling your estate will be easier if all parties involved work well together.

Be sure to name a successor executor in case the primary executor dies before you or cannot serve.

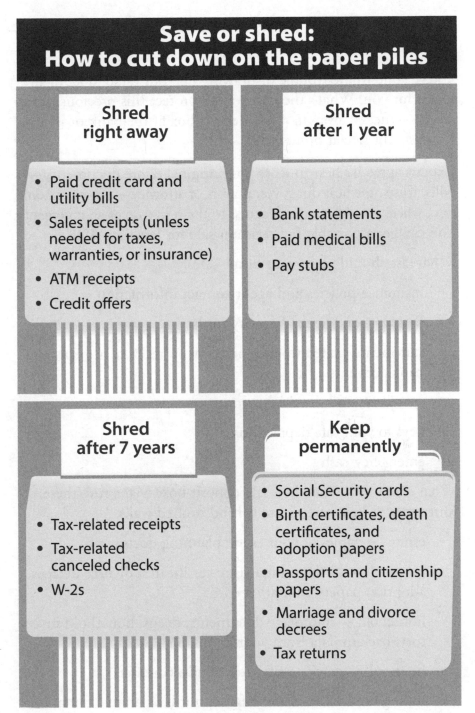

Save or shred:
How to cut down on the paper piles

Shred right away

- Paid credit card and utility bills
- Sales receipts (unless needed for taxes, warranties, or insurance)
- ATM receipts
- Credit offers

Shred after 1 year

- Bank statements
- Paid medical bills
- Pay stubs

Shred after 7 years

- Tax-related receipts
- Tax-related canceled checks
- W-2s

Keep permanently

- Social Security cards
- Birth certificates, death certificates, and adoption papers
- Passports and citizenship papers
- Marriage and divorce decrees
- Tax returns

Safe and sound: Where to store hard-to-replace docs and more

You've gone to the trouble of drawing up your estate documents. Good for you. What's the best way to protect this precious paperwork — tucked away in a safe deposit box at the bank or in a fire-resistant safe at home?

Experts agree it's best to store your original estate documents — wills, trusts, medical directives, powers of attorney — in your home safe, where you'll have quick access to them in case of an emergency. You can get a portable fire-resistant safe for less than $50.

What else should go in your home safe?

- insurance policies and agent contact information

- passports and Social Security cards

- statements related to your investment, retirement plan, and bank accounts

- spare keys and the title to your car

- keys to your safe deposit box

- emergency cash

What should you store in a safe deposit box? Make sure these four types of items are secure behind vaulted walls.

- estate — copies of your estate planning documents

- personal — birth and marriage certificates, divorce decrees, adoption papers, military records

- household — mortgage documents, deeds, household inventory, backup data from your computer

- financial — stock certificates, bonds, contracts

Depending on the size of the safe deposit box, annual rental fees usually run between $25 and $150.

AGE IN PLACE

ESSENTIAL GUIDE TO LIVING OUT YOUR GOLDEN YEARS IN YOUR OWN HOME

Home solutions

"There's no place like home." It's been 80 years since moviegoers first heard Dorothy deliver that classic line in "The Wizard of Oz." A lot has changed since then, but not seniors' belief in her heartfelt words. Nearly 9 in 10 people 65 and older would prefer staying in their current home as they get older, a way of life called aging in place.

But doing so requires planning. After all, you could end up living in an unsafe environment if your home isn't set up to help you transition into your later years. Something as simple as an upturned edge on a throw rug could cause you to trip, break a bone, and lose your independence.

In fact, falls are the No. 1 cause of injuries among seniors. That's why it helps to know these eight tips to protect you from taking a tumble.

- Wear non-slip, high-backed shoes with insoles. Avoid dangerous flip flops and high heels.

- Have your eyes checked once a year. Don't wear multi-focal lenses when climbing stairs.

- Put a non-slip, rubber mat in the shower and tub.

- Keep flashlights handy, including one by the bed.

- Know your pet's location to avoid tripping over him.

- Plug in night lights between your bedroom and bathroom.

- Ask your doctor to review your medications to see if they might make you dizzy.

- Remove clutter and objects you could stumble over, like lamp cords, from hallways.

You've got many options when it comes to creating an age-friendly home. Read on for some simple, low-cost ways to ready your house for your golden years.

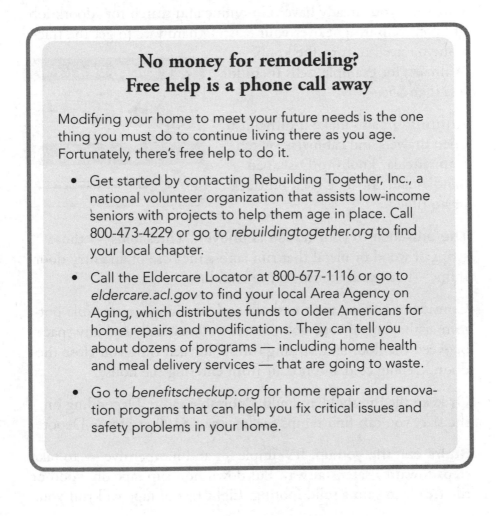

No money for remodeling?
Free help is a phone call away

Modifying your home to meet your future needs is the one thing you must do to continue living there as you age. Fortunately, there's free help to do it.

- Get started by contacting Rebuilding Together, Inc., a national volunteer organization that assists low-income seniors with projects to help them age in place. Call 800-473-4229 or go to *rebuildingtogether.org* to find your local chapter.

- Call the Eldercare Locator at 800-677-1116 or go to *eldercare.acl.gov* to find your local Area Agency on Aging, which distributes funds to older Americans for home repairs and modifications. They can tell you about dozens of programs — including home health and meal delivery services — that are going to waste.

- Go to *benefitscheckup.org* for home repair and renovation programs that can help you fix critical issues and safety problems in your home.

8 roadblocks to aging in place (and simple, affordable fixes)

Arthritis leaves you without a firm hold. Can't seem to get a tight grip to twist doorknobs? Here's a simple fix. Change out your old round knobs with lever-style handles. Slightly push the outer edge with your fingertips, hand, or even your elbow and like magic, you're ready to open the door. You'll find lots of styles at your local home-improvement store.

Like what you already have? Go online and search for "doorknob gripper." Slip it right over your existing hardware to get the traction you need to turn the knob. Walmart, for example, sells them for less than $5.

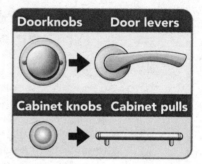

Arthritis can also make it difficult to open drawers and cabinets. Switch from circular knobs to D-shaped handles and you'll be back on track in no time.

The entrance to your house is uneven. Thresholds — those strips of wood or metal that run across the base of an entry door frame — can easily cause you to stumble.

Consider removing the threshold and attaching a retractible bottom at the foot of your door. It will automatically seal any space between the floor and missing threshold each time you close the door, keeping cold and hot air from entering the house.

Or keep the threshold and add a portable ramp. Depending on the size, you can find ramps for less than $100 at Home Depot.

Stairs can trip you up. It's simple — and inexpensive — to take steps toward a safer stairway. Put down non-slip tape on wood or tile treads to gain a solid footing. Eight feet of tape will run you less than $6 at Lowe's. But what if you have carpet? Make sure it's stretched snugly against the outer edge of each tread.

In either case, be sure you can distinguish one step from the next. Add a visual contrast at the outside of each tread with colored painter's tape.

Thinking about replacing your worn-out flooring? You're more likely to trip over a high-pile carpet, so choose a style no more than 1/2-inch thick. Remember, though, that wheelchairs don't roll as well over carpeting as they do over hard flooring.

Multitasking makes falls more likely. Fumbling with keys, groceries, and mail at the front door can make you wobbly on your feet. Avoid the problem by placing a table or bench nearby — preferably at waist level — for resting your bags. This way, you can keep your hands and arms free of heavy items that might throw you off balance.

You can say goodbye to house keys once and for all with a combination code lock. Or try unlocking the door wirelessly with a smartphone or remote-controlled fob.

You can't reach items in your kitchen. Crouching down or standing on a step stool to pull something off a shelf is a recipe for disaster. The answer? Better organization.

Make sure the items you use on a daily basis are within easy access. Keep plates, glasses, and utensils, for example, in a cabinet and drawer next to the stove. Place them between waist and shoulder height. And the turkey baster and eggnog cups you only use at Christmas? Store them on an out-of-the-way shelf and get help retrieving them.

Want to stop cluttering up your cabinets with loose pot and pan lids? Attach a magazine rack to the inside of the cupboard for storage.

It's a good idea to organize your pantry, too. Put food items you use most often, like cereal, canned goods, and pastas, in the front row. Store smaller items, like spices and extracts, on a Lazy Susan inside a cabinet for easy access.

Slick surfaces make you unsteady. Bathrooms are especially dangerous, with lots of hard surfaces in a small space. One cost-effective way to make this room safer? Install grab bars in the shower and tub to make getting in and out easier. A hand-held shower head, combined with a shower seat, also make bathing easier.

While you're at it, consider mounting a grab bar by the toilet. It will give you extra support when sitting down or standing up — times when your blood pressure is more likely to drop and make you dizzy.

> People with low vision can't always distinguish colors, but they often detect visual contrast. If you're visually impaired, try using towels, washcloths, and bath mats that contrast sharply with the color of your tub, tile, and floor. For more tips, go to *visionaware.org/info/for-seniors/retirement-living/12*.

You fear stumbling in the dark. Seeing clearly is a priority when it comes to avoiding obstacles in your path. Make sure you're never left in the dark by installing battery-powered lights that go on automatically when you need to see. How do they know when to turn on and off? Motion sensor technology detects when you enter or exit a room.

You also might consider similar lights for the walkway leading up to your house. Prices start at around $15 for a pack of two. Other senior-friendly options? Try a touch-activated lamp on your nightstand. Gently tap the base of the lamp and presto, you've got light. No need to feel around in the darkness for a pull chain or tiny knob.

Opening your front door is dangerous. Let's face it. You may not be as tall as you once were. That can make once-easy tasks — like looking out your door's peephole — a lot harder.

Not to worry. Adding a second, lower peephole is a relatively easy project. Directions can be found online or you can hire someone for the job. Cost of a new one? Less than $10 at your local home-improvement store.

You can also find larger, battery-operated peepholes, which for about $60 and up, provide a much clearer image of your visitor on a screen. This way you'll be sure to properly identify the person before opening the door.

Hit a home run: Find the perfect senior-friendly residence

Planning on moving now that you're retired? If so, you're in good company. Baby boomers between the ages of 53 and 71 are responsible for more than 30 percent of all home purchases, according to the National Association of Realtors.

Of course, seniors wading into the real estate market have different priorities than, say, millennials just graduating from college. Whether you're downsizing to a seaside condo or buying into a senior-living community, you'll want to consider the following when shopping for new digs.

The outside is as important as the inside. Before entering the house, make sure the address number is visible from the street. That way, medical personnel can find you in case of an emergency. And be sure to examine the pavement leading up to the house. Is it level and free of holes?

Next, take a good look at the yard. Ask yourself if you want the responsibility of weeding, fertilizing, and mowing. If not, you'll have to take into account the added expense of hiring a lawn service.

And don't forget about location. The time may come when you can't drive anymore. Look for a home near public transportation or within walking distance of shops.

Fewer floors mean less climbing. Going up and down the stairs might not be a problem now. But what about 10 years down the road? Think about limiting your search to a single-level ranch or a two-story with a master bedroom and attached bath on the first floor.

Ideally, you won't have steps leading to the front door, says Steve Hoffacker, a certified aging-in-place specialist. But sometimes they might be the only thing standing in the way of an otherwise perfect home. If that's the case, why not look at all your options?

"There might be a side door that has just one step, or maybe you could enter the house through the garage," Hoffacker suggests.

Accessibility is key to lifelong use. Check to see that doorways are 36 inches wide, the minimum recommended width for allowing persons with disabilities to pass through.

Do you have to step over a curb to get into the shower? "Actually try to get into the tub," Hoffacker advises. "If you find that you can't get your leg over the side, then that's not the house for you."

And the kitchen? Look for low cabinets or shelves, Hoffacker says, so you won't lose your balance reaching for food items and dishes. A fully accessible kitchen will also feature a 30-inch-high eating surface for use by someone in a wheelchair or by small grandchildren.

Stay safe — and independent — with these low-cost repairs

It's often the little things that count. That's certainly the case when it comes to remaining independent in your home, says Steve Hoffacker, a certified aging-in-place specialist and master instructor.

Just a few simple, inexpensive repairs can go a long way toward improving the quality of your life, he says. And the good part is you don't have to tackle several DIY projects at once.

"Home improvements are not an all-or-nothing situation," Hoffacker says. "Do a little when you can."

Hoffacker, who lives in Florida, says there is no specific age in which to begin preparations to age in place. After all, each person has different needs at various times in their lives.

Still, he's got a few suggestions that will work for any senior looking for safety and independence in the home. His top ones?

- Change out your old toggle light switches with larger rocker switches. Why? Seniors can experience vision and mobility problems, making it difficult to turn traditional switches on and off.

- Replace your old lightbulbs, which can cause eye fatigue, with energy-efficient LED bulbs. The newer bulbs can last for decades, Hoffacker says, so you don't have to worry about changing them.

- Take out your two-handled faucet in the kitchen and install a single, lever-handled replacement. It's easier to maneuver when your hands are full.

Hoffacker says you can do these projects on your own or have a relative or neighbor help. The result? "Your home will be more accessible today than it was yesterday," he says.

Security and emergencies

"Be prepared." Anyone who has ever earned a merit badge recognizes the famous motto for the Boy Scouts, coined in 1907 by founder Robert Baden-Powell. He later explained that Scouts should be prepared for any accident or emergency. And never be taken by surprise.

Just like the Scouts, you need to be ready for any situation that comes up. In this chapter you'll learn penny-pinching tips that will help you handle storms and natural disasters, prevent robberies and break-ins, and cope with unexpected dangers at home.

Because if you're confident in your ability to handle any emergency, you'll feel safe and secure in your own home — an important aspect of staying independent as you age.

4 methods to master any disaster that comes your way

Gather gadgets and gizmos to keep you safe. Essential safety products are missing from most people's homes. And in an emergency, they could be priceless. Do you have these potential lifesavers?

- battery-operated radio
- fire extinguisher
- first aid kit
- flashlight
- multipurpose tool
- escape ladder
- power generator
- extra batteries

Make an action plan to shield what matters most. According to the Federal Emergency Management Agency (FEMA), more than 60 percent of people have not worked out an emergency plan with their family. Get busy on yours with these tips.

- Create a record of important phone numbers. FEMA recommends storing them in a safe place, like your wallet. Make sure your list includes your doctor and pharmacy. And your veterinarian, if appropriate.

- Name an out-of-town contact. Select a relative or friend who lives in another state, if possible. During and after a storm, long-distance phone service may be more reliable than local service in the disaster area.

- Choose shelter locations. Identify a shelter-in-place spot in your home where you can go during a crisis, and determine two ways out of each room in your house. Also, pick two meeting places outside your home where your family can reunite in an emergency.

- Review your plan regularly, and update it whenever your circumstances change.

Be in the know so you're ready for anything. Your TV, radio, and cellphone can keep you up to date with what's happening in your community.

- Stay tuned to local TV news for emergency information like boil-water advisories and evacuation orders.

- Tune your weather radio to your local weather station so you'll know about weather alerts all day, every day.

- Use your cellphone to monitor Wireless Emergency Alerts (WEAs), messages sent by the government to notify you about extreme weather or other emergencies in your area. You will receive these automatically on your phone, unless you've opted out.

You can also call FEMA for disaster assistance at 800-621-3362. The Disaster Distress Helpline, a crisis-support system for people experiencing emotional distress related to a natural or human-caused disaster, can be reached 24 hours a day at 800-985-5990.

Protecting your home could lower your premiums. Tornadoes, hail, hurricanes. All natural disasters that can cause costly damage to your home, and put you in danger. Protect your property — and maybe even cash in on discounts — with these pointers.

- Seal up all openings from wind and rain. Reinforce windows and doors, too. Adding a few upgrades to your home — like reinforced shutters and a wind-resistant roof — could help you snag an insurance discount.

- To protect your home from tornadoes, install windows and patio doors made with impact-resistant glass. If you live in a tornado-prone area, a storm shelter is your best protection.

- An impact-resistant roof is a good defense against hail. Upgrade yours, and you may be rewarded with a lower insurance premium.

> Your insurance company will require a detailed list of everything lost or destroyed during an emergency. Get writer's cramp just thinking about preparing an inventory before disaster strikes? Use your cellphone to make a video instead. Record furnishings, major appliances, contents of closets, and items on bookshelves. Then store the video on a USB flash drive, and stash it in a safe deposit box.

- Ask your local fire department to inspect your property, and get tips on fireproofing your house. Some insurance companies, particularly in the western states, offer wildfire defense programs that provide consultations, monitoring, and last-minute preparation tips — at no cost to you.

To find out what discounts are available to you, contact your insurance company today.

Protect yourself from this invisible danger with a $20 fix

Carbon monoxide (CO) is a colorless, tasteless, and odorless gas that can cause headaches, fatigue, and shortness of breath. Even death. An inexpensive carbon monoxide detector can protect you and your family from this silent killer.

If your home has fuel-burning appliances, like a gas dryer or range, place a monitor on each level of your home — including the basement — and near an attached garage.

Some detectors sell for less than $20 online. Look for the Underwriters Laboratories (UL) seal to make sure your detectors meet safety standards, and install devices according to package instructions. Test the detectors monthly, and vacuum occasionally to reduce dust in the sensors.

If your alarm sounds, don't try to find the source of the CO. Instead, evacuate your house, call 911, and stay out until the authorities give you the all-clear.

Stay safe and secure in your home with these simple tips

Just watching the local news about break-ins and robberies can send shivers up and down your spine. Want to feel safer in your own home? Here are three simple, no-cost security measures you can do today so you'll be better prepared if the unthinkable happens.

Lock 'em out with inexpensive hacks. About 30 percent of burglars come in through an open or unlocked door. And more than one-third break in through the front door.

"Most residential burglars will take the path of least resistance," says Detective Sergeant L.D. White of Georgia's Cobb County

Police Department. "Homeowners have to make it as difficult as possible for a burglar to even attempt to break in."

- Keep doors and windows closed and locked, even when you're home.

- Make deadbolts sturdier. Buy a security-grade strike plate with 3-inch screws for under $3. Install them on every exterior door with a deadbolt lock.

- Mount a simple $5 slide lock on the inside of your garage door to keep thieves from lifting it open.

Sidestep stranger danger at your front door. Experts warn that some door-to-door salespeople may be burglars. For example, someone may pose as a home security system salesperson so he can enter your house and case the joint for a later burglary. To help prevent robberies and other crimes, don't open the door when a stranger knocks or rings your doorbell.

- When delivery people come to your door, ask to see their identification. Call their company to confirm their ID. If you have any doubt, call the police and report the stranger.

- Do not let strangers into your home to use the phone. And don't assume that a female stranger isn't dangerous. Some burglars are women, or they may work in a team with a man.

- Invest in a $5 peephole. It's easy to install and can save you from opening up to potential intruders.

- Check out a "smart" doorbell, like Ring or SkyBell, that will send an alert to your smartphone when someone presses the button or merely skulks within a few feet of your door. Tap the alert and you'll see a live video feed of your doorway via a built-in wireless camera. Using your phone, you can speak with the person at the door.

Bright lights keep burglars at bay. Shine a light on crime to deter thieves and burglars.

- The entrances to your home should be well-lit. And don't forget garages, driveways, and alleys. Check lightbulbs regularly to make sure they're still working.

- Be sure your house number can be seen by the police, firemen, and other emergency workers, but don't put your family name on the mailbox. A burglar could use that information to find your phone number and call your house. If no one answers, they'll know you're away, and your house becomes an easy target.

- When it's dark, remember to close your curtains to protect your property, says Sergeant Brian Eden of the Peachtree City Police Department in Georgia. "Close your blinds at night. That will prevent people from being able to see straight through your house — and see that nice TV or anything else you may have." A no-cost tip that's simple and effective.

Sound the alarm — without breaking the bank

Homes without any kind of alarm system are as much as 300 percent more likely to get burglarized than alarmed homes. Here are two ways to protect your home without spending wads of cash.

- Buy an alarm kit online or from your local home improvement store for around $200. You get a keypad, door and window sensors, and even motion sensors similar to those found in more expensive systems. That's a savings of up to $1,400 since you'll install the kit yourself. Plus, because you also do the monitoring, you'll save $180 to $720 in monthly fees during the first year alone.

- For an even cheaper option, buy standalone door and window alarms priced as low as $11 a pair. You could put alarms on 14 windows and two doors for under $100. They attach with adhesive pads and sound off loudly if a door or window is opened. Since they run on batteries, they will work even during a power outage.

Burglar-proof your home without an alarm

In-home care

Nancy's garden was the pride of the neighborhood until she fell and broke her arm. She found she couldn't care for it — or herself — anymore. She considered a nursing home, but that meant giving up her prized petunias. Instead, Nancy found an in-home caregiver who helped her stay in her house of 45 years.

Nancy's helper only cooked and cleaned, but in-home care offers everything from companionship to medical assistance. It's a great way to stay at home when you might otherwise need to turn to an assisted living facility. You'll save money, too, since it's often cheaper than a nursing home.

But cheaper doesn't mean free. It still comes with a cost most people don't plan for. Experts say 7 out of every 10 seniors haven't put aside money for a caretaker. Instead they plan to ask their children or spouse to look after them, which only passes expenses on to loved ones. More than half of all friends and family caregivers reach into their own pockets to make ends meet.

Certain benefit programs might offset the cost. Research these options to see if you can afford to hire help or pay your family.

- Medicaid subsidizes the price of a caregiver, but rules vary from state to state.

- Veteran-specific programs like Aid and Attendance provide funds to supplement the costs of in-home care.

- Private charities and support groups offer some support for seniors who need assistance.

- Medicare covers eligible home health services if you meet all the qualifications.

Self-care for the caregiver — how to lift your spirits and fight fatigue

What if you don't need care, but you find yourself looking after a friend or loved one? Studies show that people who take care of family members are twice as likely to suffer from depression as the general population.

Just like a doctor wouldn't go to work sick, you can't help others if you aren't well yourself. Here are a few ways to make sure you don't neglect your own needs and health.

- Try to keep up with the hobbies and activities that make you happy.

- Get light exercise at least a few times a week.

- Call or visit your friends often to stay connected. They might be able to give you a break from your duties if you feel overwhelmed.

Track down trusted care in 4 simple steps

Size up your needs before you start the search. The first thing you should do when considering in-home care for yourself or a loved one is determine what you're looking for. List everything you need — like companionship, help with chores, and assistance with tasks like bathing. Is this best-suited to someone who can help around the house or a medical professional?

You also need to decide on a budget. This will help you nail down what kind of care you can afford and how often your caregiver can work.

Check to see if insurance will cover your caretaker. Curb the costs by asking if community organizations, churches, or family members can help provide similar services.

Vet the candidates to find the perfect pick. Once you narrow down your needs you can start your search. You have two main options — go through an agency or hire someone directly.

The agency is the easiest path. They look up qualifications, run background checks, and negotiate salaries. Ask around for referrals or go online to research reputable agencies in your area.

This convenience comes with a price, though. A caregiver hired by an agency costs roughly two times more than someone you hire yourself.

Direct hires are cheaper, but the onus of screening the caretaker is on you.

- Ask tough questions about their qualifications and get at least three references.
- Run a criminal background check.
- Check to be sure the interviewee can legally work in America.
- Set up a backup plan in case your caretaker calls in sick.

Write out the rules and seal the deal. After you find the perfect candidate, draw up the contract. Avoid any confusion by clearly defining household rules, hours worked, and wages paid.

Consider bringing in your caregiver for a two-week trial before you hire them. That way you can test the waters before committing to a long-term deal.

It's a good idea to ask a friend or family member to drop by unannounced while your caretaker is over to check for any signs you could be in danger.

Stay above water with a payroll plan. If you go with an agency, they will handle payment options and tax forms for you. But if you're on your own, you have a few things to hash out.

First, figure out what to pay your caregiver. Research the average costs for similar services in your area. Remember that the cost of care will go up if you need more help.

You also need to ensure you don't break any local or federal laws. Consider reaching out to an attorney or accountant to help set up your payroll properly. And don't forget that you need to provide tax statements for your caregivers, too.

For more tips on staying safe, choosing a caregiver, and finding an agency, see *Protect yourself from fraudsters in your home* and *Choosing a caregiver: How to ensure you're in safe hands* in the *Financial abuse* chapter.

Dodge pricey penalties with this legal secret

Have you heard about the Medicaid penalty period? When you apply for benefits, Uncle Sam noses through the last five years of your bank records. If the government thinks you gave away money to family so you could qualify for Medicaid, you'll have to wait months — even years — before you're eligible again.

But you can receive in-home family care without jeopardizing your Medicaid qualification. All you need to do is draw up a contract between you and the family member who will take care of you. The contract legalizes the arrangement, making it less likely Medicaid will consider the money a gift. Plus the payments help reduce the size of your estate, which will speed up your Medicaid qualification.

A caregiver contract, sometimes called a personal service or care agreement, should clearly spell out several things.

- The caregiver's duties. This might include running errands, paying bills, or cooking meals, and how many hours a week they'll spend caring for you.

- How much they'll be paid. Call a few local home health agencies and ask what they charge for the kinds of services your caregiver will perform. Then pay your family member based on those rates. Don't be tempted to overpay just because they're family.

- How they'll be paid. You can pay your relative hourly with a paycheck or upfront with a lump sum. Hourly is less likely to make Medicaid or the IRS suspicious.

Spend a little money to have an elder-law attorney draw up the contract so it stands up to Medicaid scrutiny down the road. And be sure to discuss the details with the rest of your family to avoid hurt feelings and estate battles later on.

Want free in-home care? Follow this ingenious advice

"Home sharing is an opportunity for a healthier or younger person to move in and help out around the house," says Karen Heyward-West, director of Homesharing at St. Ambrose Housing Aid Center in Maryland. "As a result, people live longer and they are able to stay in their homes."

Shared housing programs, like St. Ambrose's, match roommates with homeowners who need support, whether financial or health-related. A homeowner can rent out an extra room, get help with her house or personal care, or both. Heyward-West has paired dozens of home-seekers with seniors who need in-home care.

One standout success story began when a 59-year-old woman developed health problems. Faced with the prospect of leaving her home, she reached out to St. Ambrose to find someone who could help with upkeep.

"The match lasted 26 years," Heyward-West says. "They became family."

If you want to find a roommate who will help look after your house or provide basic health care, check out local nonprofits or go online to *nationalsharedhousing.org/program-directory* to see if resources are available in your community.

To learn more about how shared housing can help trim your bills, see *Save money and have fun with home sharing* in the *Shared and community housing* chapter.

Gadgets, apps, and technology

Chances are, you don't keep up with the latest technology. Experts say 7 out of every 10 seniors don't bother with smartphones. And 4 out of 10 don't even use the internet.

A new field of study — dubbed gerontechnology — might change your mind. It focuses on how technology can help older adults stay independent.

If you turn your nose up at the newest gadgets and apps, you could miss out on the chance to remain in your home. The market is bursting at the seams with technology specifically designed for retirees. These tools remind you when to take your pills, call 911 if you fall, and even help you keep up with your hobbies.

The best part? The price. You may think cutting-edge gizmos cost an arm and a leg, but they don't hold a candle to the cost of health care. A nursing home would run you at least $90,000 a year. And a full-time in-home caregiver comes in at $50,000.

But the cost of a high-end home monitor that learns your daily routine and alerts loved ones if something is out of the ordinary? Under $1,000 a year.

Read on to find out how assistive technology can help you stay safe and secure at home throughout your golden years.

5 tech tools that keep you healthy at home

Emergency alerts let you call for help. Falls can be deadly, especially if hours pass before you call 911. And you can't ask someone to keep an eye on you every single second, right?

Turns out, you can, with Personal Emergency Response Systems (PERS). These devices — which you can wear as necklaces, bracelets, or belts — allow you to call for help.

> Smartphone savvy? You can find free apps that schedule medication reminders. The best ones even let your caregiver or family members know when you take your pills, give you information about side effects, and help you reschedule missed doses.

An unmonitored device that calls a friend or family member at the press of a button will cost you a one-time payment of around $25. Need a more advanced device that detects falls automatically, alerts an ambulance, and calls a dispatch center? They're a bit pricier, with fees that clock in around $25 to $50 a month.

Remote monitors show your loved ones how you're doing. Are your children always worrying about your well-being? Do they want to hire someone to come over every day? Maybe you don't want a stranger in the house, but you don't want your family to fret, either. So what can you do?

Remote monitoring systems are a good compromise. You get to stay home alone, and your loved ones get some peace of mind. Monitors range from sensors that only alert your family when you're up and about to cameras that let them drop in remotely to check on you.

Never miss a dose with medication reminders. Not sure if you took your medicine today? Sometimes keeping track of your pills seems harder than juggling a dozen balls.

- Phone call services can help you remember your meds. For a small monthly fee, you can set up daily calls to remind you it's time for a dose. Prices range from $4 to $30 monthly, and the more expensive options also monitor your health and safety.

- Smart pillboxes sound alarms and automatically dispense your pills when it's time for a dose. You'll pay about $20 and up for dispensers you fill and program yourself. The more complex devices have monthly subscription fees starting around $60. These are usually linked with services that call or text your loved ones if you miss a dose.

Wearable gadgets keep track of your vital signs. You could spend thousands every year on a nurse who comes over each day to check your blood pressure and heart rate. Or you could make a single payment of a few hundred dollars and get a smart watch or wearable gadget that lets you keep an eye on your own vitals.

The prices depend on what device you go for, and some options are only available with a prescription. A few of the high-end products even send alerts to medical professionals if they detect potential health problems.

Gadgets that once only gave you medical readings, like glucose monitors, are also getting high-tech makeovers. These upgrades sync with your phone so you can keep an eye on your health and track any changes.

Eat, drink, and stay healthy with smartphone apps. Your stomach used to rumble if you missed a meal. These days you hardly notice if you don't sit down to eat. Like most seniors, your appetite and thirst have diminished as you've aged. But poor nutrition puts you at risk for diseases like osteoporosis and heart disease, so a healthy diet is still important.

Search the internet for nutrition apps, or ask your doctor to recommend one. They can remind you when to drink water or help you keep track of your meals. The best part? They're free.

Money-saving programs you need to know about

Not sure if your insurance will foot the bill for assistive tech? Check these resources to see if they'll help with the costs.

- Medicare Part B pays for some medical assistive technology. To see if you're covered, call 800-633-4227.

- Medicaid might help with the cost of technology for your house, like adaptive lighting or stair lifts. Call 877-267-2323 to find out more.

- State assistive technology programs can help you afford tools that let you live independently. To find a program near you, go online to *at3center.net/state program* and select State AT Programs and your state from the drop-down menus.

- The Department of Veterans Affairs is another avenue to try if you're eligible for veteran benefits. It also provides training programs to teach you how to make the most of your assistive device. Call 844-698-2311 to see what you're entitled to.

Get by with a little help from your virtual friends

A voice-activated assistant seems like it belongs in George Jetson's house, not yours. But this technology isn't far-flung science fiction. You can have your own digital helper for less than the cost of a week's worth of groceries.

Tech companies like Amazon, Apple, and Google all make home speakers equipped with these digital aides. The prices range from $50 to a few hundred dollars, depending on the brand and size.

Simply activate your assistant with a phrase, then give it a command. The gadget can set medication reminders, turn down the volume on the TV, play audiobooks, and do countless other tasks that make your life easier.

You'll need to hook the speaker up to the internet and pair it with any smart devices you have. If you run into trouble, check to see if your local computer store will lend a hand with the setup.

Audiobooks: Perfect solution for small-print struggles

A gripping mystery novel. A sweeping romance. A thought-provoking biography. Whatever your taste in reading, you don't have to let failing eyesight deprive you of this great pleasure. Your solution lies with the National Library Service's (NLS) That All May Read program.

"One of the first things I encourage seniors to do is sign up for the talking book program," says Audrey Demmitt, a peer advisor for VisionAware who helps vision-impaired seniors live an independent life.

If you have problems seeing a printed page, simply register with the NLS program and the library will send you free audiobooks and a digital machine to play them on.

Getting a book is as easy as picking up the phone. "You call a number and say, 'I want to read the latest John Grisham, or WWII story,' or whatever else you like," Demmitt says. The library will mail the book right to your house. And sending it back is a snap. "When you're done, just flip the card over and put it back in the mail. You don't even have to write out the address."

Demmitt says the program can be life-changing. "Even if seniors resist at first, they eventually come back and say to me, 'I can read again. It's so lovely to have something to do, to listen to a book.'"

To find a participating library in your area, call 888-657-7323 or go online to *loc.gov/nls* and click on "Find Your Library" under Braille and Audio Reading Materials at the top of the page.

Hard of hearing? Easy ways to crank up the volume

The whole neighborhood knew when George was watching TV. He turned the volume up so high everyone on the street could hear it. His wife dreaded when friends visited, too. Conversations turned into shouting matches just so George could participate. And George's story isn't unique — 1 out of every 3 seniors suffers from age-related hearing loss.

Boost your hearing without breaking the bank. More than half of all seniors with hearing loss don't wear an aid. And if you count yourself among them, you're more likely to suffer problems that land you in the hospital, one study says.

Of course, no one likes struggling to hear. But hearing aids often cost upwards of $3,000 — and Medicare won't cover them — so many seniors don't have a choice. But take heart. You can find bargains if you know where to look.

Big-box stores offer hearing aids and batteries for almost half the usual price. Other organizations might subsidize the cost, too. Check to see if you're eligible through Medicaid, the Affordable Care Act, or veterans' benefits.

Tackle hearing loss with these easy-to-use gizmos. If you don't have hearing aids or prefer not to use them at home, look into these devices that can help you around the house.

- Wireless speakers or headphones that pair with your TV will let you crank up the volume without causing a racket. The prices range from $70 to $400 or more.

- Alarms that light up when the phone or doorbell rings can save you from missing important calls and visits. They range anywhere from $10 to $70.

- Free smartphone apps turn phone calls into text that you read. Other apps help amplify sound through headphones you attach to your phone.

Transportation and mobility

Aren't you glad you didn't grow up in the Amazon rainforest? Boys of the Sateré-Mawé tribe have to endure hundreds of excruciatingly painful ant bites before they're considered adults. All you had to do was pass your driver's test.

Experts estimate that most people over 16 have a license. And chances are they'll hold on to it for as long as they can.

But as you get older, the road becomes more dangerous. Arthritis sets in, your reflexes slow down, and your eyesight starts to fade. That may be why seniors are more likely to cause a collision than someone between the ages of 25 and 64.

When you're in your golden years, a single accident can hamper your ability to live on your own. Almost a quarter of all seniors who are in car crashes give up their independence due to chronic pain and injuries.

It might be time to hang up your keys if you frequently drive outside the lane, scrape the curb, or ding your car. But that doesn't mean you have to give up your independence, too. Read on to find new ways to get around without sacrificing your safety.

7 streetwise strategies to help you get around when you no longer care to drive

Hail a ride for the lion's share of savings. Taxis have been shuttling people around towns since the 17th century, when horse-drawn hackney carriages roamed the streets of London and

Paris. And if you need to take a quick trip to the store, a cab is still an option. You might even qualify for a taxi voucher program. Learn about your transportation options by calling the Eldercare Locator hotline at 800-677-1116 or searching online at *eldercare.acl.gov*.

Fast-forward to the 21st century and explore what tech-savvy seniors already know — ride-sharing services offer the convenience of a taxi, sometimes for a fraction of the cost. Just use your smartphone to hire a car whenever you need to take a trip. Apps for ride-sharing services like Lyft or Uber are free to download, and the rates are based on location, distance, and how busy the roads are.

> Grocery delivery services like Shipt, Instacart, and Jet send food right to your doorstep — perfect for when you can't get to the store. Or you can get ready-to-cook meals mailed to your house. To find out more about meal delivery, read *Nutrition in a box: Meals on demand may fit the bill* in the Groceries chapter.

Public transportation cuts costs for city dwellers. Reliable buses and subways could be the key to getting around. Mass transit is cost-effective and typically has accommodations for wheelchairs or mobility scooters.

Senior discounts are usually available, too. If you have a caregiver who helps you get around, they might be able to ride with you for free. Contact your local government or public transportation center to see what they offer.

Get back on the road with special senior services. ITN*America* helps set up rides for seniors who don't drive anymore. Simply pay a yearly membership fee with your local program to schedule rides whenever you need a lift. The charges are based on distance and pickup location, but the amount varies from state to state.

If you have an old car you're not using, you can trade it in for credits toward future rides. Go online to *itnamerica.org/find-your-itn* or call 207-857-9001 to find out more.

If ITN*America* doesn't operate in your area, check out your local senior center or volunteer organizations. They might have transportation programs that offer rides for free or at a discount.

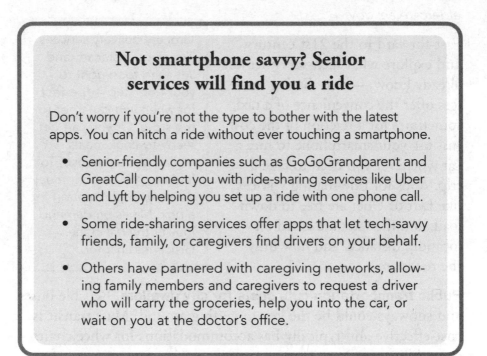

Not smartphone savvy? Senior services will find you a ride

Don't worry if you're not the type to bother with the latest apps. You can hitch a ride without ever touching a smartphone.

- Senior-friendly companies such as GoGoGrandparent and GreatCall connect you with ride-sharing services like Uber and Lyft by helping you set up a ride with one phone call.

- Some ride-sharing services offer apps that let tech-savvy friends, family, or caregivers find drivers on your behalf.

- Others have partnered with caregiving networks, allowing family members and caregivers to request a driver who will carry the groceries, help you into the car, or wait on you at the doctor's office.

Going to the doctor? You can get there for free. If you can't drive to your medical appointments, your insurance provider may have you covered. Some Medicaid programs, for example, take care of medical transportation for nonemergencies. That means you could get free rides to and from the doctor's office or hospital for approved care.

Local volunteer organizations may also provide shuttles or rides. Check with them to see if they can help arrange transportation.

Tag along with your loved ones for quality time and savings. If you need to hang up your keys, see if nearby friends or family can help you get around. Ask if you can go along when they run errands. And you can offer to chip in a few bucks for gas.

Go back to school to find a chauffeur for less. Live near a university or college? Get in touch with the student employment center. You might find a student with a clean driving record who will take you to the store in exchange for a small fee.

Self-powered transit — walking is free, easy, and good for you. If you live in an area with good sidewalks and nearby shops, why not use the oldest transportation method out there — your feet. Walking isn't only a free way to get around. It helps lower your blood pressure, fight off heart disease, and even temper arthritis pain.

Upgrade your car to stay safe on the road

Arthritic knees, diminished hand strength, hip pain, and failing eyesight all make driving more of a challenge than it was in your younger years. But these common symptoms of aging don't necessarily mean you must throw in the car keys.

The University of Florida National Older Driver Research and Training Center in conjunction with AAA have recommendations that address the challenges senior drivers face. Take advantage of existing features in your car or look for these specific elements if you're thinking of buying another vehicle.

- safety features — front and rear warning systems, antilock brakes, adjustable head restraints with extra padding, dynamic stability control, backup cameras, parallel parking assistance, and dual-stage air bags

- ergonomics — adjustable seats, low door thresholds, adjustable accelerator and brake pedals, and tilting and telescoping steering wheels

- comfort — thick steering wheels, automatic door openers and closers, power mirrors and seats, heated mirrors and seats, large dashboard buttons, pushbutton ignition, and keyless entry

In addition, you can add inexpensive assistive devices to your car — like pedal extenders, swivel seats, leg lift straps, lumbar supports, and hand controls — either through your car's manufacturer or a third party. Just make sure any add-ons don't compromise the existing safety features in your car.

Find out what adjustments are best for you by contacting an occupational therapy-driver rehabilitation specialist (OT-DRS) online at *aota.org/olderdriver* or by calling 301-652-6611. If you want help selecting a vehicle that fits your needs, use the interactive tool at *seniordriving.aaa.com/smartfeatures*.

Take back the streets with these tech tools

Can't quite make out what everyone is saying? A hearing aid will fix that. Trouble reading the small print in your favorite book? You might need a new pair of glasses. Is driving becoming too much of a hassle? Your car might need a high-tech makeover. A few cutting-edge tools could be all it takes to put you back in the driver's seat.

> Three out of 4 new-car seekers 50 and older say technology is key to keeping them safe on the streets. Blind spot and lane departure warning systems are the most sought-after and can help if you have difficulty turning your head to scan traffic.

A system that includes lane departure and forward collision warning can cost you around $1,000 including installation. And a blind spot detection system will run you about $240. Looking for cheaper options? Install your own dash cam. You can find popular models online that act as a collision warning system for around $130.

A backup camera is a great tool for parallel parking or maneuvering down that long, winding driveway. A system you put in yourself will cost less than $140 at auto parts stores or online.

If you're in the market for a new ride, you might not need to add all these bells and whistles. Most new cars come with backup cameras or warning systems as standard equipment.

Steer clear of trouble with this roadmap for safe driving

Giovanni Rozzo became famous when he was named Britain's oldest driver at 104 years old. And even though he drove for almost eight decades, he never caused so much as a fender bender. His secrets to staying safe? Avoid busy highways and don't drive at night. Here are a few more ways you can stay safe on the streets.

Put the brakes on meds that put you at risk behind the wheel. Almost half of all seniors who drive take at least seven medications. And those medications impact everyone's safety on the road.

Antihistamines for allergies or colds, antidiarrheals for stomach problems, or antiemetics for nausea can increase your risk of crashes. And that's just to name a few. If your meds cause fatigue, confusion, or blurred vision, don't drive while taking them.

Talk to your doctor about how your medicines can affect you. He'll help you understand the risk or find safer options.

Go back to school to sharpen your skills — and save cash. Driving school isn't just for teenagers. Senior driving courses are designed to help you stay safe even as you age. The best part? Passing the class could grant you up to 10 percent off your insurance bill.

Plot your route to get home safe and sound. Studies show that seniors are involved in more accidents connected to left turns than the younger set. The solution? Plan your routes ahead of time so you don't have to make as many left turns. And if you can, avoid driving during rush hour. Your risk of accidents goes down when fewer cars are on the road.

Socialization

Alelia Murphy is 114 years old, making her the oldest living woman in the United States. Murphy, who liked to kick up her heels at Harlem dance clubs, also made hats, cooked, and volunteered throughout her life. Her motto? "There's no time to sleep. Sleep when you're dead!"

While no one can promise you'll beat Murphy's record, experts agree that eating nutritious food and getting enough exercise are two of the three most important things you can do to stay healthy and independent.

So what's the third? Having more friends — you'll find that socializing helps extend your life, fight depression, and ward off dementia.

In an Australian study, older people with the largest network of good friends were more likely to survive during the 10-year follow-up period. In fact, those with the most friends were an astonishing 22 percent less likely to die than those with the least.

Researchers suspect friends may encourage older people to take better care of themselves. Friends also tend to help get you through tough times, which boosts your mood and self-esteem.

A different study from the National Institute of Mental Health found that participating in highly organized activities — volunteering your time, perhaps — is the single strongest predictor, other than not smoking, of longevity and vitality.

So make more friends, and make the most of your life.

Stay connected in 7 amazingly effortless ways

Nurture your spirit and health. Spirituality and religion are an important part of many lives and often become even more so with age. That might make it a perfect time to become more active in the religious organization you belong to.

Along with building friendships, you'll likely see a host of health benefits. Researchers at Duke University found that African Americans and female seniors who engaged in religious activity like prayer and Bible reading were less likely than others to need care in nursing homes or rehab centers. Although the exact reason isn't clear, the experts noted that religious people tend to have strong social networks to fall back on.

> Staying in contact with others is especially important if you live alone. Experts say you need to talk to someone daily. You can start by arranging a call with a family member or friend. Doing so will make you feel more sociable and also serve as a safety check.

Become a senior scholar for free. September is back-to-school time. Why not sign up for continuing education classes at your local public college? Classes are often free or discounted for adults age 60 and above. Go to *aseniorcitizenguideforcollege.com* and click on "Find Your State Tuition Waivers" in the menu at the top of the page.

Or ask your local college if you can audit a class. You won't get a grade or credit, but you'll definitely boost your knowledge. You also could try shorter-term classes offered through local community centers and libraries.

Stay in touch through technology. Computers and smartphones won't ever replace personal contact, but they sure come in handy during the times in between. Do you miss your out-of-town grandkids? Download the HomeTeam or Caribu app to spend time reading books and playing games with them.

An added bonus? Talking via electronic gadgets might help you beat the blues. A recent study found that seniors communicating through video chat functions such as Skype and FaceTime were at a significantly lower risk of depression than those using email, social networks, or instant messaging.

Find purpose in helping others. You can stay busy and help bridge the generation gap by volunteering your time and knowledge to students in high schools. Nonprofits like Big Brothers Big Sisters of America also seek older adults with life experience. Or perhaps you could donate a few hours a week to the dogs and cats in animal shelters.

"It's extremely gratifying," says Art Koff, who's been volunteering at *ICouldBe.org* for 16 years as an online mentor to inner-city students around the country. "I'd really urge any retiree who is computer literate to do it."

Unsure about all the volunteer opportunities out there? Check out *volunteermatch.org* and *nationalservice.gov/programs/senior-corps* to find the best fit for you.

Work part time to feel connected. Many retirees say they would think about returning to work if conditions were right. Many others already have. In fact, one study found that 4 in 10 currently employed workers 65 and older had previously retired.

Why go back to work? It's not necessarily for the money. Some retirees miss the challenges, the accomplishments, and the connections they felt with former co-workers. You can jump-start a part-time job search by contacting a former employer, searching the 50+ job boards, and checking your town's website for listings.

Thrive with group hobbies. Do you like to knit, garden, or play chess? Perhaps you love to read or watch films. Either way, lots of clubs cater to a particular hobby.

Go to *meetup.com* or your local senior center to find groups with similar interests. You might want to sign on sooner rather than later. Researchers have found that older seniors who are social and participate in arts and crafts run a reduced risk of developing dementia. While the data doesn't prove cause and effect, it can't hurt to have fun with people who have similar interests.

Do you avoid large parties and small talk? Then you might be an introvert — somebody who prefers time alone. Don't feel you have to change your personality in order to socialize in retirement. Instead, focus on the topics and activities you enjoy by enrolling in a class or joining a club.

Eat together for healthy interaction. Seniors, particularly those living alone, often don't eat enough or turn to prepackaged or frozen foods. After all, few people go to the trouble of cooking a big, healthy meal for just one person.

So it should come as no surprise that seniors say they are happier, enjoy the taste of food, and get more nutrition when sharing meals.

Fortunately, finding a table mate is easier than you think. Why not invite a neighbor or family over for lunch or dinner? Better yet, go shopping and cook together. Your guest will most likely be grateful for your company.

Dial up newfound friends — join a nationwide social center

Want to socialize with others from the comfort of your own home? Contact Well Connected, a nonprofit that offers classes, friendly conversation, and support groups to older adults across the country. Once you register, you can access any of its 70 activities a week via conference call.

All you need is a telephone to take part in the free service. You can also use your computer to join online groups. On average, each group has about 12 participants. Well Connected will even set up reminder calls so you don't forget to dial in.

"You can learn a foreign language, study art history, listen to poetry, play bingo, or be an armchair traveler — all over the phone," says Audrey Demmitt, a peer advisor for VisionAware, an organization dedicated to helping adults with vision loss stay independent. "It's a really great support network."

For information, call 877-797-7299 toll free, or go to *covia.org/ services/well-connected.*

Senior romance: Be a winner at the dating game

It doesn't matter if you're 25 or 75 — finding romance can be difficult at any stage of life. But older singles face an additional burden. Many are divorced or widowed after long marriages and find it stressful to jump into the dating scene.

But that shouldn't be a reason not to try. Companionship is essential to enjoying a good quality of life during retirement. That means you need to be proactive in meeting that "special someone" who helps brighten the days. Here are a couple of ways to get you on track.

Meet a potential partner close to home. Perhaps you're more of an old-school kind of person who avoids computer apps like the plague. In that case, being out and about in your town or city will greatly increase your chances of meeting someone.

One way to do so? Explore what you're passionate about, and you'll likely meet people with similar interests. That might mean going to museums, volunteering with a local charity, or joining a club.

You can also check out events at your community or senior center. They often involve day trips, an enjoyable way to spend time getting to know adults in your area. Or go to *meetup.com* to find a seniors group near you.

Let technology find a certain somebody safely. You might think seniors are brand new to the world of online dating, but that's changing fast. In fact, online dating use among 55- to 64-year-olds has doubled in recent years, according to a survey by Pew Research Center.

It's important to remember, though, that it can be risky to meet people over the internet. Here are some warning signs that the person on the other end of the profile might be a con artist.

- You're never able to meet in person.

- The individual professes love for you very quickly.

- He asks you for money to get out of a financial crisis.

Don't share your home address, Social Security number, or bank information when exchanging messages with another site member. Be sure to run a Google search on the other person, and meet in a public place for your first few dates.

Get fit as a fiddle (for free) with SilverSneakers

Think you can't afford to go to the gym? Think again. Many seniors with Medicare Advantage insurance plans have free access to gym memberships and fitness classes that cater to older adults. Dubbed SilverSneakers, the program is available at more than 16,000 locations nationwide.

Lola Bedford is a longtime fan. She and a neighbor started taking SilverSneakers yoga classes at a local Gold's Gym when Bedford was 72.

"We loved it," she says. "It was such a great experience."

Bedford says yoga didn't place undue stress on her body. "The instructor was wonderful," she explains. "We didn't get down on the floor and tie ourselves into knots." Instead, each person got a chair or a large rubber stability ball to help with balance.

And, she says, everyone had fun. "We'd get a lot of laughs out of each other," she adds.

Bedford believes she benefited from more than the increased physical activity. "I think it helped me mentally," she says. "It made me feel good about myself."

Researchers at the Massachusetts Institute of Technology would agree with her. They found in a recent study that SilverSneakers members are more physically active and less isolated or lonely than nonmembers.

The reason? Scientists say the program may cause members to feel more confident and empowered, which in turn increases their sociability.

Bedford feels a bit nostalgic about her experience with SilverSneakers. She stopped going after moving to northwest Georgia several years ago. Now 78, she's enthusiastic about returning to the program.

Fortunately, all she has to do is go to *silversneakers.com* to find a nearby location.

EVALUATE LIVING OPTIONS

ALTERNATIVE HOUSING WHEN STAYING PUT DOESN'T MAKE SENSE

Downsizing

Looking to boost your cash flow and reduce stress? Then moving to a smaller, less expensive home might make sense. Think about it — lower house payments could free up money for your retirement goals. And you may not have to spend as much time and energy on maintenance and repairs.

Of course, downsizing can also bring up all sorts of emotions. It's difficult to give up the memories associated with your home. And even the thought of trying to pare down the contents of, say, a two-story Colonial into a one-bedroom condo can be overwhelming.

But moving to a more manageable home could help you remain independent longer. Here are some reasons to consider a simpler lifestyle.

- Financial necessity. Are the costs of owning your current home stretching your budget?

- Family and friends. Will relocating bring you closer to the ones you love?

- Health concerns. Do physical limitations make moving around and upkeep difficult?

- Unused space. Are you heating and cooling rooms you rarely enter?

Think downsizing might be in your future? Read on for tips that will make the transition as smooth as possible.

Sort out the stress of decluttering with 5 organization ideas

Win half the battle with proper planning. Downsizing is often tinged with sadness, particularly if you have to sort through decades of belongings. At the same time, it can be thrilling to free yourself of so much accumulated clutter. The key to a stress-free experience? Preparing while you're healthy. Moving is hard at any age, and only becomes more difficult when you get older.

And don't wait until the eleventh hour to start downsizing. It's best to begin at least six weeks before you list your home. You'll have a big head start on organizing, and the house will be more marketable.

Divide and conquer to ease the process. Start off easy by sorting through items with little emotional attachment. Clear the bathroom, laundry room, and linen closet of things like expired medications, nearly empty bottles of detergent, and frayed towels. Be realistic. Keep only what you already use — not what you might use one day.

Same goes for the kitchen, which tends to be overstocked with unused spatulas, cookie sheets, and pots and pans. Never used the yogurt maker you got for Christmas years ago? Now is the time to mark it for donation.

> When downsizing, avoid putting items in storage "just in case" you might use them later. Doing so delays making a decision and can be expensive. The average monthly price of a 10-by-10 storage unit — about half the size of a one-car garage — runs around $120. That's $1,440 a year.

Color-code items for quick identification. When moving on to other rooms, it's a good idea to sort through large objects like furniture and exercise equipment before tackling sentimental items. Keep the measurements of your new living space in mind as you decide which pieces you'll keep.

Experts recommend placing a colored tag or sticker — green for save, blue for donate, and red for discard, for example — on large items and boxes. Immediately get rid of things marked for donation or trash. Remember — out of sight, out of mind.

Be honest with yourself to narrow down options. Can't decide on whether to keep something — maybe a book, hat, or scrapbook filled with ticket stubs? Ask yourself these questions.

- When was the last time I used this?
- Does the item have sentimental value that can't be replaced?
- Is it in good shape?
- Will I need it at my new place?
- Do I know someone who would love to have this?

Keep up your spirits with a positive attitude. One way to avoid becoming overwhelmed? Set limits — say an hour or two at a time — for each task. Taking a break gives you time to decompress and gain a sense of accomplishment at the work you've already done.

And don't forget to ask for help from friends and family. Loved ones are there for more than just lifting and hauling. They can help with the tough decisions and provide emotional support when you stop to reminisce over old family photos and mementos.

Let it go: How to shrink the drama of downsizing

Retired and drowning in possessions? You're not alone. Researchers in a national study found that people age 50 and older are less and less likely to sell or donate items they no longer need. And that's in spite of the fact that more than half of the seniors believed they had too many belongings.

A possible reason? Winnowing down a lifetime of possessions stirs up unwanted emotions, including feelings of loss and fear. Check out these surefire strategies to manage the emotional stress.

Recognize your feelings so you can move on. You've lived a long time in your home, so your mixed feelings about downsizing are only natural. Allow yourself to feel sad, and understand that you're undergoing a mourning process.

But don't lose sight of the future when you're relocating to a smaller place. Experts recommend that you talk to friends and family about your feelings. In addition, make your new home as comfortable as possible and get involved with the people and activities in your new community.

Look at the upside of downsizing to reduce anxiety. Nobody looks forward to figuring out what to keep, packing it up, and making sure it fits in the new home. But downsizing can cause additional anxiety if you're worried about the costs involved and whether or not you'll like your smaller digs.

That's why it's important to focus on the positive. Remember that you're relocating to a safer, clutter-free environment where everything you need is readily available. Getting rid of items, like outdated clothes you haven't worn in years, frees up space and simplifies the choices you have to make each day.

It's called sentimental clutter — mementos that take up precious space. If you have a collection of things you never use — say, elephant-shaped teapots — pick a favorite to display. Take a photo of the rest before giving them to family and friends or donating. This way you can remember your treasures and enjoy the gift of giving.

Sell this, not that: Your guide to hiring an estate sale company

Charged with liquidating a loved one's estate? Or maybe you're transitioning into senior living. Either way, the sorting, staging, and pricing that comes with selling off a house full of stuff is often time-consuming and exhausting.

That's why some people turn to estate sale professionals to ease the process. Follow these helpful hints to help you choose the right company.

Vet your top picks to uncover the best candidates. It's best to do your homework before hiring anyone, says Julie Hall, director of the American Society of Estate Liquidators. She suggests that you narrow your search by asking your friends, attorney, or local real estate agents for recommendations. Check for unresolved complaints with the Better Business Bureau or Angie's List.

Then, she says, check references and find out if the company is a member of a professional organization. You can also drop by local estate sales to see potential candidates in action.

Ask the right questions and avoid future surprises. After you've picked two or three companies, ask them how they'll market the sale and what security precautions they'll take. Also find out if they have theft and property damage insurance.

Remember, estate liquidators don't come cheap, with the average commission around 40 percent. But Hall warns against going with the cheapest bid. "You get what you pay for," she says. "If you go for the least expensive, something's going to suffer — maybe not enough advertising or not enough staff watching out for you and your possessions."

And don't forget to ask about additional fees, Hall says. For example, does the company charge extra to clean up after the sale?

Success hinges on proper pricing. Think those Hummel figurines and Norman Rockwell commemorative plates will fetch a fortune? Not anymore.

A combination of factors — the passing of those born during the Depression and baby boomers wanting to downsize — has caused items like heavy mahogany furniture and cut crystal cocktail shakers to flood the market. "There's too much supply and not enough demand," Hall says.

Talk with your liquidator to get a better feel for the estate's value. "Professional estate agents are savvy. They know how to advertise and how much things are worth. So even with their commission, they can bring in more," Hall says.

Get a written contract. It should say when the sale will be held, how much you'll be charged, and when you'll get paid. The contract should also describe what happens to any leftover items. But don't feel pressured into giving the green light if you're not ready. Make sure they've addressed all your concerns before you sign the bottom line.

Moving

What do an African forest elephant and the contents of a two-bedroom house have in common? They both weigh about 6,000 pounds. Yikes. Before you relocate your elephantine assets, you need to plan all the ins and outs. Consider these things when determining your destination.

- Health care. You want to make sure the hospital and doctors aren't hours away, especially if you have specific medical needs.

- Family and friends. Are you moving farther from your loved ones? If so, you're leaving your social network behind. Prioritize engagement with your new community, and look for local programs and activities you could get involved in.

- Taxes. Have you considered how a new neighborhood will affect your tax returns? You might not owe state income taxes, but a high property tax could make up for that. And some states require you to establish an official residence to get a tax break.

- Cost of living. Think about how your expenses will change. For example, a month's worth of groceries in New York City could cost you $470. The same supermarket cart might ring up to $320 in Clearwater, Florida.

- Climate. Don't move up North if you can't bear the cold winters. And think twice about heading to the South if you're not up for sweltering summers. Consider how the weather will affect factors like your health and utility bills.

- Safety. Research crime rates online at websites like *crime reports.com* or *mylocalcrime.com*. Not tech savvy? Contact the community resource officer at the city's nonemergency number and ask for a log of recent crimes in the area.

- Transportation. Are you planning to drive yourself around, or would you rather take the bus? Research the area's transportation options and how convenient it will be to travel to places you go frequently like grocery stores and shopping centers.

Now that you've figured out where you're going, it's time to confront the elephant in the room — how are you going to get three tons of stuff to your new home? With these tips and tricks, you can make moving a breeze without blasting your bank account.

4 hacks for a hassle-free move

Rejuvenate your home to reel in new buyers. Would you buy a car covered in dirt, grime, and rust? No way. The same holds true for a house. Give it a makeover before you start showing it to potential customers.

- Get the carpets cleaned, touch up the paint, and make the windows sparkle.

- Trim the hedges, mow the lawn, and take some time to make sure the exterior of the house looks great, too.

- Update the appliances. Many seniors have lived in their homes for years, and older fridges and stoves could sour some shoppers.

- Set the stage. Declutter, decorate with neutral colors, and let in some natural light.

Hire reliable help to smooth the process. You have two big things to figure out before the move — how to sell your old place and where you'll go next. Real estate agents can help you with both.

First, decide if you want to go with two agents or just one. You can often get discounts when you do all your business with the same person, but some agents specialize in either buying or selling.

If you're moving to a new town, consider hiring separate realtors for selling and buying. After all, you want to work with someone who knows the area.

Ask family or friends if they have any recommendations, too. Or head online to find well-reviewed agents.

> Hauling your personal library across the country? You might save some cash if you ship your books. Ask about the Media Mail service at your local post office and compare the cost to the estimates from your movers.

A mammoth move costs a ton — try these tricks to curb the costs. You need a truck. And movers. And gas. That adds up. The average price of a long-distance move is a whopping $4,890. Here's how to cut those costs.

* Use tech to aid your search. Free smartphone apps let you compare the costs of different moving companies. Simply plug in the distance and the items you need moved, and you'll get quotes from local movers.

* Lighten your load. The less stuff you have to move, the more you'll save. So take some time to consider what you can sell, donate, or just toss out. And read the *Downsizing* chapter to learn how to take the stress out of paring down your possessions.

* Time your move. Summer is the busiest, and therefore the most expensive, time to move. If you can, plan to relocate in the offseason. Also, consider moving during the middle of the week instead of the weekend.

* Find boxes for free. Don't buy your boxes from a moving company. You can get free ones from liquor stores, local libraries, schools, and grocery stores.

Bring a bit of home along to help you settle in. You have a lifetime of memories in your old home, so it can be tough to get used to a new house. To ease the transition, try taking pictures of your rooms and closets before you box them up. Use these photos to recreate your setup when you're unpacking. It won't be exactly the same, but it will help you feel more comfortable.

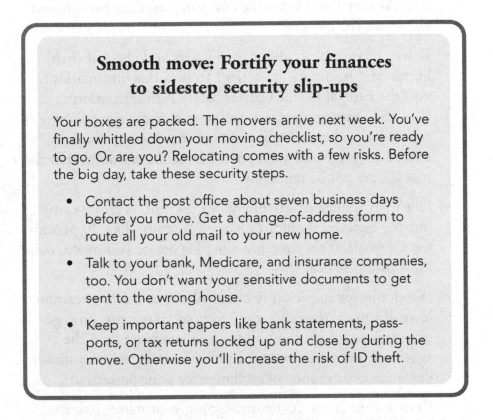

Smooth move: Fortify your finances to sidestep security slip-ups

Your boxes are packed. The movers arrive next week. You've finally whittled down your moving checklist, so you're ready to go. Or are you? Relocating comes with a few risks. Before the big day, take these security steps.

- Contact the post office about seven business days before you move. Get a change-of-address form to route all your old mail to your new home.

- Talk to your bank, Medicare, and insurance companies, too. You don't want your sensitive documents to get sent to the wrong house.

- Keep important papers like bank statements, passports, or tax returns locked up and close by during the move. Otherwise you'll increase the risk of ID theft.

Pick the perfect movers with these simple steps

Broken furniture. Shattered mirrors. Missing jewelry. That's the price of hiring the wrong movers. Track down a company you can trust to look after your belongings by following this advice.

- Get an in-person estimate. Companies within 50 miles of your current house are required by law to come to your home to evaluate the costs. Find out if the estimate is binding or not. If it is, the quote will guarantee the price.

However, a nonbinding estimate is just a ballpark guess. The final bill could wind up a good bit higher.

- Ask questions about the moving team. How much experience do they have? Does the company conduct background checks on the movers?

- Research complaints about the movers and check if their license and insurance are active. To find this information, visit the Federal Motor Carrier Safety Administration's (FMCSA) movers database online at *ai.fmcsa.dot.gov/hhg/search.asp* and type in the name of the moving company. Lapsed coverage and an expired license are warnings that the mover may not be reputable.

- Don't pay a huge chunk of change upfront. A trustworthy moving business shouldn't charge you more than 20 percent for a deposit. If they require a big fee before you move, walk away from the deal.

- Watch out for suspiciously cheap offers, too. Some scammers lowball you on the price, only to hold your items hostage until you pay them thousands of dollars more than the agreed-upon fee. Contact the police immediately if a mover demands extra money in exchange for your possessions.

- Review your contracts before signing your name. Ask the movers about extra fees — like those for carrying items up a flight of stairs — and check to see if they're included in the paperwork. Take time to review everything thoroughly, otherwise you might be surprised by the final bill.

- Weigh the costs of coverage. Say the mover drops your brand-new 65-inch TV. They'll cover the cost, right? Wrong. At minimum, moving companies will only pay back 60 cents per pound on damaged or lost items.

  Even if you go with the top-tier, full-value protection, they won't necessarily pay for items valued at $100 or more per pound — like jewelry, antiques, or electronics. You can consider buying third-party moving insurance, but check with your homeowners policy first. You could already be covered.

Stress-free transition: Prepare for your next chapter with expert advice

"We make the move easier and relieve the stress," says Kaye Ginsberg, owner of Peace of Mind Transitions, a senior move management company based out of Atlanta, Georgia.

Professionals like Ginsberg create a comprehensive moving plan to help you with the physical and emotional aspects of relocating. They can help sort and pack your belongings, coordinate with movers, and even set up a floor plan for your new home.

And when you arrive, they'll help get everything in order. "When a traditional moving company unpacks, they just put everything out on a table or a counter," Ginsberg says. "But when we unpack, we reorganize the kitchen and the closets, put up all the decorative items, hang pictures, and even make the beds."

Plus move mangers make sure your home is senior friendly. "As you get older, your range of motion is minimized," she says. "So a lot of times we'll put pullout drawers in the lower cabinets, and we'll put items like dishes there because that's easier for you to manage."

They also adjust storage rods so you can reach everything in your closet, and set up furniture to accommodate walkers and wheelchairs.

To find a senior move manager near you, go online to the National Association of Senior Move Managers' website — *nasmm.org* — and click "Find a Senior Move Manager."

Shared and community housing

So you don't want to live alone in your old family home. And you're not ready to move to an assisted living facility. The good news is you still have plenty of options when it comes to housing.

You could share your space with a roommate — just like sitcom stars Laverne and Shirley. Or you could even settle down with relatives like the crew in "The Addams Family."

The trick is finding out which one is best for you. Read on to discover the benefits of alternative housing. You may find an option that helps you stay independent and comfortable for years to come.

Top 3 benefits of creative living arrangements

Celebrate independence by lodging close to loved ones. Looking for an inexpensive way to live near your family, but not with them? ECHO, which stands for Elder Cottage Housing Opportunity, might just be the ticket.

Often called "granny flats" and "in-law suites," ECHO is a small, temporary housing unit — often 400 to 800 square feet — installed in the backyard of a relative's home. ECHO homes include all the amenities you'll need, including a kitchen and bathroom, but on a smaller scale.

It's a win-win situation. The kids and grandkids can assist you if you need it, but you'll still be independent and have your privacy.

Move in with family and watch your pennies grow. More and more seniors agree that sharing a home with relatives might be a great alternative to living alone. In fact, the number of people

65 and older residing in a grown child's home nearly doubled between 2001 and 2016.

One reason? Economics. After all, sharing a home offsets housing costs. But it's about more than just saving money. Family caregivers can more easily attend to the physical and emotional needs of aging retirees if they all live under one roof.

Enjoy the social rewards of community living. Looking forward to aging in place and being around lots of other people? Then consider cohousing, a style of living in which you have a strong sense of fellowship with your neighbors.

Members in a cohousing community typically own their homes or apartments. The residences tend to cluster around a common house where neighbors can gather for a shared meal or do laundry.

Cohousing members plan group activities and manage communal gardens and walkways. They also gather for events and share resources like lawn mowers and tools. Of course, you can opt out of any activity whenever you want. Learn more about existing communities at *cohousing.org*.

Save money and have fun with home sharing

Remember the TV show "The Golden Girls"? Hard to believe, but it's been over 30 years since viewers first tuned in to Dorothy, Rose, Blanche, and Sophia sharing the ups and downs of senior life in Miami.

Although the roommates occasionally clashed, they were always there for each other in the end. And that's just one of the benefits that can come with shared housing.

Looking for a housemate? Try finding a match at *seniorhome shares.com, silvernest.com,* or *goldengirlsnetwork.com.* Or visit *nationalsharedhousing.org* and click on the Directory button for a state-by-state listing of home-share programs. Nonprofits and agencies that provide housing services often offer home-share services and information.

"When we look at our outcomes for seniors, home sharing extends their lives," says Karen Heyward-West, director of Homesharing at St. Ambrose Housing Aid Center in Maryland. "They're able to remain in the home by having someone there to support them."

It turns out that having a housemate does more than add years to your life. It can add life to your years.

Lighten your load and gain peace of mind. You can cut your monthly mortgage payment and utility bills in half if you and your roomie split everything down the middle. Shared housing offers other perks, too.

- Lessens loneliness. You'll have someone to spend time with. If you're widowed or divorced, this style of living can help you find companionship and friendship.

- Helps you keep up with upkeep. An extra set of hands can really help with cleaning, cooking, gardening, and repairs.

- Strengthens your weaknesses. If you don't like to cook, choose someone who does.

- Beefs up security. Having someone else in the house can make you feel safer.

- Spreads your wings. A housemate may provide transportation if you no longer drive.

A little bit of effort goes a long way. "There's a big difference between sharing a home and renting a room," Heyward-West says. "Everyone going into it needs to accept the home-sharing philosophy. It doesn't mean, 'I have my room, I lock my door,' and that's it. You're sharing space like the living room and the use of things like the washer and dryer. Both parties are sharing in the upkeep of the home."

That's why this solution might not work for everyone. You must be flexible enough to allow someone else the use of your entire home.

Consider entering a shared-housing arrangement on a trial basis to see if it's the right fit. And be sure to screen a potential housemate for a criminal background or issues with alcohol or drugs.

Coming of age: How to find the best in senior living

Linda Sciullo took a leap of faith on her 65th birthday. That's the day the newly retired book editor moved from her metro Atlanta home to The Villages, a central Florida active adult community catering to people age 55 and up.

She hasn't looked back since. "I am very happy," Sciullo says nearly four years into her new life. "It was the perfect move for me."

Like many retirees living in The Villages, Sciullo thrives on a busy schedule. She takes advantage of the community's many amenities, including yoga and zumba classes, day trips, billiards, and golf.

The Villages, the largest retirement community in the world, has more than 2,700 social clubs to choose from.

"I kind of have to force myself to stay home on some days," Sciullo says.

Sciullo is the first to admit that her new home might not be a good fit for a homebody who, for example, likes to spend a lot of time reading or watching television.

"It's not a typical retirement community," she says. "This is a place for very active people." Her advice? Find a place that fits your personality. That means visiting different communities in an area.

"Do a lot of research," Sciullo suggests. "And weigh the good with the bad."

Renting before buying is another option, she says. This way you can get to know several different neighborhoods before making a decision.

Other things to consider before buying into senior living? Cost, location, current residents, activities, and management of the community should all come into play.

Nursing homes and assisted living

Your home is a familiar place full of memories, so it's natural to want to live there as long as possible.

Unfortunately, health issues sometimes make it too difficult to manage the everyday tasks — cooking, cleaning, dressing — necessary for independent living. In fact, half of the people turning 65 today will develop a disability that requires long-term care.

That's why it's smart to think about future living arrangements before you need to make a change. After all, it's best to explore your options and make a thoughtful decision while you're healthy.

Here are ways to make sure you and your loved ones make the right choice.

You may be forced to pick up the tab for your parents' nursing home bills if they can't afford to pay them. Some 30 U.S. states have filial responsibility laws requiring adult children to help pay for a parent's long-term care expenses. The laws are rarely enforced, but this might change as the population ages and the cost of health care skyrockets.

4 steps to finding quality care at the best price

Identify your needs for perfect placement. Lots of older folks move into assisted living communities as an alternative to remaining in their homes. They live in a residential setting but receive help with things like medication management, washing, and dressing.

Assisted living is a great alternative if you are able to get around on your own, are sociable and alert, and don't need medical care on an ongoing basis.

On the other hand, a nursing home is a better option for seniors with complex medical conditions. Nursing home residents are more likely to share a room, while those in assisted living generally have their own apartments.

Seek help to curb the cost of care. It's no surprise that the cost of senior care continues to climb. While prices vary from state to state, the national median cost for a one-bedroom unit in a private-pay assisted living community is $4,000 per month, or $48,000 per year. Expect to pay more than double that for a private room in a nursing home.

Unfortunately, Medicare won't pick up the tab for assisted living or long-term care in a nursing home. But several private health and long-term care insurance policies will pay some of the costs. Call your provider to learn about your coverage.

In addition, contact Medicaid to see if you're eligible for assistance. You'll find the phone number for the State Medical Assistance Office in charge of your state's Medicaid program at *medicare.gov/contacts* or call 800-MEDICARE.

> Veterans and their spouses who require help with activities like bathing, eating, and dressing may qualify for extra benefits from the U.S. Department of Veterans Affairs (VA). The money can pay for in-home care, assisted living, or a nursing home. The catch? You must be eligible for a VA pension.

Find your fit at the right locale. Search the phone book and the internet for a list of long-term care communities in your area. Ask your physician, clergy, and friends if they can recommend a local facility. You can also check with your state health or welfare departments.

The national Eldercare Locator, at *eldercare.gov*, and the National Center for Assisted Living, at *ahcancal.org/ncal*, are also good resources.

Family members can compare the quality of local nursing homes at *projects.propublica.org/nursing-homes* or read customer reviews at *yelp.com*.

Visit the locations that appeal to you at different times of day to get a picture of what life will be like. Talk with administrators, staff, and residents.

Read the fine print to avoid surprise charges. Assisted living communities have several types of pricing structures, so be sure you understand what you're paying for.

Some charge a single fee for room and board and another for care. Others charge individually for each service or have an "all inclusive" pricing model where everyone pays the same price, regardless of the level of care provided.

Make sure your admission contract states the following:

- a resident's rights and obligations.

- the services included.

- the basic monthly fee and all items that cost extra.

- information on cost-of-living increases.

- transfer, discharge, and leave of absence policies.

- whether the facility is Medicaid or Medicare certified.

Concerned about your facility's standards? The Centers for Medicare & Medicaid Services provides a list of nursing homes found to have serious quality issues. Go to *cms.gov* and type "SFFList" into the search bar to find the latest Special Focus Facility background info and list. Or contact your state's long-term care ombudsman (*ltcombudsman.org*) about a facility's complaint record.

It's always a good idea to have an attorney look over any legally binding document before you sign it.

Long-term housing checklist:
Must-ask questions for finding the right residence

Touring a nursing home or assisted living facility? Here's what to look for.

Gauge the atmosphere.
- [ ] Is the lobby open and welcoming?
- [ ] Are the furniture, windows, and floors clean?
- [ ] Do you hear comforting sounds like music, laughter, and conversation?
- [ ] Is the building well-ventilated and fresh-smelling?

Talk with residents.
- [ ] Are they pleased with the care they receive?
- [ ] What is a typical day like?
- [ ] Can family members participate in events?
- [ ] Do they have regrets about choosing this facility?

Stop in for lunch or dinner.
- [ ] Is the food fresh, nutritious, and appetizing?
- [ ] Does the menu feature several entrees to choose from?
- [ ] Can the kitchen cater to dietary needs or special requests?
- [ ] Are residents permitted to eat in their rooms?

Check out the activities.
- [ ] Does the calendar of events match your interests?
- [ ] Are events well-attended?
- [ ] Do they offer outings away from the community?
- [ ] Are religious services available?

Look at staffing patterns.
- [ ] Do they have enough staff on hand to meet your needs?
- [ ] Do employees treat residents with dignity and respect?
- [ ] Are background checks performed before hiring staff?
- [ ] How much training do staff members have?

Radical redesign in nursing homes offers comfort along with care

For lots of people, the words "nursing home" spark thoughts of shared rooms, medicine carts, and a hospital-like atmosphere. That's not the case for seniors living in Green House skilled-nursing homes.

Green House residents — usually 10 to 12 per household — have their own private bedrooms and share a living room, open kitchen, and dining table long enough for communal meals.

The idea behind the project, which launched in 2003, is to make the seniors feel as if they are living in a home, rather than an institution.

"It's so important that the residents have some autonomy and control," says Susan Ryan, senior director of The Green House Project.

The seniors in a Green House home, for example, have round-the-clock kitchen access and provide input on meal planning. That means weight loss among residents is rarely an issue, Ryan says. And unlike in traditional nursing homes, there's plenty of outdoor space for residents to gather and engage with each other.

Low employee turnover is also essential to the program. "We take consistent staffing very, very seriously," Ryan says. "In order to build knowing and trusting relationships with residents, you need to have the same people coming into the home."

The results? Ryan says the small size of Green House communities allows for relationship building among staff and seniors. "That yields very positive benefits for the residents' physical, emotional, and mental health," she says.

Ryan says the 285 Green House homes scattered across the United States accept Medicaid. The cost to private-pay residents is comparable or slightly higher than those in traditional nursing homes. For more information, visit *thegreenhouseproject.org*.

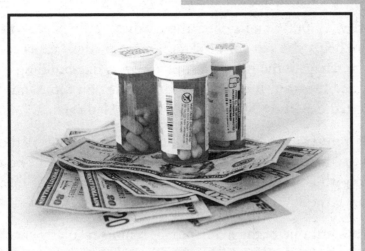

UPGRADE
HEALTH
COVERAGE

WISE MOVES TO BOOST
BENEFITS WITHOUT
PAYING MORE

Medicare

Every day, 10,000 seniors enter the Medicare minefield. The program helps you pay for post-retirement medical expenses, but trying to navigate the rules without a plan is like building a house without a blueprint. It could end up costing you thousands in unexpected expenses. The same is true for Medicare.

Take it from Dan. After he retired, he put off joining Medicare Part B for three years. When he finally got around to it, he was slapped with a 30 percent late-enrollment penalty. That meant he owed an extra $500 a year in premiums.

And that's just one of the many pitfalls seniors regularly encounter. Experts estimate that the average Medicare beneficiary pays $8,000 out of pocket on health care every year. You can bring those costs down with a little knowledge and planning.

Find out how you can make the most of Medicare and get what you're entitled to without busting your bank account.

4 strategies to save on Medicare and keep more money in your pocket

Call in the cavalry for "Extra Help" with the bills. Can't afford to pay for all your prescriptions? Extra Help is an official program that offsets Part D premiums and lowers the cost of prescription drugs for people who need financial aid.

To join the program, your household income must be under $18,120 if you're single, or $24,690 if you're married. You also can't have more than $28,150 in savings, cash, or other investments. Plus you'll need to be on a Medicare drug plan.

If you qualify for the Extra Help program but don't have Part D, Medicare may automatically enroll you in a drug plan so you can participate. But you would have to give up your current insurance.

> You can't add to your health savings account after Medicare kicks in, but you can still put it to good use. Withdraw the money you've already stowed away to pay for Part B premiums, Medicare Advantage plans, and prescription drug coverage. The best part? You won't owe taxes on any money you take out.

If you want to keep your employer or union coverage, you'll need to opt out of Extra Help and Part D. When you get a letter saying you've been signed up for the program, call the number and let them know you don't want to participate.

And don't worry — you can join Part D and Extra Help later without penalty as long as your current plan pays at least as much as Medicare's standard drug coverage.

Still interested even though you don't meet all the requirements? Exceptions can be made if you have dependents, live in certain states, or are currently working. Go online to *socialsecurity.gov/i1020* or call Social Security at 800-772-1213 to find out how to apply.

Crunch the numbers to sidestep future fees. Don't celebrate your great stock market returns just yet — you might end up with a high-income surcharge. That's because your Medicare premiums go up along with your earnings. People in the top income bracket could pay an extra $5,000 a year in premiums and drug coverage.

The calculations are based on the tax returns you filed the previous year. So if you withdraw retirement funds, sell a vacation home, or do anything else that could be counted as income, think about how it will affect your Medicare costs down the line.

- Think the surcharges are too high? Call Social Security or go online to *ssa.gov/benefits/disability/appeal.html* and click

"Reconsideration" then "Request Non-Medical Reconsideration" to file an appeal.

- Recently retired? Just married? Reevaluate your Medicare costs to lower your payments. If you've experience a life-changing event that alters your income — such as the death of a spouse, change in marital status, loss of a pension — fill out an SSA-44 form. You can find it online at *ssa.gov/forms/ssa-44.pdf*.

Reexamine your coverage to save on premiums. Every year, new plans hit the market. If you don't take time to look at them, you might miss out on huge savings. These plans could cover more services, lower your premiums, or let you use different doctors and pharmacies.

Information about updates roll out in September, and then you have from October 15 to December 7 to enroll in a new plan.

For help making a decision, call 800-MEDICARE, use the plan finder online at *medicare.gov/find-a-plan*, or look at your most recent "Medicare & You" handbook. Free counseling is also available from your State Health Insurance Assistance Program (SHIP). Visit *shiptacenter.org*, or reach out to your Medicare office to get in touch with a local advisor.

Check out these savings programs to stay above water. Need help paying your Medicare bills? Think about applying to a Medicare Savings Program offered by your state.

- Qualified Medicare Beneficiary (QMB) Program. This helps offset the cost of premiums for both parts A and B. Providers can't charge you for copayments, deductibles, or coinsurance when you get services or items covered by Medicare.

- Specified Low-Income Medicare Beneficiary (SLMB) Program. Recipients get help covering the cost of Part B premiums.

- Qualifying Individual (QI) Program. You get help paying for Part B premiums, but funds are limited. Apply early because QI is run on a first-come, first-served basis.

- Qualified Disabled and Working Individuals (QDWI) Program. QDWI can curb the cost of Part A premiums for people who work and have a disability.

To find a program in your state, go to *medicare.gov/contacts* and click on "Medicare Savings Programs (MSPs)."

Over 65? Don't pay a penny for these common medical services

The only thing better than getting a bargain on state-of-the-art health care is getting it for free. And Medicare gives you plenty of no-cost services you can take advantage of.

> Many Medicare beneficiaries don't take advantage of hospice benefits. If you have a terminal illness, Medicare will cover drugs, treatments, and in-home care. Because all your caregiving needs will be met, experts say you'll live more comfortably, and maybe even longer.

Fight future ailments with complimentary care. Only 1 out of 10 seniors takes advantage of the free annual doctor's visit granted by Medicare Part B. Plus you're entitled to tests, procedures, and vaccines that will help prevent diseases.

You can get yearly bone density tests, flu shots, and cancer screenings — and that's just to name a few.

Go back to class on a scholarship from "Medicare U." Want more than just medical tests? Medicare will teach you how to stay fit and make the most of your golden years.

You'll find free sessions that cover nutrition and managing heart disease — and counseling to help you quit smoking.

You won't believe your eyes — glasses and eye exams at no cost. Quit squinting at every page you read. Medicare will cover the cost of corrective lenses if you've had cataract surgery. And if you're at risk for certain conditions, you can get free yearly exams to check for signs of diabetic retinopathy and glaucoma.

For more information on all these freebies, go online to *medicare.gov/coverage* and search for procedures, medical equipment, and classes to see if the costs are covered.

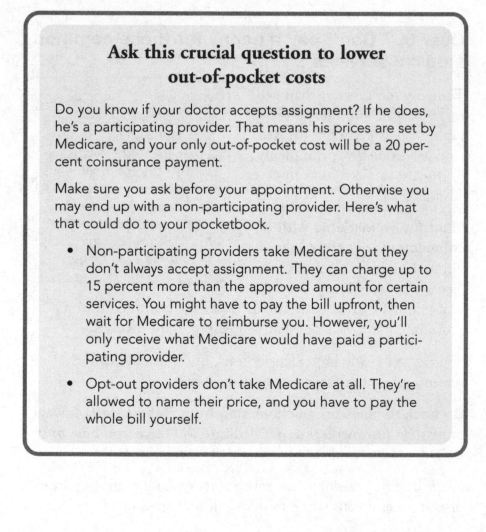

Ask this crucial question to lower out-of-pocket costs

Do you know if your doctor accepts assignment? If he does, he's a participating provider. That means his prices are set by Medicare, and your only out-of-pocket cost will be a 20 percent coinsurance payment.

Make sure you ask before your appointment. Otherwise you may end up with a non-participating provider. Here's what that could do to your pocketbook.

- Non-participating providers take Medicare but they don't always accept assignment. They can charge up to 15 percent more than the approved amount for certain services. You might have to pay the bill upfront, then wait for Medicare to reimburse you. However, you'll only receive what Medicare would have paid a participating provider.

- Opt-out providers don't take Medicare at all. They're allowed to name their price, and you have to pay the whole bill yourself.

Can you take 'Advantage' of a cost-saving plan?

You've got the A, B, and D of Medicare sorted out. But wait —
where's the C? Part C, better known as Medicare Advantage, is
private insurance that can replace your Original Medicare coverage.
Here's why 1 out of 3 seniors go for it — and why you might, too.

- Affordability. Medicare Advantage plans often have very
  low or no premiums. But they make up for it with a higher
  deductible. If you're healthy and don't go to the doctor
  often, you could stand to save with an Advantage plan.

- Ease of use. With Medicare Advantage, you won't have to
  keep track of extra insurance cards or think about what is
  covered by parts B or D. Everything is packaged together, so
  it's easy to check on your prescriptions or find out if a doctor
  is in your network.

- Extra benefits. Need to get a root canal? New eyeglasses?
  Then a Medicare Advantage plan might make sense. It often
  covers things not included in Original Medicare.

- Maximum out-of-pocket limits. Original Medicare won't cap
  your personal expenses. So that means if you have high medical bills, you're on the hook for thousands of dollars. That's
  not the case with an Advantage plan. The law limits providers
  from charging you more than $6,700 a year for Medicare-
  covered services. Many insurers set the limit even lower, so
  you won't have to worry about the high cost of care.

That said, Medicare Advantage isn't the best choice for everybody.
With it, you can only use certain providers, so your options are
limited by your insurance's network. That could be a problem if
you travel frequently.

And unlike Original Medicare, Advantage plans often require
referrals from a primary care doctor if you need to see a specialist,
get specialized equipment, or hire home health care.

> ## Free course helps you steer clear of diabetes
>
> More than a third of American adults have elevated blood sugar, a condition that puts them at prime risk for type 2 diabetes. Fortunately, it's not too late to ward off this deadly disease. And Medicare will give you just the boost you need.
>
> The new Medicare Diabetes Prevention Program offers access to at least 16 classes that will teach you how to make lifestyle changes, get more exercise, and control your weight. And the best part? No out-of-pocket cost.
>
> If you have prediabetes and Part B coverage, call Medicare or go online to check out the program and see if you meet the other qualifications.

Total protection: How to plug the gaps in your coverage

Greg thought he didn't need Medigap because he was already paying Part B premiums. That all changed when complications from heart surgery kept him in the hospital for months. Medicare only covered 80 percent of the $80,000 doctor's bill, which meant he had to pay $16,000 out of his own pocket.

Medigap can help offset those costs, which is why a quarter of people on Medicare have some kind of supplemental insurance. The plans aren't one size fits all, though. Here's how to find the perfect one for you.

Narrow down your needs to get the best coverage. Decide if you'll go with Medicare Advantage or Medigap. Jim Blankenship, certified financial planner and author of "A Medicare Owner's Manual: Your Guide to Medicare Benefits," says to consider these points.

- Where you live. Do you travel often or head south for the winter? Then consider Medigap. "Medicare Advantage coverage is generally regional," he says. "If you go with Medigap, you'll be covered by any facility or provider that accepts Medicare."

- Your choice of providers. Need certain specialists for your specific medical issues? Medigap doesn't require a referral as long as the specialist takes Medicare.

- The cost of care. Medigap may seem more expensive at first, but if you take frequent trips to the doctor it could be a money-saver. "The upfront costs of Medigap are generally higher than Medicare Advantage," says Blankenship. "But in the long run, depending on your health situation, Medigap may be cheaper because it provides more complete coverage."

> The best time to apply for Medigap is during the open enrollment period after you turn 65 and join Medicare Part B. Companies can't deny you coverage or charge higher rates due to pre-existing conditions during this six-month stretch. Not in open enrollment? Call Medicare to see if you have a guaranteed issue right that gives you the same benefits.

Shop around to find the perfect plan. Medigap plans share identical benefits no matter where you buy them, but they're sold by private companies. That means availability and prices vary based on where you live.

Take a look at all the different plans to see what you want covered. You can go online to *medicare.gov/find-a-plan*, call Medicare's hotline at 800-633-4227, or talk to your local State Health Insurance Assistance Program (SHIP) about options.

Next, take time to contact local providers and ask them a few questions. Find out what plans they offer, what the premiums are, and if the prices have increased over the past few years.

Cross the t's and dot the i's to avoid pricey penalties. After you've chosen your plan and completed your application, decide when you want your policy to kick in. Most companies let coverage start the first of the month after you fill out your application.

A couple of days after you submit all the paperwork, check with your insurance company to make sure everything is in order. Otherwise you might be in for a nasty surprise.

"Things get lost, various different things happen to good applications, but if you don't follow up with it you're stuck if it doesn't go through," Blankenship says. "You could wind up with penalties that you didn't anticipate."

If you haven't received confirmation of coverage within 30 days of submitting your application, call the insurance company. After 60 days without confirmation, reach out to your state insurance department.

Manage Medicare easily with this state-of-the-art fix

Would you like to control all your Medicare documents with the push of a button? Now you can. All you have to do is sign up online, and the Medicare world will be at your fingertips.

Registering is easy. Go to *MyMedicare.gov*, click "Create an Account," and type in your information. Then you can track your Medicare claim status, manage your prescriptions, find approved providers in your area, and more.

An added bonus? You can use the website to get early alerts if anyone tries to file a claim using your identity. Plus you'll freeze out thieves who might want to create an account in your name. For more information about protecting yourself, see the *Identity theft* chapter.

Medicaid and financial aid programs

Elaine always thought her savings and Social Security would provide a comfortable retirement. But then she was laid off in her late 50s and forced to tap into her 401(k) early. A decade later, Elaine is one of millions of seniors on a fixed income who struggle to pay for rent, food, and medicine.

And, like others in her age group, she doesn't take advantage of the resources that could make her life more comfortable.

Take, for example, the Supplemental Nutrition Assistance Program (SNAP) that helps low-income individuals and families buy food. According to the National Council on Aging, 3 out of 5 seniors who qualify for the program don't participate. That means some 5 million seniors are missing out on benefits.

How much could you get? It depends on your circumstances, but a single woman like Elaine could expect about $134 a month. That's an extra $1,608 a year to spend on nutritious fare to help her stay in tiptop shape — and keep the doctor away.

Why don't more older adults apply? Some are afraid that others will look down on them for accepting help. Others have heard myths about the program or aren't aware they're eligible to enroll.

Fortunately, there's hope — and support — for seniors who need help paying for health expenses and more. Read on to learn how to connect with the public and private assistance programs that could make your golden years so much better.

Boost your health care experience with these 4 little-known Medicaid truths

Tons of long-term care options are covered. You might already know that Medicaid covers long-term nursing home fees. In fact, Medicaid pays for the care of 6 in 10 nursing home residents in the U.S. But did you know that the program also pays for services to help keep seniors in their homes as long as possible?

While each state has flexibility on the assistance it provides, benefits often include in-home medical visits, assistance with activities like bathing and getting dressed, and even help with household chores like grocery shopping and laundry. Home modifications — think wheelchair ramps and walk-in bathtubs — are often paid for, at least in part, by Medicaid.

Family can get paid for caregiving. Medicaid allows you to hire family members to provide you with personal care. Generally, the Medicaid office gives you cash directly to pay your caregiver or uses a financial management company to handle their salary.

The majority of states don't allow spouses to be hired as paid caregivers. But adult children, in-laws, and grandchildren — even ex-spouses — are usually permitted to do so. How much will they make? They're typically paid several dollars less than the state's average hourly rate for home care.

Are you a senior whose income is too high to qualify for Medicaid? You may still get coverage if you have significant medical expenses that reduce your income below a certain level. Check to see if your state has a "medically needy" pathway to Medicaid eligibility.

"Dually eligible" means Medicare gaps get filled. Having trouble keeping up with Medicare-related costs? Medicaid might be able to fix the problem. The program assists 1 in 5 Medicare beneficiaries with expenses like premiums and copayments. Some of the other perks? In addition to standard Medicaid benefits, many states cover optional services like prescription drugs, eyeglasses, dental care, and physical therapy.

Plus Medicaid runs four savings programs for low-income seniors on Medicare. Each has unique income limits, but you can save a lot on Medicare premiums and other out-of-pocket medical expenses if you're eligible. For more information, see *4 strategies to save on Medicare and keep more money in your pocket* in the *Medicare* chapter.

More pre-retirees now qualify for coverage. Seniors without employee-sponsored health insurance in their pre-Medicare years often can't afford health care coverage. The Affordable Care Act, a cornerstone of the Obama administration, sought to ease the situation by expanding Medicaid coverage so more adults under the age of 65 can qualify. How much can a pre-retiree now earn and still be eligible? Up to $17,236 a year. It's a little bit more if you live in Alaska or Hawaii.

Of course, there's a catch. Not all of the states have adopted the Medicaid expansion plan. Want to know if you're eligible based on income alone? Go to *healthcare.gov/lower-costs*.

Need a leg up? Find free government benefits the easy way

Everybody needs a little help from time to time, and seniors are no exception. But let's face it. Few people have the time and energy to sort through all the government programs out there.

Not knowing your options can keep you from getting what you deserve. Need a hand when it comes to the best places to look? Turn to these valuable resources.

Online tool links you to benefits. The National Council on Aging has launched a free screening service of thousands of benefit programs at *benefitscheckup.org*. Tucked away in the database are over 2,500 public and private programs from all 50 states and the District of Columbia. So far the nonprofit has helped 7.5 million people collect over $29 billion in benefits.

All you have to do is answer a few simple questions to find the programs that meet your unique needs. You may get assistance with these types of expenses:

- health care and medication

- food and clothing

- housing and utilities

- legal representation

- transportation

> The Eldercare Locator is a nationwide service that connects older Americans and their caregivers with community-based services like health insurance counseling and long-term care support. Call the Eldercare Locator at 800-677-1116 or go to *eldercare.acl.gov*. Another option? Go to *Benefits.gov* to check your eligibility for federal and state benefit programs.

Dial your way to community assistance. Want to speak directly with someone? Then dial 211. It's a little-known phone number that will lead you to dozens of local services. And it's free and confidential.

Specialists will listen to your concerns and find the best local resources to address them. Operators can link you with all sorts of support, including food and shelter assistance, education and job training, home health care, support groups, and crisis intervention services. The service is available 24 hours a day, seven days a week.

Take advantage of free or low-cost health care. Forget about Medicare limitations. The Hill-Burton program could pay all your hospital and nursing home costs. It started way back in 1946, when the federal government funded upgrades at various hospitals, nursing homes, and clinics. In return, the health care providers promised to treat a certain number of patients each year for free or at a reduced cost. About 140 health facilities still do.

You might be eligible for assistance if your income falls within the federal poverty guidelines. Reduced-cost treatment is sometimes provided for those who earn more. To find participating medical centers near you, go to *hrsa.gov* and search for "Hill-Burton Facilities Obligated." You can apply at the facility's billing department or admissions office.

State of play: The ins and outs of qualifying for Medicaid

Real estate agents have been saying for years that the most important factor in determining a property's value is "location, location, location." Oddly enough, the same can be said for Medicaid.

It's true. Whether or not you'll receive Medicaid hinges on where you live. Although the federal government partially funds the program, the states have a lot of control over eligibility.

Most of them, however, use a formula based on income and family size. Generally, you may be eligible for some form of benefit if you earn less than 100 percent to 200 percent of the federal poverty level and are elderly, pregnant, disabled, a child, or a caretaker.

Almost every state has several Medicaid programs. And while all the states cover certain services — nursing home and hospital care, for example — dozens of other benefits are considered optional.

Find out more about particular state programs at *medicaid.gov/state-overviews*.

Medications and supplements

Way back in 1965, a hamburger and Coke set you back a quarter, and you probably shelled out no more than $200 a year for health care. Now you're hard-pressed to find a Happy Meal for less than $2.50. And health care? The average yearly costs per person are an eye-popping $10,000 — and they don't show any signs of slowing down.

One of the biggest culprits? Astronomical drug prices that hit seniors hard. The average cost of a brand-name prescription to treat a chronic condition comes in at over $5,800 a year.

You probably know just how hard it is to balance a budget while paying for your meds. But you shouldn't have to make the choice between filling your prescriptions and buying groceries for the week.

With a little know-how and a few tricks, you might be able to lower your costs considerably.

Slash your Rx costs by thousands with these 10 top tips

Go generic to cut your costs. Tired of paying for brand-name prescription drugs? Try their cheaper cousins. The active ingredients are the same, and the Food and Drug Administration's regulations are just as strict.

You probably do it all the time with over-the-counter drugs. If you can save money buying the Walmart brand of acetaminophen instead of Tylenol, you don't think twice about it. You should have the same attitude toward prescription generic drugs.

Talk to your doctor if she recommends a name brand, and ask if a generic will do instead. She may have a specific reason for requesting that particular drug. For example, certain blood-thinning or thyroid medications can be dangerous if the dosage is off even a little, so you may need to stick to the name brand.

Stock up on savings when you buy in bulk. You might get a discount on your prescription if you buy enough for 90 days instead of 30. Talk to your pharmacist or doctor to see if you stand to save.

Don't waste money buying more pills than you need, though. If your doctor only wants you to take something for a month, you'll waste money by ordering a three-month supply.

Clip coupons to avoid breaking the bank. Drug manufacturers occasionally offer coupons that could shave hundreds off prescription prices. To see if any are available, talk to your doctor or pharmacist.

Some coupons might not be compatible with your insurance. In that case, it might be cheaper to buy the drugs out of pocket and submit a claim for reimbursement.

Seek out the best pharmacy for your wallet. Medicare, as well as other insurance options, have preferred pharmacies. When you get your drugs there, your out-of-pocket costs will be much lower than if you went elsewhere.

Don't have a preferred pharmacy option from your insurance? Shop around and compare prices for different drugs at several pharmacies. Even though the medicine is the same, the price could vary. And if you have certain medical conditions, specialty pharmacies could help you find financial assistance and other money-saving resources.

Sign up for discount programs to score great deals. Certain pharmacies have programs that give you bargains on generic drugs. However, they often require annual membership fees.

Some supermarket pharmacies also offer free prescriptions, regardless of your insurance. You might have to enroll in their loyalty program to access these benefits. Reach out to your pharmacy to see what they have available.

Take advantage of freebies to avoid outrageous prices. Don't pay for prescriptions, especially when you might qualify to get them for free. Look at prescription assistance programs if you need help paying for the medicine you need.

Websites like *rxassist.org* will help you track down programs that provide financial assistance or help you find free medications.

Nonprofit groups, like the Partnership for Prescription Assistance at *pparx.org*, also help low-income seniors find free drugs. Look into similar nonprofits near you, or check to see if you're eligible for government-run programs.

Reevaluate your meds to save on care. Recent surveys have found that, when people ask their doctor to review their current medications, he will take them off at least one drug. That's money back in your pocket.

Save money by substituting. Your doctor may help you figure out other cost-saving methods, like switching to a lower dose or a cheaper drug, or taking a higher dose less often. Or ask about using an older drug, which may be cheaper than the fancy new models.

Consider splitting your pills to halve your costs. You may be able to cut your prescription costs in half by splitting your pills. If this works with your medication, you can buy higher-dose pills for the same price, then cut the pills in half for cost savings. It won't work for all drugs, so talk to your doctor before you try this clever — and perfectly legal — trick.

Alternative treatments could keep you from going broke. Don't want to pay thousands for risky prescriptions? Talk to your doctor about a therapeutic treatment. For example, you may decide to try melatonin supplements instead of a prescription drug that treats insomnia.

Your insurance will often cover the costs of alternative treatments if they've been prescribed by a doctor.

Steer clear of dangerous prescriptions with this expert advice

Believe it or not, 1 in 3 seniors are prescribed drugs that could be harmful. Do you know if you're one of them?

Rasheeda McNeal, a certified pharmacy technician, says the best way to avoid risky medicines is to be aware of how drugs affect your body. Seniors need to be especially careful of the side effects caused by opioids and other long-term prescriptions.

"We ask seniors to look for things like drowsiness, dizziness, hot flashes, or sudden chills," she says. "Anything that's out of the norm."

And be aware that a new prescription may not mix well with your other medications. "You need to make sure your medicines won't interact with medicines you already take," McNeal says. "For example, you might need a special cough syrup because codeine can make statins last longer in your body than they're supposed to."

To make sure you're avoiding dangerous drugs and adverse interactions, check out these resources.

- Log on to pill identifier websites like *medscape.com* or *drugs.com*. "You can see what your pills look like and all the possible adverse reactions," McNeal says.

- Ask for a Generic Brand Reference. Most pharmacies have a book of popular medications and their generic equivalents. It gives you information about the medicine and potential dangerous side effects.

- Talk to your doctor to see if any of your prescriptions are on the American Geriatric Society's Beers list — a catalog of drugs that could potentially cause problems for older adults. If so, ask if there are any safer alternatives you could try.

Over-prescribed antibiotics affect your health — and your wallet

The cost of treating drug-resistant bacteria clocks in at a whopping $2 billion every year. That's enough cash to give every person in America a crisp $5 bill and still have money left over.

Experts say these superbugs are caused by unnecessary antibiotics. And according to the Centers for Disease Control, only 2 out of 3 antibiotic prescriptions are actually needed. Doctors write that third one for a variety of reasons — sometimes just because they know patients don't want to leave empty-handed.

Next time you're sick, talk to your doctor about whether an antibiotic is necessary. You don't want to pay for a drug you don't need or risk the dangerous side effects.

If your doctor does tell you to take a certain medication, make sure to follow the instructions. You're at risk for another illness if you stop taking your pills before the dose is finished.

Pay now and save later — when cash prices cut the cost of your meds

Nancy had no idea her prescription copays were actually more expensive than buying her medicine out of pocket. And how could she — the pharmacists never told her how much she stood to save.

Insurance companies used to have contracts with pharmacies that barred workers from telling you how much medicine would cost if you paid with cash instead of using your insurance.

Fortunately, new laws have banned these "gag clauses." Now you can compare the costs when you fill a prescription. And you might find an even better deal when you pay on your own, especially if you have coupons or discount programs.

Make sure to ask the pharmacist. He doesn't have to offer information on prices unless you bring it up first.

One big benefit — if you're on Medicare Part D or part of an Advantage plan, you can count those cash payments as out-of-pocket expenses. That will help get you out of the dreaded coverage gap known as the donut hole.

Don't spend bundles on bogus supplements

The supplement industry rakes in more money than professional basketball, football, and baseball — combined. But even though Americans spend an astonishing $37 billion on supplements every year, they're often not getting their money's worth.

You've read that supplements can improve your health. So what's the problem? Supplement sellers don't need approval from the Food and Drug Administration before they send their products out to store shelves.

That means the actual ingredients could vary widely from the extract used in the studies. In fact, experts say the amount of the active ingredient in some supplements can change from batch to batch. So how can you avoid spending hard-earned cash on duds?

- Look for seals of approval like the ones you see here. The U.S. Pharmacopeia (USP) and National Sanitation Foundation (NSF) will put a stamp on supplement labels that prove the bottle actually contains the listed ingredients. Read these labels carefully. Some brands put fake certifications on their bottles that look almost identical to the real ones.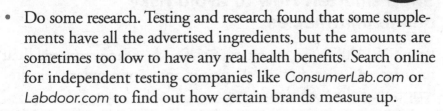

- Do some research. Testing and research found that some supplements have all the advertised ingredients, but the amounts are sometimes too low to have any real health benefits. Search online for independent testing companies like *ConsumerLab.com* or *Labdoor.com* to find out how certain brands measure up.

- Take health claims with a grain of salt. Manufacturers are allowed to list whatever health claims they want on their supplements, but that doesn't make them true. Don't fall for shifty marketing. Talk with your doctor to get a better idea of which supplements could benefit you.

Think twice before heading north for cheap meds

Have you ever considered going to Canada to get a bargain on your prescriptions? Canadian brand-name drugs are usually cheaper than their American counterparts. Before you hop on the next plane north, evaluate these factors to see if buying foreign meds is the right choice for you.

- Cost. Factor in the expenses from shipping, travel, and currency conversion and then compare the prices to U.S. generics. You might find you won't save any money.

- Safety. Foreign tests and guidelines don't always meet the standards set by the U.S. Food and Drug Administration (FDA). Talk to a doctor you trust to avoid buying unsafe medicine.

- Legality. Importing unapproved prescriptions is illegal, but the FDA makes certain exceptions. For example, if you have a serious condition and the drug you need is not available in the U.S., they may allow you to bring in a 90-day supply. Make sure you meet all the criteria before taking the plunge.

Shop smarter: How to avoid risky online pharmacies

People these days use the internet to file their taxes, manage their finances, and even do their shopping. Some even order their prescriptions online. So should you?

Watch out for these red flags to avoid risky suppliers. The U.S. Food and Drug Administration found that only 3 percent of online pharmacies meet safety standards. Keep an eye on these warning signs to avoid suspect operations.

- The site has no licensed pharmacist on staff to answer questions about your medications. If you don't see a phone number or staff list on the website, don't do business with it.

- You're able to buy and order medications without a valid prescription. Not only is this dangerous to your health, it's against the law.

- The business isn't based in the United States. This could be a sign that the drugs aren't safe. And shipping medicine internationally could be illegal.

- The pharmacy isn't licensed. To find out if an online pharmacy is up to snuff, check with your state board of pharmacy.

- The website hasn't been certified by the National Association of Boards of Pharmacy. This organization signs off on dependable online pharmacies and gives them a seal of approval. To get more information and check certifications, go online to *safe.pharmacy*.

> Tried to get meds online and received what looks like an FDA warning letter instead? You may have ordered from an illegal online pharmacy. The FDA warns that scammers are sending these notes, possibly hoping to bilk you out of money by promising not to pursue legal action. Don't respond to the fake letter. Instead, the FDA says to email details of the letter to *FDAInternetPharmacyTask Force-CDER@fda.hhs.gov*.

Get mail-order prescriptions without jeopardizing your safety. Retail pharmacies have a host of experts who can store, ship, and manage your medications. You don't get that same assurance if you order drugs over the internet.

Certain meds need to be stored at specific temperatures. That's why your pill bottles often say to keep them in a cool, dark place or to avoid high heat.

Talk to your online pharmacy about including temperature indicators in your prescriptions to ensure they were shipped properly. Otherwise, it might be best to stick with a brick-and-mortar store.

Make sure online ordering will actually save you cash. If you order your drugs through the mail or online, sit down and do the math to see if it makes financial sense. Experts from the Centers for Medicare & Medicaid Services found that getting drugs shipped to you is often more expensive than going to the store.

Preferred drug no longer covered? Try these simple steps

Rebecca spent years trying to find the perfect prescription to manage her osteoarthritis. She finally found a drug that worked, only to discover her insurance company planned to stop covering it next year. If you're in a similar situation, what can you do?

- Ask your doctor about alternative options or similar drugs that are still covered by insurance.

- No other meds fit the bill? Ask your insurer about an exemption. Your doctor will need to tell your insurance company there's no other option. However, your insurer could require you to take cheaper alternatives for a while. If the less-expensive drugs aren't as effective or cause side effects, your insurance company will then cover a higher-tier drug.

- Look for coupons and assistance programs to help you afford to buy your drugs out of pocket. You can also search for low-cost prescriptions at big-box and warehouse stores.

Doctor visits

Can you describe all your aches, pains, and ailments in fewer than 20 words? According to a recent study, that's about all you'll get at the doctor's office. Many physicians only spend 11 seconds listening to you before they interrupt.

You invest a lot of time and money in health care. Be a smart patient by partnering with the right doctor. With a little know-how, you can find a physician who will give you the quality care you deserve.

- Find a doctor in your network. If a practice isn't covered by your insurance, you'll probably pay through the nose every time you go for a checkup.

- Ask friends and family for recommendations. Your loved ones will have firsthand experience of what it's like to work with a doctor they trust.

- Look out for red flags. Want to know if a doctor has a history of complaints? Go online to *docinfo.org*. This website — which is run by the Federation of State Medical Boards — lists physician information like certifications, active licenses, and disciplinary actions.

- Visit the doctor's office. Some places will let you schedule a tour of the facility and have an in-person meeting with the doctor you're considering. Call ahead to see if you have that option.

6 easy-peasy practices to make the most of your doctor visit

Log all your symptoms to pinpoint any problems. Stomachache? Back pain? Write it down. Keep a journal of anything out of the usual so you can bring it up later when you're talking to your doctor.

Do your best to be as detailed as possible. For example, if you noticed a headache after your morning walk, note the date, time, and what you were doing before it started hurting. Think about how your doctor might describe the pain, too. Was it sharp and throbbing or dull and aching?

Plan ahead to get the answers to all your questions. Do you want to ask the doctor about something specific? Write down your questions in advance and bring them along. You might not remember everything by the time you actually meet with your physician.

Remember to bring a pen and paper along so you can take notes during your visit. And if you have questions but don't want to interrupt the doctor, you can use them to jot down a few things to ask later.

Ward off medical mishaps with a little preparation. Even the best doctor is only human. So if you don't tell him that you're taking a new drug for, say, high cholesterol, he might miss it. Next thing you know, he's prescribed an antibiotic that causes a dangerous interaction.

Even when you tell a doctor which meds you take, he still needs to know the brand, dosage, and how often you take them. To help your physician out, make a list of every medicine, vitamin, and supplement you're on. And be specific. If it's easier, put all your pill bottles and supplements into a bag and bring them along.

Seeing a specialist or going back and forth between doctors? Bring your medical records with you. You can arrange to have them sent over before your appointment.

Don't want to go it alone? Find someone who can lend a hand. Consider asking a close friend or family member to come along for the visit. An extra set of ears will help you keep track of everything the doctor tells you. Plus they can take notes when you're busy chatting with the doctor.

It's important to find someone you trust who listens well, is willing to be assertive, and doesn't mind asking questions. Before the visit, brief your advocate on what questions you have and what the appointment will be about.

If you can't find anyone to tag along, you can always ask your doctor to write down the important points or any instructions.

Tackle your biggest issues first to avoid wasting time on small potatoes. If you have more than one health issue to discuss, decide which is the most important to you. That's the one you should ask your doctor about first because he'll usually give it more attention.

Have a long list of concerns? Let the doctor's office know when you call to schedule the appointment. You may be able to request a longer visit.

> Next time you head to the doctor's office, consider seeing a physician's assistant (PA). He will often have more time to talk with you than a doctor would, so you can ask more questions. And the best part? The cost may be lower.

Curb confusion to capitalize on your visits. If you leave the doctor's office scratching your head, you're not going to make the most of your doc's advice. Don't be afraid to ask questions if you need clarification. A good doctor will take the time to make sure you know exactly what's going on in your body.

You need to completely understand the treatment plan, especially if you intend to see a specialist or get a second opinion. Still want to know more? Ask the doctor about websites or books where you can research the condition yourself.

Think twice, act once — get a second opinion to avoid making a major mistake

Roger's doctor recommended invasive surgery to treat his chronic knee pain. Yet after sinking thousands of dollars into a risky procedure and spending months in rehab, Roger's pain persisted. He found a new doctor, and a combination of therapy and drugs finally got him back on his feet. Of course, he could have avoided the unnecessary operation in the first place if he had sought a second opinion.

Need extra advice? Here's when you should start the search. You don't need to consult another doctor if you have a minor issue like a common cold or don't have time to get another opinion, as in the case of emergency surgery. Most experts recommend seeking out a second opinion if you're in one of these situations.

- Your doctor recommends a complex, risky, or expensive treatment. For example, you should consider getting more advice before a major surgery.

- You have a diagnosis of a rare or serious illness. Even if the diagnosis is the same, another doctor may give you different treatment options.

- You're given a few choices. For instance, your physician says your options are therapy, drugs, or surgery. You might want to get another professional's perspective, especially if you're on the fence or need more information.

Ask around to find a fresh perspective. Start by asking your doctor if he has any recommendations for second opinions. Many people worry they will offend their physician when they seek out more advice, but it's nothing to be concerned about. You can also ask your friends and family for a recommendation.

Let the doctor know you're looking for a second opinion when you make the appointment, and tell him what your diagnosis is. Bring along test results, scans, and other medical records.

And do your best to avoid telling him how you feel about certain treatments, otherwise you could influence his advice.

Connect with a virtual doctor to lower the cost of care

Can't find a ride to the doctor's office after your knee surgery? Don't worry, a new technology — known as telemedicine — lets you connect with doctors right from the comfort of your couch. As long as you have an internet connection, you'll never need to worry about missing an appointment again.

Get expert advice from anywhere on the globe. Telemedicine lets you interact with your doctor using a personal device such as a computer or tablet. You can share your concerns, discuss symptoms, and receive treatment options in real time via technology like video conferencing.

While a physician won't be able to physically examine you, he can still check up on certain conditions. For example, you can share digital pictures of rashes or lumps. Or if you have a chronic condition like diabetes, you can track your blood sugar and send the results to your doctor.

Consult online doctors to slash your bills. One of the biggest draws of telemedicine is the cost. A virtual visit typically ranges from $40 to $70, while a trip to a brick-and-mortar doctor's office might run you $130 to $180. Check with your insurance company to see what it will cover.

Use this tool wisely to avoid dangerous drawbacks. You wouldn't use a screwdriver to hammer nails. And you shouldn't use telemedicine as a replacement for every in-person trip to the doctor, either. Instead, it's best to use this tool to supplement your current health care routine.

People often turn to online doctors for everyday ailments like the flu or common cold. For seniors, minor conditions could lead to serious health problems, so it's better to get a physical examination when you can.

Experts often recommend reserving telemedicine for managing chronic conditions or monitoring post-surgery recovery. Talk to your doctor to see if he thinks you could benefit from using these services.

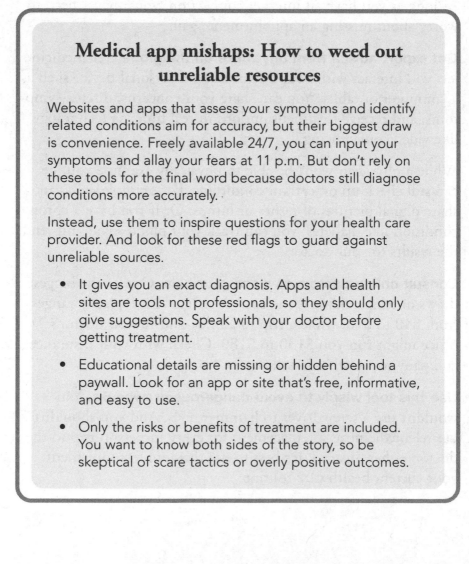

Medical app mishaps: How to weed out unreliable resources

Websites and apps that assess your symptoms and identify related conditions aim for accuracy, but their biggest draw is convenience. Freely available 24/7, you can input your symptoms and allay your fears at 11 p.m. But don't rely on these tools for the final word because doctors still diagnose conditions more accurately.

Instead, use them to inspire questions for your health care provider. And look for these red flags to guard against unreliable sources.

- It gives you an exact diagnosis. Apps and health sites are tools not professionals, so they should only give suggestions. Speak with your doctor before getting treatment.

- Educational details are missing or hidden behind a paywall. Look for an app or site that's free, informative, and easy to use.

- Only the risks or benefits of treatment are included. You want to know both sides of the story, so be skeptical of scare tactics or overly positive outcomes.

Medical services and procedures

Ever put in drops for dry eye only to spill most of the pricey medicine down your cheeks? It's not your fault. Drug companies make the dropper dispense more than your eye can hold. After all, they want you to use up the contents of the bottle quickly. And considering that Americans spend $3.5 billion a year on eyedrops, that's a lot of money down the drain.

Wasted medication is just one way your hard-earned money gets squandered. Experts estimate that the U.S. health care system wastes a colossal $750 billion a year on things like unnecessary services and procedures, excessive administrative costs, and overpricing.

Of course, you can't fix this national problem all by yourself. But you can make sure to spend your health care funds in a way that gets you the biggest bang for the buck.

- Find a primary care provider that you like and trust. Talk honestly with him about your health to ensure you get the right care.

- Remember that costs for medical services vary by location. Go to *healthcarebluebook.com* to learn how much you should pay for treatment in your area.

- Before you schedule an expensive procedure, ask your doctor the one question that could save you money — do I really need to have this done? Ask him what it's for, how it will impact your health, and what risks or side effects are involved. Ask about other options and if your condition will get better or worse without treatment.

There are certainly times you should say yes to tests in order to protect your health. But sometimes, you can just say no. Talk it over with your doctor before you decide.

5 drugs and medical procedures you might not really need

Cardiac stress test. Back in the day, it was common for healthy folks to take an exercise stress test that involved walking on a treadmill during a physical exam. After all, it's a great way for the doctor to see how well your heart works when forced to pump the hardest.

Decided to go ahead with a diagnostic test? You'll be billed for the service if your insurance company denies payment. To avoid this, make sure the testing facility confirms with your insurer — before the procedure is performed — that the test is approved.

But experts have changed their tune. In fact, the U.S. Preventive Services Task Force, an independent panel that evaluates research and makes recommendations concerning preventive services, discourages stress testing for people who don't have symptoms or strong risk factors for coronary artery disease (CAD).

Why not? This type of exam doesn't catch all cases of CAD and sometimes leads to false diagnoses of the disease. Inaccurate results could lead to more unnecessary and expensive tests.

Sleeping pills. Find it hard to fall or stay asleep? You're in good company. Insomnia affects almost half of all seniors, according to the National Institutes of Health, and can lead to memory loss, depression, and irritability.

Doctors often prescribe sleeping pills, such as Restoril and Ambien, to help get you back into normal sleep patterns. But it turns out seniors can be hurt by dangerous side effects. Such medications, called sedative-hypnotics, can double your risk of getting into a car accident, falling, and breaking a hip.

Instead, talk to your doctor about relieving your insomnia through lifestyle changes like cutting back on caffeine and taking a warm bath before bed. For more tips on getting quality shut-eye, see *10 simple tips for sound and restful sleep every night* in the *Insomnia* chapter.

Total-body scans. Lots of imaging centers market whole-body scanning — a test that takes pictures of your entire body — as a way to detect early signs of cancer. But there's no data suggesting the procedure is of any benefit to people without symptoms.

To make matters worse, total-body scans can miss signs of cancer that other tests — a mammogram, for example — would probably detect, the American College of Preventive Medicine warns. Plus some scans deliver a considerable amount of radiation, which can increase your risk of cancer. Whole-body computerized tomography (CT) scans, for example, deliver four times the amount of natural radiation that experts think people are exposed to in a year.

Nonsteroidal anti-inflammatory drugs (NSAIDs). Lots of people turn to NSAIDs — aspirin, ibuprofen, and prescriptions like Celebrex and Voltaren — for relief from chronic pain or inflammation. In fact, they're some of the most commonly prescribed drugs among older adults.

But you might want to think twice before taking them because, once you hit a certain age, NSAIDs put you at a higher risk for kidney damage, gastrointestinal bleeding, and high blood pressure.

What should you do if you're in pain? Experts from the American Geriatric Society say to limit NSAIDs to the lowest effective dose and the shortest duration needed to ease your discomfort. You can also ask your doctor about alternatives such as Tylenol, the brand name for acetaminophen, or other inflammation treatments like rest, ice, compression, and elevation.

MRI for lower back pain. MRI stands for magnetic resonance imaging. To have an MRI, you'll lie inside a large, tube-like magnet where radio waves and a magnetic field will make pictures of the organs and tissues in your body.

During the first six weeks of back pain, think twice about this test if you have no other severe conditions like fever, sudden back pain with trauma, or kidney infection, advises the American Academy of Family Physicians. They say imaging of the spine so early on increases costs without improving patient outcomes. Check with your doctor if you have questions about your condition.

> Maybe you need financial assistance to treat a vision problem. Perhaps you can't afford new prescription eye-glasses. The National Eye Institute, a division of the National Institutes of Health, provides a list of agencies that can help at *nei.nih.gov/ health/financialaid*.

Cap high dental costs and cement your savings

Dental disasters like a damaged front tooth will put a crimp in your confidence, not to mention your smile. So it's important to see a dentist as soon as possible. But what do you do if you don't have the money for treatment?

It's a situation that happens to lots of seniors. In fact, more than half of older Americans say they haven't visited the dentist in the past year due to the cost of care. After all, traditional Medicare doesn't cover routine services like cleanings and fillings, and Medicaid coverage is often limited. So how do you find dental care you can afford?

Turn to the Health Center Program from the Bureau of Primary Health Care, a service of the Health Resources and Services Administration. This little-known government program works with 1,400 health centers across the country to offer medical services for free or at a reduced cost. Some 1,050 of them provide dental care. To find a health center near you, go to *findahealthcenter.hrsa.gov*.

Dental schools are also a good source of reduced-cost treatment. At facilities with clinics, students gain experience by providing care under the supervision of licensed dentists — while you get a discount. For a list of schools, go to *ada.org/267.aspx*.

Dodging the drill: Stop cavities in their tracks without breaking the bank

So you need to get a tooth filled but can't stand the thought of all that pesky poking. You may be in luck. Now there's a low-cost, painless alternative to fillings.

It's called silver diamine fluoride, a liquid the dentist paints directly onto a cavity. The mixture hardens over several weeks, killing harmful bacteria and strengthening the structure of your tooth. The treatment can slow decay enough to avoid or delay the need of a more expensive filling.

On the downside, silver diamine fluoride turns the damaged area of the tooth black. But that's not too big a deal if the cavity is in the back of your mouth or near your gumline.

A resin composite filling might cost $155. But you could expect to pay about $25 for a cavity to be painted over with silver diamine fluoride.

Are you covered? Top medical procedures insurance won't pay for

Susan hated her droopy eyelids and sagging cheeks. Not to mention the deep "marionette lines" that ran from the corners of her mouth to her chin. Tired of looking older than she felt, the 64-year-old decided to visit a plastic surgeon.

Susan was excited to learn that a face-lift could make her look years younger. But there was bad news, too. The majority of health insurance companies, Susan's included, won't cover the cost of cosmetic surgery unless it's medically necessary.

It's one of many popular medical treatments that insurers consider nonessential. Avoid getting blindsided like Susan by familiarizing yourself with these procedures most insurers won't cover.

- vision services like eyeglasses, contact lenses, and laser surgery
- private nursing care
- hearing aids
- cosmetic dentistry
- acupuncture and other alternative therapies

So what do you do if you want an uncovered service? You can pay for a wide range of medical expenses with pretax dollars from your health savings account. Just make sure they're considered qualified medical expenses in IRS Publication 502.

You could also negotiate for a lower fee with your health care provider. Don't forget to ask about low-interest finance options.

Patients with passports: The pros and cons of getting health care abroad

Perhaps vision and dental care aren't included in your insurance plan. Or maybe your carpal tunnel syndrome has gotten so bad that you require surgery. Either way, you might consider becoming a medical tourist — a person who travels abroad for health care.

You wouldn't be alone. Nearly 2 million Americans are expected to cross the border for a medical procedure this year.

One of the top reasons? Savings can range from 20 to 90 percent. A $50,000 knee replacement in the U.S., for example, might run around $23,000 in Costa Rica, including airfare and lodging. Other top destinations include Brazil, India, Malaysia, Mexico, and Singapore.

Of course, receiving medical care abroad can be risky. Communication can be an issue if you don't speak the host country's language. Medication could be of poor quality. And flying after surgery increases your risk of blood clots.

That's why you need to do your homework before booking a flight. The Centers for Disease Control and Prevention recommends that you contact a travel medicine specialist for advice about six weeks before departure.

You'll also need to check the qualifications of your health care providers and the credentials of the facility you've chosen. Accrediting groups, including Joint Commission International and DNV GL Healthcare, provide the names of facilities that meet their accreditation standards.

Feast your eyes on these 'spec'tacular savings

Tired of paying top dollar for prescription eyeglasses? Now you don't have to. Shop online and get a dandy pair of specs for hundreds less than retail.

Visit *goggles4u.com* or *zennioptical.com*, for example, and set your sights on everything from specialty lenses to designer frames. Prices start at less than $8 a pair. To order, all you need is an updated prescription from your eye doctor that includes the distance in millimeters between your pupils.

Can't figure out which type of frame looks best on you? Then go to *allaboutvision.com/eyeglasses* for a primer on choosing a frame that suits the shape of your face.

Maybe you're still unsure about going this route. Lots of online retailers, including *glasses.com*, *eyebuydirect.com*, and *glassesusa.com* allow you to download a photo of yourself so you can "try on" frames online.

Hospitalizations

A stay in the hospital is often a scary experience. But so are the bills that arrive soon after. Open your mailbox and you're likely to find multiple bills for different services, some of which you might not even remember.

Patients with insurance aren't off the hook either. Nearly 6 in 10 Americans say they've received a surprise medical bill for services they thought their insurers would pay for.

Fortunately, you have more options than you may realize when it comes to driving down the cost of hospitalization.

6 time-tested tactics for cutting your hospital bill before admission

Study your insurance plan. You can avoid lots of billing problems by understanding the basics of your insurance plan — the size of your deductible and the limits on your treatment options. Many people don't realize their insurance won't cover numerous prescriptions, procedures, and therapies. Your best bet? Read your health plan documents so you know what costs you'll be responsible for.

Be sure to ask your doctor if you're being admitted as an inpatient or outpatient. That's because your admission status dictates how your insurer — whether it's a private company or Medicare — covers your hospital stay. The wrong designation can make a huge difference in how much you'll pay.

Choose the right facility. Have an ear infection but your doctor's office is closed? Consider going to an urgent care center instead of the emergency room. You'll probably save hundreds, if not thousands, of dollars and get treated a lot sooner. Urgent care centers are usually open evenings and weekends. Many accept health insurance, so check to see if yours is in network.

On the other hand, emergency rooms are best for treating severe and life-threatening conditions like severe chest pains, deep wounds, or head trauma.

Research costs online. Soaring health care costs and higher out-of-pocket expenses have made consumers more conscious of pricing. But the amount you'll pay for a procedure varies greatly by location and can be difficult to pin down.

To get the best rate, call area hospitals for estimates. Some facilities post pricing tools on their websites, and in many cases you can log in to your insurer's site to compare your share of the bill at different hospitals.

> Medicare Part A covers inpatient care at a hospital, as well as short-term care in a nursing home, hospice services, and some home health care. Most people don't have to pay a premium for Part A, but you're responsible for copays and a yearly deductible.

Don't know what the fair price for a particular procedure should be? Find out online at *clearhealthcosts.com*, *healthcarebluebook.com*, or *newchoicehealth.com*.

Stay in network. Have you ever been in the hospital, thought you were covered by insurance, and then ended up with a bill way higher than you expected? You might have been treated by an out-of-network physician who hadn't agreed to a negotiated rate with your insurer. Ouch.

Here's how to lower your risk of being hit with surprise charges.

- Before getting treatment, check that both the hospital and your doctor are in network.

- Ask your doctor to order bloodwork, MRIs, and other tests from in-network labs.

- If possible, request that any specialists — anesthesiologists, radiologists, pathologists — also are in network.

- If you must sign a statement of financial responsibility, write in that you agree only if your care is in network.

Negotiate better terms. It's a little-known fact that it's possible to haggle down your hospital bill even before you've received any care. So be polite yet firm when calling the billing office for a reduced rate. Frame your request around your ability — or inability — to pay. Above all, be persistent. If an administrator denies your request, find out the name of his manager and call back.

Another option? Offer to pay a percentage upfront. Lots of hospitals offer discounts — some up to 20 percent — for patients who pay in advance. Such plans have become popular because they reduce the hospital's risk of not being paid at all.

Check into charity status. Find out if your local hospital is not-for-profit. If so, call and ask to speak to a financial counselor about charity care, which covers "medically necessary" treatment like inpatient stays and emergency room visits. Depending on your income, you could get 50, 75, or even 100 percent off your hospital bill. But you have to ask because hospitals might not volunteer information about these programs.

Is the hospital for-profit? Don't worry. You may still qualify for financial assistance, so be sure to ask.

Key steps to finding quality care close to home

Looking for a report card on how well your area hospitals compare with each other? You're in luck.

The Centers for Medicare & Medicaid Services rates 4,000 hospitals nationwide on issues like surgery complication rates, mortality rates, and effectiveness of care. Go to *medicare.gov/hospitalcompare* and type in your ZIP code to see how well the hospitals measure up.

You'll also want to see if the hospital is accredited by The Joint Commission, a nonprofit with a mission to improve the quality of U.S. health care. Find out by searching online at *qualitycheck.org*.

Feel better faster by slashing your statement after your visit

Discouraged by medical bills now that you're out of the hospital? Consider these steps to help you drop your bottom line.

- File an appeal. Generally, you have 60 to 90 days to appeal in writing if your bill is incorrect. Use your itemized statement and insurance explanation of benefits (EOB) to pinpoint incorrect charges.

- Negotiate. Call the hospital billing department and request a discount based on financial need. Offer to pay in cash or on a payment plan.

- Enlist help. Bring a professional patient advocate into the mix to look over your bills and help you lower your overall costs. Fees can range widely from $75 to $225 per hour. Locate an advocate online at *advoconnection.com*. Some charitable organizations, like the Patient Advocate Foundation, provide these services for free.

Anatomy of error: Diagnose billing mistakes to keep your finances in fine fettle

Would you agree to buy a car without knowing the sticker price? Probably not. But that's how it works in the health care industry. You often have no idea how much you'll pay for treatment until after hospital administrators finish negotiating rates with your insurance company. Only then do you get the bill.

And after all that, you could still face thousands of dollars in bogus charges. Groups that review bills for patients believe 8 in 10 medical bills contain costly errors.

Fortunately, you can learn how to spot and resolve the most common hospital billing mistakes. All you need is an itemized account — not a summary — of all the services you received. Here's what to look for.

- Duplicate charges for the same test or procedure. This can happen, for example, if both a doctor and nurse note in your chart that you had a blood test. The billing department sees two separate entries, so you could get billed twice.

- Phantom tests. Sometimes a doctor will order, then cancel, a test. Have a loved one keep track of what procedures you have done so you don't get billed for services you didn't receive.

> Medical debt can severely damage your credit score. Fortunately, the three major credit reporting bureaus — Experian, Equifax, and TransUnion — must now wait 180 days before adding an unpaid medical bill on your credit report. That gives you extra time to resolve issues with your insurer or health care provider.

- Incorrect length of stay. You'll probably be charged for the day of admission but not the day of discharge. Don't get stuck paying for both. Also, make sure you're not charged for a private room if you shared space with another patient.

- Unbundled fees. This occurs when a procedure should be billed as one item but is instead billed by its separate, more expensive components. You may be charged for the use of an operating room, but then get stuck paying separately for items — paper gowns and latex gloves — that should be included in the fee.

- Medicine charges. Don't pay for a name-brand drug if your doctor ordered a generic. And if you brought your medicine from home, check that you weren't charged for it.

- Operating room time. Hospitals usually bill for operating room time by the minute. Compare the anesthesiologist's record of time in surgery with the hospital's billing of the procedure to be sure they match.

It's up to you to resolve the overcharge if you spot a problem. Contact your insurance company and the hospital's billing department to try to fix the error. Be sure to write down the date, time, and name of the person you speak to in case you have to refer back to your conversation at a later date.

It's worth disputing mistakes on your bill, even if your insurance provider would cover the extra cost. High charges can count toward your lifetime spending cap, and you might need those funds later.

Cope with a hospital stay the healthy way

No doubt about it — going to the hospital can save your life. But it can also be hazardous to your health. That's because medical mishaps — think medication mix-ups and the spread of infectious diseases — occur all the time. A Johns Hopkins University study even suggests that medical errors are the third-highest cause of death in the U.S.

That's why experts want you to be proactive about your hospital care. Follow these tips to help ensure a successful stay.

- Bring a list of the drugs you're taking to the hospital so your doctors can check for potential interactions.

- Build a relationship with your medical team. Write down their names so you don't forget.

- Ask questions if you're unsure about any aspect of your care.

- Remember, anything you touch can harbor bacteria. Wash your hands and use alcohol-based sanitizer often.

- Get moving, if possible, to help prevent bedsores and blood clots.

- Schedule surgery for Tuesday, Wednesday, or Thursday morning. These tend to be better-staffed times.

Need help navigating the health care maze? Call a patient advocate

Are hospital bills piling up, but your insurance company won't approve your claim? Or maybe you're having problems paying your Medicare deductible after going to the emergency room.

Then it might be time to contact an advocacy group like the Patient Advocate Foundation (PAF), a Virginia-based nonprofit that draws on the experience of medical professionals, social workers, billing and coding experts, and more. Their case managers help you get access to the care you need by resolving issues like insurance denials and medical debt. Your only requirement? You have to be suffering from a chronic, life-threatening, or debilitating disease.

"Last year 44 percent of our patients were Medicare beneficiaries," says Beth Moore, PAF's executive vice president of corporate communications. One of their biggest issues is not being able to afford copays and out-of pocket expenses, she says. "We find resources for these seniors that they might not know how to tap into."

PAF also helps with things like enrolling in Medicare, an often confusing process, and securing transportation assistance for medical appointments.

Their case management services, which helped nearly 25,000 people last year, are free of charge to patients regardless of their income.

Moore understands that retirees often have a deep sense of pride and prefer to be self-sufficient. But, she adds, that's no reason to try to muddle through when feeling overwhelmed with health care-related concerns.

Her advice? Seek professional help early.

"Often you're not asking for anything special," she says. "Rather, these are services that you're entitled to."

You can request assistance from PAF by calling 800-532-5274 or by going to *patientadvocate.org*.

Long-term care insurance

Mary couldn't live on her own after falling and breaking her hip. She needed to move to a nursing home, but the price of a room clocked in at a whopping $7,500 a month. And Medicare wouldn't foot the bill.

Unfortunately, Mary's story is all too common. A recent study found that 7 out of 10 seniors will need long-term care at some point in their lives. That could mean help with daily tasks like cooking, cleaning, and shopping. Or it could be round-the-clock supervision at a nursing home.

Either way, long-term care is expensive. An in-home caregiver will run you around $50,000 a year, and a nursing home is twice that much. How do you afford these sky-high rates? That's where long-term care insurance comes in.

It will help you cover the costs of treatments and services you need to live comfortably. And while insurance isn't as expensive as paying out of pocket, it's still not cheap. If you buy your policy at 65, you can expect to pay at least $3,000 a year in premiums. Luckily, you can cut the price of your policy with a few smart moves.

5 tried-and-true methods to curb the cost of coverage

The early bird gets the best premiums. The sooner you shop for long-term care insurance (LTCI), the cheaper your monthly payments will be. That's because insurers raise their rates as you age. For example, if you and your spouse buy a policy at 65 instead of 60, it might cost $2,500 more in premiums every year.

Experts say the best time to apply for LTCI is before you go on Medicare. "When individuals qualify for Medicare at 65, it includes some enormously valuable preventive health tests and screenings," says Jesse Slome, the executive director of the American Association for Long-Term Care Insurance. "But those same screenings are likely to uncover health conditions that might make you ineligible for any kind of long-term care insurance."

And don't wait too long to look into your options, either. Most companies don't even give long-term care insurance to people over the age of 75.

"Your money pays for long-term care insurance," says Slome. "But your health really buys it."

Don't let the rising cost of care inflate your bills. Prices go up over time. Remember back in 1970 when milk was $1.30 a gallon? Now it's nearly double that. Unfortunately, health care costs are on the rise, too.

That's why many LTCI policies include inflation protection, which increases your coverage limit over time so you can afford long-term care years after deciding on a plan. The more protection you want, the more you'll have to pay in premiums. But you may not need such a big buffer.

Consider cutting back on the inflation protection in your policy to reduce your premiums. Some experts recommend going from 5 to 3 percent, but exact adjustments depend on how much health care prices are expected to increase in your area. Speak with your insurance company to see what options you have.

Slim down your coverage to slash your payments. One way to stretch your savings is to shorten your benefit period.

Insurance companies use your benefit period to determine how much money your policy will pay out. So if you have a five-year benefit period that covers $250 a day, the plan will pay out a maximum of $426,250. You could cut your period down to three years to reduce your premiums.

But keep in mind you'll have $152,500 less in coverage. If you think you might need extensive care, you could be in hot water after you've used up all your benefits.

Good savings come to those who wait. Some LTCI plans require you to pay your own bills for a period of time before the benefits kick in. And if you lengthen your waiting period, you'll usually pay less in premiums.

For example, if your current policy doesn't require you to pay anything out of pocket before receiving care, you can lower your premiums by extending your waiting period — sometimes called an elimination period — to 90 days.

Be careful if you go this route, though. Unless you have cash to cover your expenses, you could struggle to pay for a nursing home or caregiver while you wait for your coverage to start.

Pay up now to save more later. Let's say you wanted to read the news every day. You could go out to a newsstand and pick up a paper for a couple of dollars each morning. Or you could pony up for a yearly subscription, which would save you hundreds in the long run. The same idea holds true for LTCI.

Insurance companies cut you a deal if you pay upfront. Instead of shelling out for your premiums every month, see if you can pay for the whole year at once. Experts say this might shave 8 percent off your bill. So if your costs are $3,000 a year, you could save up to $240.

Simplify your search with these tips for finding the perfect policy

Don't get overwhelmed when you search for long-term care insurance (LTCI). You can easily buy a policy directly from a financial planner, an insurance agent, or a broker. But before you take the plunge, keep these tips in mind.

- Look for state-approved insurers. States regulate which companies can sell LTCI and what products they can offer.

- Watch out for rising premiums. Ask about their premium rate history to make sure you won't be blindsided by a significant change.

- Over 100 companies offer LTCI across the country, so compare policies from at least three companies to find the best deal for you.

- Pay attention to the details. Understand how much or how long the policy will pay, and make sure you have the option to cancel your policy after a 30-day review.

Can't qualify for Medicaid? These tricks may fit the bill

You might count on Medicaid to pay for your long-term care. But if your income is too high or you have more than $2,000 in assets, most states won't give you any benefits. So what are you to do?

Partner up to protect your assets. In certain states, you can purchase a form of long-term care insurance called a Partnership-qualified policy. These government-approved plans might help you qualify for Medicaid even if your assets exceed the state-set limits.

Just ask Caroline. She bought one of these policies that had a maximum lifetime benefit of $175,000. After living in a nursing home for two years, she hit the limit on her plan. Caroline hoped Medicaid would pay for her care, but her bank accounts and savings bonds added up to over $65,000.

Normally, that would keep her from receiving benefits because her savings were way over the $2,000 limit. But Partnership-qualified plans let you keep assets up to the amount paid under the policy — in her case, $175,000 — and still get government help.

Spend down safely with smart strategies. Want to qualify for Medicaid but have too much money in the bank? Many people choose to spend down their assets until they meet the requirements.

You can pay off debts, buy qualified annuities, or even put money toward the cost of care. You have to be careful, though. If you don't follow the government guidelines for spending your money, you could be hit with a penalty that will stop you from receiving benefits. Consider consulting an attorney or financial advisor if you want to go this route.

> Medicaid pays for nursing home services, in-home medical care, and even assistance with daily tasks like cooking, cleaning, and shopping. The specifics vary depending on where you live, so reach out to your local Medicaid office for more information.

For details on how to get in-home family care without jeopardizing your Medicaid qualification, read *Dodge pricey penalties with this legal secret* in the *In-home care* chapter.

Get some TLC for your LTC needs with these alternate options

Resources are more abundant than ever before to help you and your family afford the care you need — even if you don't have long-term care insurance (LTCI). Check out these additional ways to pay for quality care.

Hybrid policy. Often less expensive than traditional LTCI policies, hybrids pair life insurance with long-term care coverage under one premium.

Accelerated death benefit (ADB). It sounds ominous, but this tax-free advance on your life insurance death benefit allows you to tap into a portion of your ADB to help cover the cost of care. Read your policy carefully to see if this option is already included in your plan, or call your provider to add it as a rider. It may come with an extra charge.

> Is your LTCI tax qualified? Then you can withdraw money tax-free from your health savings account (HSA) to pay for LTCI premiums for yourself, a spouse, or current dependents. The amount will depend upon whose premium you're paying based on their age. You may also use HSA funds to pay for other qualified long-term care expenses.

And pay attention to the fine print. To claim your ADB with a long-term care rider, for example, you generally must be unable to perform at least two activities of daily living, such as bathing and dressing, for a certain period of time — say, 90 days. With a chronic illness rider, on the other hand, your doctor usually has to certify that the illness is likely to continue for the rest of your life.

Viatical settlement. This arrangement allows you to sell your life insurance policy to a third party for a lump-sum payment, which you can use to pay for long-term care. It's an option if you're terminally ill with less than two years to live, and the payment is based on your life expectancy.

Deferred income annuity. Annuities provide guaranteed income regardless of your health condition. And a recent change in the law allows you to use some annuity profits tax-free for long-term care premiums.

What type should you get? Many experts recommend a qualified longevity annuity contract (QLAC), which you can purchase with retirement account funds to lower your required minimum distributions. You may convert up to $130,000 of your 401(k) or IRA into a QLAC.

Reverse mortgage. If you are at least 62 and own your home, you may qualify for this variation on a home equity loan. You receive a cash loan from the bank that does not have to be repaid as long as you live in your home. But keep in mind that if you leave your house for 12 months or more — to live in a nursing home, for instance — then repayment will be due. To find out more, read the *Reverse mortgages* chapter.

Aid and Attendance program. Honorably discharged wartime veterans age 65 or older who need help with daily activities may be eligible for this benefit from the Department of Veterans Affairs. The program offsets the cost of care at home or in an assisted living facility or a nursing home. Surviving spouses are also eligible.

Health care directives

You might be surprised to learn that 2 in 3 adults have not completed an advance directive. It's a legal document that outlines the life-preserving measures you want — or don't want — if you're unable to speak for yourself. But avoiding this sensitive topic can be devastating to you and your loved ones.

Here are some of the things that can happen if you don't put your preferences on paper.

- You may receive treatment that goes against your beliefs.

- Doctors can use extreme measures to keep you alive.

- Family members might argue over what medical procedures they think you would want.

Fortunately, you can get the care you desire and relieve loved ones of having to make decisions on your behalf. A simple plan will give you — and your family — peace of mind.

5 documents you need in case something happens to you

Living will. This document tells your doctors and family the type of care you want if you're terminally ill or in a permanent coma and can't communicate. Would you want, for example, artificial respiration or a feeding tube at the end of your life? What about pain relief?

Each state has its own rules when it comes to living wills. You can either hire an attorney for help in drafting yours or ask your doctor or local health department to provide you with the proper documents.

Durable power of attorney for health care. A living will, which typically deals with end-of-life issues, doesn't cover every medical possibility. That's where a durable power of attorney for health care comes in. It's a legal document giving someone power to make health care decisions for you — consenting to surgery or moving you to another hospital, for example — if you're incapable of doing so.

It's best to choose someone you trust, perhaps a friend or relative who lives nearby. You'll also want to name an alternate agent in case your first choice is unable to fill the job.

Experts recommend you name a durable power of attorney for health care when you draft your living will. The combined documentation is called an advance directive. To get your copy, go to *caringinfo.org* and click the blue box labeled "Download your state specific Advance Directive."

Do-not-resuscitate order (DNR). This form documents your wish not to receive CPR or other invasive treatments if you stop breathing or your heart stops beating. Your doctor, who must sign the DNR for it to go into effect, will provide you with your state's form.

Keep the DNR by your bedside or on your refrigerator door, where emergency medical technicians can easily see it. Be sure your health care proxy and medical providers have copies.

Physician Orders for Life-Sustaining Treatment (POLST). This document, which can be used in addition to — or in place of — a DNR, is useful if you're seriously ill and nearing the end of life. It tells medical professionals what treatments you want, or don't want, in an emergency. POLSTs should be written with the help of a health care professional, who must sign it.

Keep it in a visible place at home, and make sure a duplicate is in your medical records. The form varies from state to state and is often brightly colored so it can easily be found.

Health information release. Doctors are often tightlipped when it comes to patient privacy. Sometimes they incorrectly claim that federal law prohibits them from discussing your condition — even with family members. This can be stressful for relatives and even dangerous for a senior who needs help in making an informed medical decision.

Why not be proactive and avoid the problem altogether? Ask your doctor to give you a health information release form. This way he'll have written permission to discuss your health care with specific family members, friends, or clergy.

Click your way to secure health care directives

You know you don't want to be kept on life support if something happens, but how do you share your wishes with your loved ones? These three services make the process painless.

- MyDirectives is a free planning service for medical emergencies. Use it to identify who you want to represent you, share treatment goals, and make a personal statement video. Available online and in the Apple App Store, you can find details at *mydirectives.com*.

- Cake offers a free interactive checklist for end-of-life planning including health care directives. Answer a series of questions and upload documents before sharing your profile with loved ones to keep them in the loop. Explore more at *joincake.com*.

- Everplans helps you create your directives online through a set of questions. Designate deputies — people you trust — to share details of your Everplan with them. Get started at *Everplans.com*.

Whichever service you choose, you'll rest easy knowing your wishes are just clicks away.

The power of the pen: Put your health care wishes in writing

Think it's time-consuming to fill out an advance directive? Then you'd be surprised to learn it takes just five minutes to complete. Once you have the proper forms, all you need to do is write in the name and address of your health care agent and initial a few boxes.

"It doesn't require a lawyer. If you can read and comprehend English you should be fine," says Donald Hawbaker, an elder law attorney in Griffin, Georgia.

You shouldn't wait until you're frail or sick to complete an advance directive, he advises. After all, nobody knows when tragedy might strike.

"Everybody over the age of 18 should have one," Hawbaker says. "People think life will progress with a statistically pre-dictable sequence of events, but it doesn't."

Hawbaker, who prepares advance directives when working on a client's estate plan, admits to not having filled out his own advance directive until he faced surgery.

"It was a matter of not taking care of business," he says. "You know, life gets in the way."

Waiting until you're in the hospital is not a good idea, Hawbaker says, because you'll need two witnesses to sign the document. Neither of them can be your health care agent — usually a member of the family — or someone on the hospital staff. That can leave you scrambling for wit-nesses, just when you need them most.

"You're down to availing yourself of the kindness of strangers in the next hospital room," he says.

Advance directive: How to help your loved ones help you

So you've completed your advance directive. It's one of the most important steps for making sure you're taken care of if you can't make medical decisions for yourself. Here's how to make sure your loved ones carry out your wishes.

Tell your family. Make your end-of-life wishes clear to your family and doctors. Knowing how you want to live your last days will make it easier for them to make tough decisions on your behalf.

Get it on record. Give your doctors copies of your advance directive, and make sure they add it to your medical file. The same goes if you enter assisted living or a nursing home. Give copies to family members, close friends, and the person you've chosen to make medical decisions for you.

Cover your travel. If you split your time living between two states, fill out separate forms for each one. Give a copy to your doctors and local hospitals in both locales.

Get straight answers to senior questions

Estate planning, advance directives, Medicare, oh my! Ever feel like you're Dorothy lost in the woods looking for Oz? Having a thorough and informed resource on hand to guide you is like having a yellow brick road. Legal professionals at *SeniorLaw.com* pave the way for you online.

This New York law firm specializes in elder law. Their website features links to services and information on advance directives, health care proxies, nursing homes, reverse mortgages, estate planning, federal and state resources, and more. Find answers at *seniorlaw.com/elder-law-legal-resources-on-the-web.*

LIVE WELL

SCIENCE-BACKED TIPS TO
TACKLE YOUR BIGGEST
HEALTH CONCERNS

Chronic pain

Everybody experiences pain at one time or another — whether it's the razor-edged bite of a paper cut or the aching throb of a stubbed toe. The discomfort, which alerts you to an injury, is usually short-lived.

That's not the case, though, with chronic pain — a common condition among seniors. The suffering can last for months or years, limiting your ability to manage daily chores and go out with friends. Persistent pain has many causes.

- Sometimes an old injury is the culprit. Your body may have healed, but damaged nerves keep the pain lingering like a bad memory.

- Then there's the chronic pain from conditions like fibromyalgia and irritable bowel syndrome. Symptoms flare and fade, but the problem never goes away.

- Among the senior set, long-term pain often stems from years of wear and tear on your spine. That can cause your back, hips, knees, and neck to hurt.

Of course, nobody can turn back time. But you have plenty of ways to keep a step ahead. One place to consider? Your diet.

That's because research suggests that foods high in antioxidants and omega-3 fatty acids may help reduce pain-causing inflammation. So try filling up on fruits, nuts, green leafy vegetables, whole grains, legumes, fatty fish, and olive oil — all staples of the Mediterranean diet.

Read on for more tips to help you stay free of chronic pain.

3 blueprints to take a bite out of back aches

Walk away from pain without physical therapy. Think everyday aches and pains come naturally with aging? Think again. You can reduce or even eliminate nagging back pain simply by putting one foot in front of the other.

That's according to an Israeli study that found brisk walking drops lower back pain just as well as strength training programs, which often require specialized equipment and professional supervision at rehabilitation clinics.

The researchers recruited 52 patients with lower back pain and asked them to participate in specific exercise programs twice a week for six weeks. One group completed a muscle strengthening program. The others did an aerobic walking program, starting with 20 minutes of walking and progressing to 40 minutes as their endurance grew.

The result? The walking group saw just as many improvements in pain levels, endurance, feelings of disability, and avoidance of daily activities.

How can walking be as successful as a program using special gear? Researchers believe walking at a quick pace works your abdominal and back muscles just as much as exercises targeting those areas.

Get the sole truth on back pain

Want to work the muscles in your back without having to huff and puff your way through squats and lunges? Rocker bottom shoes could be the answer.

That's the finding of Spanish researchers who followed 40 people with lower back pain over four weeks. During that time, for a minimum of six hours a day, half of the participants wore shoes with thick soles that curved upward at the heel and toe. The remainder wore their normal shoes.

The researchers tested core muscle activity and range of motion in their lower backs. They found significant improvements among wearers of the rocker bottom shoes compared with the other group. The researchers say those changes may be why they could perform everyday tasks that were previously too painful.

Get your back on track with yog-ahhh. Did you know that many people do exactly the wrong thing for back pain? They lay in bed, thinking rest is the best treatment. The surprising truth is you should remain active to prevent muscle spasms and weakness in your back.

Although you want to avoid activities that worsen your pain, it's best to stay mobile and stick to your daily schedule as much as possible. If you must lie down, do so for only a few hours at a time.

Looking for quick relief? You'll be happy to hear yoga is just what the doctor ordered. That's according to scientists who evaluated 228 adults with chronic back pain. They divided participants into three groups, two of which participated in either yoga or intensive stretching in class and at home. The third group received a self-help book on pain management.

- At the end of three months, those in the yoga and stretching classes reported better back movement and less back pain than those in the self-help group. In fact, the two forms of exercise were equally effective.

- And, it turns out, the yoga and stretching groups had an easier time tossing out their pain pills. Compared with the self-care group, twice as many participants in the yoga and stretching classes reported lowering their medication use. That's great news for seniors, who need to be extra cautious about the potential side effects of opioid painkillers.

So are you ready to give yoga and stretching a try? Check with your doctor to see if it's right for you. Attend a class to learn the best poses for lower back pain. This knee-to-chest stretch is a gentle place to start.

1. Lie on your back with your knees bent.

2. Lift one knee to your chest by pulling your thigh or shin toward you.

3. Keep your back flat while you hold the stretch, then lower your leg to its original position.

4. Repeat with the other knee, then again with both knees.

Icy-hot home remedy tends tender backs. Some back pain comes from the stress and strain of overworked muscles — think lifting boxes in the garage. Other times, all it takes is a simple movement like reaching for the top shelf in the kitchen. And don't forget chronic aches that flare up when aggravated or just always seem to be hanging around.

So what do you do for quick relief — heat or ice? Experts say do what works for you. Here are some simple guidelines.

- Ice is often recommended for strains and recent injuries to reduce inflammation and tissue damage — both of which are linked to chronic pain. Use cold compresses or an ice pack for 15 minutes at a time when your back first starts hurting. This will help numb the pain and reduce swelling.

- Heat is often best for relieving chronic irritation and loosening up stiff muscles. If you've been injured, switch to heating pads or a hot water bottle after icing for a couple of days to relax the muscles and increase blood flow to the affected area.

- What about when you're exercising with chronic pain? Some people prefer heat therapy before workouts to warm up muscles and cold therapy after to fight inflammation.

Remember, back pain can signal a more serious issue if it is accompanied by symptoms such as numbness, fever, or loss of bladder control. If that's the case, be sure to contact your health care professional.

Insider tips to relieve discomfort and stay independent

Want to avoid years of back pain? Physical therapist Sherri Betz has some advice for you — get out of your chair and stand up straight. "You should avoid sitting. And be on your feet at least four hours a day to keep your bones healthy," urges Betz.

Poor posture, meanwhile, wreaks havoc on the muscles and ligaments in your back. That's because a rounded back causes your head — which weighs around 10 pounds — to tilt forward. "That puts an incredible load on your spine," she says.

Betz strongly recommends group exercise classes for seniors with back pain. They'll help you stay motivated and are a great way to socialize. And, there's an added bonus. Exercise keeps your legs strong — the single most important factor in maintaining your independence, Betz says.

So how do you know if your legs are weak? "You're in trouble if you can't get out of a chair without using your hands," she warns. "It's a huge red flag that you'll end up with a walker or need assisted living."

Betz, who is also a spokesperson for the American Physical Therapy Association, advocates the single-leg heel raise for keeping your legs in top shape. "Just stand on one leg and raise your heel up and down 10 times every day," she says. It'll do wonders for your balance, Betz explains, as well as strengthen your foot and entire leg.

Marshal the art of tai chi to ease fibromyalgia symptoms

Tingling and numbness in your hands and feet. Stiff joints and muscles. Sleep problems and fatigue. They're just a few of the symptoms of fibromyalgia, a painful condition affecting your bones and muscles. While there's no known cure, doctors often prescribe aerobic exercise as part of a treatment plan.

But how can you take up swimming, tennis, or cycling if just the thought of walking to the mailbox fills you with dread? Turns out you might not have to. That's because the ancient Chinese discipline of tai chi — a series of low-impact, dance-like moves that seamlessly flow into one another — may be more effective in treating your fibromyalgia than aerobic exercise.

That's what a new study published in *The BMJ* reveals. More than 200 adults with fibromyalgia were randomly assigned to either tai chi or aerobic exercise classes. Researchers evaluated several aspects of their physical and mental health including:

- symptoms like fatigue, depression, anxiety, and intensity of pain.

- how they coped with symptoms.

- their ability to perform daily tasks.

Those who did tai chi twice a week saw greater improvements in their symptoms and other assessment factors after both six months and a year, compared with those who did the same amount of aerobic exercise.

And it turns out that slow and steady really does win the race. Among the individuals studying tai chi, those who took classes for six months felt better than those who took classes for just three months.

Love hurts: Spousal spats may aggravate pain

It's no secret that arguing with your husband or wife can put you in a bad mood. But did you know that a spat with your better half might worsen your chronic pain?

That's what happened to two groups of older adults — one with osteoarthritis and the other with diabetes — in a recent study. The participants kept diaries over several weeks, jotting down notes on their mood, how well they were getting along with their spouses, and the severity of their symptoms.

Sure enough, both groups reported being in a worse mood on the days they experienced tension within their marriage. That, in turn, led them to feel greater pain or have more severe symptoms.

Keep diabetes from getting on your nerves with ALC

At first the symptoms were so subtle Julie barely noticed — just a slight tingling in her feet. Then came shooting pain at night, followed by patches of numbness up to her ankles. Within months Julie was so unsteady on her feet that she feared falling and breaking a bone. Wondering if it could be related to her diabetes, the 65-year-old finally called her doctor.

The diagnosis? Peripheral neuropathy — a condition affecting up to half of all people with diabetes. The cause? Chronically high blood sugar levels that damage the nerves in their feet. Fortunately, many people like Julie find relief through a healthy diet and exercise — both of which help keep blood sugar levels in check.

New research also suggests that taking supplements of the amino acid acetyl-L-carnitine (ALC) may lessen the pain associated with diabetic neuropathy and improve nerve function. Why? ALC may provide the extra energy nerve cells need to regenerate while also helping your brain produce natural painkillers.

For folks who want to try out acetyl-L-carnitine supplements, experts at the Linus Pauling Institute recommend a daily dose of 500 to 1,000 milligrams. But before you start taking ALC, be sure to check with your doctor, particularly if you're taking beta blockers, blood thinners, or thyroid medication.

Cook up digestive relief with the low-FODMAP diet

Imagine having to cancel a dinner date because your tight, ballooning belly won't stop rumbling and gurgling. Or avoiding public places because you're afraid you won't have immediate access to a restroom. Scenarios like these happen all too often if you're among the 10 to 15 percent of American adults with irritable bowel syndrome (IBS).

Get to know the ABCs of IBS. Symptoms can be so distressing that IBS patients in one survey say they would give up, on average, 15 years of their lives in exchange for relief from the chronic cramping, gas, diarrhea, and constipation.

Doctors don't know the causes of IBS, but genetics may play a part. It's also possible that faulty communication between the brain and digestive system causes food to move too slowly or quickly through the large intestine.

Unfortunately, there's no cure. But don't despair. It turns out the food on your plate can make a huge difference when it comes to treating IBS.

Low-FODMAP foods soothe digestive woes. Research suggests that a diet low in carbohydrates known as FODMAPs — short for Fermentable Oligosaccharides, Disaccharides, Monosaccharides, and Polyols — reduces symptoms.

In the largest U.S. study of its kind, research dietitians monitored the progress of 84 IBS patients. About half followed the low-FODMAP diet over a month. The other half cut down on known IBS triggers like alcohol and large meals during the same period.

At the end of the study, more than 50 percent of the patients on the low-FODMAP diet saw a major drop in abdominal pain. That compares with just 20 percent of the control group.

Those eliminating FODMAPs also reported relief from IBS symptoms like bloating and diarrhea. Not surprisingly, they also experienced greater improvements in their quality of life and anxiety levels than those not following the diet.

Carbs are key to treating symptoms. So why does the eating plan work? Researchers believe some folks have difficulty digesting FODMAPs. That gives carbohydrates extra time to ferment in the gut, creating the perfect environment for bloating and diarrhea.

Considering the low-FODMAP diet? It comes in two parts.

- Elimination phase. Give up FODMAP-rich foods for several weeks. If you're sensitive to FODMAPs, you'll start to feel better pretty quickly.

- Reintroduction phase. Slowly begin eating high-FODMAP foods, one at a time, to identify the ones that cause your IBS symptoms to return.

The following table gives an overview of some high-FODMAP foods you'll have to avoid at first. Be sure to check with your doctor before changing your diet.

FODMAP	Top food sources
Oligosaccharides (fructans, galactans)	wheat, rye, onions, garlic, artichokes, most legumes
Disaccharides (lactose)	milk, yogurt, ice cream, cottage cheese
Monosaccharides (excess fructose)	honey, agave, apples, pears, watermelon
Polyols (sorbitol, mannitol)	stone fruits, mushrooms, cauliflower, sugar-free gum and candy

Depression

Joe made a speedy recovery in the hospital after his heart attack last year. But once he came home, his wife, Nancy, noticed disturbing personality changes in her 72-year-old husband.

Joe no longer lit up like a Christmas tree when the grandkids visited. A lifelong golfer, he paced the carpet instead of swinging a 5-iron. Even worse, Joe stopped bathing and angrily complained that Nancy's cooking made his stomach hurt. "The tide turned when he wouldn't come out of the bedroom," Nancy said. "I knew I had to do something."

The pair sought medical help. A physical exam and lab tests ruled out medical issues and confirmed the doctor's suspicion — clinical depression. Nancy was shocked. Joe never once complained of feeling blue.

The doctor explained that older people don't always feel sad or worthless when they're depressed. They might be tired and grumpy instead. In fact, some of the signs of depression in the elderly — memory loss, restlessness, and confusion — are often misdiagnosed as dementia.

One clue that helped in the doctor's diagnosis? Medical problems like heart disease, cancer, and diabetes sometimes trigger depression in older people.

Because Joe was diagnosed with a serious form of depression, the doctor recommended a combination of antidepressant medication and therapy. Nancy is happy to see he's returning to his old self.

It's important to get professional help if your life feels overwhelming, especially if you have thoughts of suicide. But even if your symptoms aren't as serious, you may still be suffering. The good news is you

can overcome mild depression through diet and lifestyle changes.
Take a look at the natural remedies on the following pages. They'll
help you feel better — both physically and mentally.

4 ways to deep-six depression

Beware of medications that put you at risk. A 2018 University
of Illinois study says more than 1 in 3 U.S. adults may be taking
prescription medicines that can cause depression.

The scientists analyzed the medication use of some 26,000 adults
over a nine-year period. They found that more than 200 commonly
used prescription drugs — blood pressure and heart medications,
antacids, and painkillers — have depression or suicide listed as
possible side effects.

Take more than one of these drugs? You'll carry a greater risk of
becoming depressed, the study says. The researchers found 15 percent of adults who used three or more of the drugs at the same time
became depressed. That compares with 5 percent of those not using
any and 9 percent of those taking two of the drugs.

Other common medications to look out for include ones used to
treat allergies, anxiety, and seizures. Be sure to ask your doctor
about possible side effects before starting any medication.

Build your muscles to beat the blues. Ever hear of a runner's
high, that euphoric feeling joggers get after pounding a few miles
of pavement? Turns out you don't have to run a marathon to get
that natural boost.

In fact, evidence shows that even small amounts of exercise — as
little as one to two hours a week — can keep you from getting
the blues. So where's a good place to start? You might consider
resistance training, the kind of exercise that builds muscle
strength and tone.

New research says any amount of weight-bearing exercise — whether you hit the gym every day or just twice a week — reduces the symptoms of depression. And the benefits are the same whether you're male or female, young or old.

Don't belong to a gym? Here are a couple of exercises to try at home.

- Hold a soup can in each hand next to the sides of your legs. Keep your arms straight and palms facing forward. Bend your elbows and raise the cans up to your shoulders. Then slowly lower the soup cans back down. Repeat.

- To strengthen your legs, stand up and slowly rise up on your toes. Hold briefly, then return your heels to the floor. Repeat. Hold on to a chair or counter if you need help balancing.

Feed your body right to boost your mood. It looks like fresh fruits, vegetables, and whole grains benefit more than just your physical health. New research says following a Mediterranean-style diet may be the key to ridding yourself of depression.

That's according to Australian scientists who recruited 67 depressed adults for a three-month study. Each ate a relatively unhealthy diet that was heavy on sweets, salty snacks, and processed meats like hot dogs and salami. Most were being treated for their depression.

Once the study began, half the participants adopted a Mediterranean-style diet rich in vegetables, fruits, whole grains, and olive oil. The other half kept their old eating habits. Guess what happened after 12 weeks? More than 30 percent of the people on the Mediterranean-style diet were no longer depressed. That compares with 8 percent in the other group.

The researchers didn't give a reason for the results. But a previous Spanish study on depression and the Mediterranean diet says those foods may fight inflammation, improve blood flow, and repair cell damage. That, in turn, could lower your risk of becoming depressed.

Put a lid on depression the Mediterranean way

Want to create your own mood-boosting meals? Here's what participants ate during the recent three-month study on diet and depression.

Food	Servings
whole grains	5-8 daily
vegetables	6 daily
fruit	3 daily
legumes	3-4 weekly
low-fat, unsweetened dairy	2 daily
raw, unsalted nuts	1 daily
fish	at least 2 weekly
lean red meat	3-4 weekly
chicken	2-3 weekly
eggs	up to 6 weekly

Don't forget to include 3 tablespoons of olive oil in your diet each day. Limit red wine to two glasses a day at mealtime. And have no more than three servings a week of "extras" such as sweets, fried foods, processed meats, and refined cereal.

Give bad sleep habits a wake-up call. Find yourself cranky and grumpy after tossing and turning all night? Poor sleep is both a common symptom and a risk factor for depression.

So is getting a better night's sleep the answer? It appears to help, according to a study of 44 military personnel with insomnia. They received cognitive behavioral therapy, a treatment that included visits to a specialist who helped them change their sleep habits.

The soldiers who showed improvements in their sleep also reported feeling less depressed. Those who continued with sleep problems saw no change in their mood.

What about the other extreme? Although we often link insomnia to depression, in truth some 15 percent of people with depression sleep too much. That can make their depression worse and lead to physical problems such as headaches, back pain, obesity, and heart disease.

Experts recommend seven to nine hours of sleep to feel your best. For tips on developing healthy sleep habits and getting the rest you need, see the *Insomnia* chapter.

No. 1 way to boost the 'happy' chemicals in your brain

Exercise helps trigger the release of chemicals that boost your mood, relieve stress, and improve your sleep. But how do you get motivated to exercise if depression has sapped the energy out of you? Follow these tips to take the first step.

- Set realistic goals. If you're just starting out, you might try walking down the block and back, or simply do stretches while watching TV.

- Be consistent. Exercise at the same time each day.

- Don't be hard on yourself if you miss a session. The important thing is to get back on track.

- Keep a log of your progress to see how much you've accomplished.

- Use a pedometer to count your steps.

- Make it fun. Walk with a friend or join an exercise class.

- Reward yourself for meeting your goals.

Band together to brush off the blues

It's been more than 2,300 years since the Greek philosopher Aristotle wrote, "Man is by nature a social animal." His idea holds true today, especially when it comes to your health. That's because loneliness — that aching feeling you get from a lack of companionship — often causes depression.

But building a strong connection to a social group helps depressed people recover. That's according to Australian researchers who surveyed clinically depressed patients three months after they joined groups with activities like soccer, sewing, and yoga. Others participated in talk therapy sessions twice a week for a month.

In both cases, the scientists found that the patients who didn't strongly identify with their group had a roughly 50 percent chance of being depressed at the end of their trial. And those who felt a strong connection? Less than a third were still clinically depressed after that time.

> Talking to a loved one with depression? Here's the best approach to take. Depression isn't a choice, so it's best not to tell the person to get over it or snap out of it. Instead, ask what you can do to help and then follow through.

Because feeling connected to your group is so important, make sure you find something you'll enjoy doing with others. Here are a few things you can do in groups to boost your mood.

Sing your heart out and put some pep in your step. Like to belt out a tune or two? A new study has found that singing will improve your mood — if you croon with others.

British researchers followed members of the Sing Your Heart Out project, which runs singing workshops for people with mental health issues, including depression and anxiety. They interviewed participants and organizers over six months, and found that singing in a group contributes to recovery.

The reason? It appears the participants enjoy the activity because they're under no pressure to discuss their condition. And weekly attendance provides the chorus with structure, support, and social contact — all of which help members improve their mood and function better.

Draw on your inner Picasso to lower stress. Grab your watercolors and head for an art class. It will likely lift your spirits, according to a Swedish study of nearly 80 people with severe depression.

While all of them received medication and talk therapy, only half went to art therapy classes to doodle, paint, and talk about what the artwork meant to them. So what happened after 10 sessions? The budding artists felt less anxious, more emotionally involved, and better able to start projects on their own. The other group saw no change.

In a separate study from Drexel University, researchers found that creating art lowered levels of cortisol — a stress-related hormone linked to depression — in the majority of participants.

Balance your mind and body to boost your mood. Taking up tai chi — a gentle, flowing Chinese exercise routine — might just be the ticket if you're down in the dumps. A 12-week study from Massachusetts General Hospital found that practicing tai chi significantly reduces symptoms of depression.

Researchers divided 50 Chinese-Americans into three groups. All had been diagnosed with mild to moderate depression and weren't receiving any other treatment. The first group attended tai chi classes and were asked to also practice at home, while the second group participated in mental health educational sessions. The third had only psychological assessments.

What happened at the end of three months? The tai chi group had a significantly greater improvement in depressive symptoms than either of the other two groups.

Along with the gentle mind-body workout tai chi provides, you'll benefit from the social aspect of group exercise. Check with your health club, community center, or YMCA to find out if they offer classes. You can find a list of local instructors at *americantaichi.net*.

Defeat depression: Keep the mind and spirit in tune

Counselor Beau Brezina spends a lot of time listening to folks struggling with depression. What does he hear from the senior set? Feelings of frustration and sadness over lost independence.

Sometimes their depression begins, he says, after health issues force them to stop driving. It makes them feel dependent on others. "They say they feel less strong as a person and more like a burden," says Brezina, a discipleship counselor at Christian Families Today in Newnan, Georgia.

Brezina says therapy, medication, and a focus on exercise, sleep, and diet are all good ways to combat depression. But he believes seniors need something beyond that. After all, he says, they're living in a country that values youth, productivity, and strength. "All of those things are stacked against the elderly because they can't bring them to the table," he says.

In fact, studies show that basing your self worth on external factors that often change — like what other people think about you — is harmful to your mental health.

Brezina would agree. He helps his clients find their self worth from an internal factor that never changes — the love of Christ the Savior. "Jesus Christ has come to give you life," he tells his clients. "That gives you worth, value, acceptance, and adequacy."

Rx for retirement: How to dodge the second-act slump

Ready to kick back and enjoy the fruits of your labor? You deserve it. But if you're not prepared, retirement can be stressful and lead to depression.

It makes sense if you think about it. Some retirees have a hard time recapturing the sense of purpose their jobs gave them. Then there's the homefront to consider — it can be difficult for couples to get used to being together all day. So how do you get a grip on the situation?

Working part time can help with the transition. Not having to punch a time clock has lots of perks. But it can also be stressful if you don't know how to fill the empty hours.

Why not bridge the gap between work and play? A study of nearly 12,200 retirees concluded that those who took a temporary or part-time job had fewer major diseases and functioned better than people who stopped working altogether.

Or consider donating your time. A separate study found that retirees who volunteered had fewer signs of depression than those who didn't.

Make an effort to stay on the same page. Your retirement will go more smoothly if you talk to your spouse about the kind of lifestyle you want in your golden years. Discuss how you want to share your time and divide up household chores. You'll avoid negative feelings — and unnecessary tension — if each partner's expectations are met.

Find your passion to keep boredom at bay. Now is the time to pursue activities that make you happiest. Perhaps you've always loved to write fiction or bake Italian pastries. You might just turn what used to be a hobby into a second career.

Don't know yet where your passion lies? Take classes or join clubs in your area. The important thing is to keep yourself open to new ideas.

6 ways to keep grief from spiraling into depression

Grief — it's a natural response to the death of a loved one. It can drain you emotionally, stirring up a roller-coaster ride of emotions that often range from shock and sadness to guilt and anger.

Of course, people experience grief differently. But everyone can use these coping strategies to help get through the loss.

- Tell friends and family how you feel. Ask for help if you need it.

- Don't ignore your health. Eat well, exercise, and schedule routine doctor visits. Take your medication.

- Communicate with someone daily. It can be as simple as a phone call or email.

- Find a support group for mourners. Hospitals and religious groups are a good place to start.

- Express your feelings through music, journaling, or painting.

- Seek professional help if you find yourself overwhelmed and unable to perform daily tasks. If left unchecked, grief can lead to depression or worsen the symptoms in someone already depressed.

Dizziness

Remember spinning around as a child, purposely making yourself dizzy till you tumbled to the floor? It was a lot of fun years ago, but the thought of it now might make you green around the gills. Maybe that's nature's way of telling you that feeling lightheaded and wobbly is no laughing matter once you've passed a certain age.

In fact, toppling over after a dizzy spell can be downright scary. That's because falls are the leading cause of injuries — broken wrists, concussions, and fractured hips — among older Americans.

And many seniors, even if they don't get hurt, become afraid it will happen again. So they become less active, which increases their risk of taking a spill in the future.

You can help prevent falls by removing clutter from the stairways and tossing out slippery throw rugs. And exercise will improve lower body strength and help you with walking and balance. As for dizziness — which affects 30 percent of people 60 and older — here's what to do.

If you feel woozy, lie down on a sofa or bed to encourage blood flow to your brain. After a few minutes, sit up gradually. Stay sitting for a few more minutes before slowly rising to your feet.

But why not prevent dizziness in the first place? The following pointers will help keep you clearheaded and on your feet.

4 clues to counterbalance dizzy spells (and why you're getting them in the first place)

Go straight to the heart of blood pressure woes. Ever feel faint right after getting up from a chair? The medical name for it — orthostatic hypotension — really just means your blood pressure takes a dive when you stand up. Why does it happen? Turns out there could be lots of reasons, including age.

When you stand up, gravity causes blood to pool in your legs and stomach area. Normally, special cells near your heart and neck arteries sense the drop in blood pressure, causing your brain to tell the heart to beat faster and pump more blood.

But in older folks, these cells might not work as well as they used to. In some cases, the heart just can't beat fast enough to make up for the drop in pressure. Low blood sugar, diabetes, thyroid problems, and dehydration can also contribute to the problem.

Ever think a soup and salad could make you dizzy? It's true. Up to a third of older adults suffer from lightheadedness caused by a drop in blood pressure after eating. How to avoid it? Try drinking water before eating and opt for smaller meals that favor slowly digested beans and whole grains.

Your best bet? Have your doctor find out why you're getting dizzy. He'll most likely look at your gait and balance, as well as how well your central nervous system works. He also might run tests on your blood, ears, and heart. In the meantime, follow this advice.

- Improve circulation by pumping your feet and ankles a few times before standing up.

- Avoid crossing your legs when sitting and get enough exercise to increase your blood flow.

- Be sure to drink enough water — room temperature is best.

Don't fall for dizzying side effects. Prescription drugs work wonders when it comes to, say, clearing up pneumonia or lowering cholesterol. At the same time, they can have serious side effects.

Take, for example, opioids. They make a dramatic difference in the lives of people experiencing severe pain. But they can also make you feel drowsy and dizzy.

Canadian researchers decided to investigate further, and found that opioids might make you a prime candidate for falling. They surveyed almost 68,000 seniors who were admitted to trauma centers over a decade.

Guess what the scientists found? Patients with recent opioid prescriptions were more than twice as likely to be hurt in a fall than from another injury. Of course, painkillers aren't the only drugs that can make your head spin. Antidepressants, muscle relaxants, and blood pressure pills also fit the bill.

What should you do if you've been prescribed a medication known to trigger dizziness? Luckily, you've got options. Ask your doctor if losing weight with a healthy exercise and diet plan will reduce your need for the drug. You can also find out if a different medication, combination of drugs, or alternative therapy might do the trick instead.

Load up on B12 to stay on your feet. You might already know that vitamin B12 deficiency can cause confusion, depression, and memory problems. It can even cause your hands and feet to go numb.

Here's one more to add to the list — dizziness. If you become anemic because you're not getting enough of this important nutrient, you may feel short of breath and dizzy. That's because your red blood cells aren't carrying enough oxygen from your lungs to the rest of your body.

So what can you do? Have your doctor test your vitamin B12 level. If it's low, load up on clams, oysters, and liver — three of the vitamin's best sources. Add variety with nutrient-packed foods like eggs, milk, fortified breakfast cereal, salmon, mackerel, and tuna.

Be aware that some people have problems absorbing B12 from food and supplements. Luckily, you can also get your boost from injections prescribed by your doctor.

Strike crystal clear balance in your inner ear. Sometimes just a small tilt of the head or turning over in bed is enough to send your head into a spin. That's the case with benign paroxysmal positional vertigo (BPPV), a common condition caused by tiny calcium crystals inside your ear.

Normally, the crystals help you keep a sense of balance. But the opposite occurs when they break loose and float from their proper home in your inner ear. The shifting creates a false sense of movement, making you feel as if you or the room is twirling round and round. Although the condition isn't life-threatening, it could cause you to lose your footing and break a bone.

Fortunately your doctor can combat the effects of BPPV with a highly effective treatment — called the Epley maneuver — that involves a series of head and body movements that dislodge the crystals. After the procedure, do this to give the crystals time to settle in their proper place.

> Worried about those dizzy spells? Call your doctor if they occur more than once and are severe. He'll probably be able to diagnose and treat the cause. Call 911 if you're dizzy and have other symptoms, such as a severe headache, trouble walking, or chest pains. These could be signs of a stroke or heart attack.

- Wait 10 minutes before having someone drive you home.

- Over the next 48 hours, sleep with the back of your head at a 45 degree angle.

- Try not to tilt your head during the day.

Ask your doctor to teach you the Epley maneuver so you can perform the routine at home if your BPPV returns.

> ## Vertigo verdict: The right remedy soothes symptoms and nerves
>
> Allen Baldwin was at work when vertigo hit like a ton of bricks. "I had to lay down on the office floor," he says. "Things were really spinning bad. I was nauseous and sweaty." He describes the feeling as being whipped around on a carnival ride.
>
> Baldwin lay still, unable to raise his head without the symptoms worsening. His wife rushed him to the hospital, where he was diagnosed with vertigo. Fortunately, the condition disappeared on its own within several hours.
>
> Then nothing. Eight years passed before the familiar spinning and nausea returned. A doctor's visit confirmed what Baldwin suspected. His vertigo had returned.
>
> This time the doctor treated the 64-year-old's condition with the Epley maneuver, turning Baldwin's head at various angles. The aim? Return displaced calcium crystals in his inner ear — the cause of benign paroxysmal positional vertigo — back to where they belonged.
>
> "There was noticeable improvement after that," Baldwin says.
>
> He finds it comforting to know what is wrong. After all, his vertigo could have been caused by something far more serious — like a concussion or stroke.
>
> And only a doctor can eliminate those possibilities. So be sure to prepare for your visit.
>
> "They ask you a lot of questions, like, have you had a car accident?" Baldwin says. "Have you had a fall? Have you bumped your head?"

Visiting the doctor? Put the proper spin on your symptoms

Going to the doctor because you've been feeling dizzy? Knowing the proper medical terminology will go a long way in helping him make a diagnosis.

Dizziness actually describes two feelings — lightheadedness and vertigo.

- When you're lightheaded, you feel woozy and off balance. You might think you're about to faint.

- Vertigo, on the other hand, is a feeling that you or the room is spinning. It might seem as if you're falling or tilting to the side.

You'll want to describe your symptoms to the doctor. Tell him what causes you to feel dizzy, as well as how long the symptoms last. Be sure to let him know about any medications, supplements, and vitamins you take.

It might be helpful to keep a diary of what happens each time you get dizzy. This way you'll remember everything during your appointment.

Hearing loss

Do you often ask people to repeat themselves? Has it become a struggle to talk over the phone? Maybe loved ones complain that your television is too loud.

If so, you already have a lot in common with about 1 in 3 adults between the ages of 65 and 74 — that's how widespread hearing problems are. Nearly half of folks older than 75 are in the same boat.

You may not be surprised that hearing loss can damage your relationships. After all, socializing can be stressful and embarrassing if you can't participate in a conversation. But did you know hearing troubles can also have lasting effects on your health? Here are two reasons why you'll want to have your ears checked at the first sign of a problem.

- Age-related hearing loss — the kind that usually affects both ears gradually due to changes in your inner ear — has been linked to a drop in memory and thinking skills as well as the development of dementia.

- People with mild hearing loss are nearly three times more likely to have a recent history of falling, according to one study.

A possible reason? Researchers think hearing issues send your brain into overdrive as you try to process sound. That leaves less brainpower for forming memories and maintaining balance.

Wearing earplugs whenever you encounter loud noises is just one way to protect your hearing. For the latest buzz on hearing loss prevention, listen in on these helpful hints.

> ## From hear on: Overcoming the silent relationship killer
>
> "Patience and a sense of humor are key," says Helene, "when your husband or wife suffers from hearing loss."
>
> Helene, 62, should know. Her father was hard of hearing. And her husband of nearly two decades has been deaf in his right ear since childhood. "It doesn't work to get aggravated," she adds. "You've just got to adapt."
>
> How did she do it? By trial and error. Helene learned over the years not to shout to her husband, Pete, from another room. "Too much chance of miscommunication," she explains.
>
> Instead, she taps Pete's arm gently to get his attention and directly faces him before speaking at a natural volume. "It's important to speak slowly and not mumble," she says.
>
> Does she have any advice for others in similar situations? Yes — don't give in to frustration. Sometimes, Helene says, she finds herself having to repeat the same sentence over and over. She's been tempted to sidestep the problem and tell Pete that what she was saying wasn't all that important.
>
> But by then, Helene says, he's already put a lot of energy into trying to understand her. It just wouldn't be fair, she adds.
>
> "It takes two to make any marriage work, but when one has a handicap, they both have to work a little harder."

5 sound ways to aid your ears against damage

Load up on veggies to keep trouble out of earshot. It turns out that when free radicals — rogue molecules that damage healthy cells — form in your inner ear, they magnify your chances of hearing loss.

But you can avoid falling victim. Scientists have learned that people who eat healthy amounts of magnesium and antioxidants, like beta carotene and vitamin C, can hear tones and frequencies better.

So head over to the produce aisle. It's where you'll find beta carotene-packed foods, like sweet potatoes and cantaloupe, and citrus fruits loaded with vitamin C. Mix up your meals with magnesium-heavy green leafy vegetables like kale, collard greens, and spinach.

Make a splash by matching delish dishes with ear-soothing sides. Don't forget to pair up some fresh fish and healthy oils with those veggies. That's the advice of researchers who followed the eating patterns of more than 70,000 women in the Nurses' Health Study II over two decades.

The result? Those who followed either a Mediterranean diet — heavy in extra-virgin olive oil, whole grains, fish, and vegetables — or the veggie-rich, low-sodium DASH diet saw the best results. In fact, they had about a 30 percent lower risk of hearing loss compared to those who adopted less healthy dining habits.

"Eating well contributes to overall good health, and it may also be helpful in reducing the risk of hearing loss," says study co-author Dr. Sharon Curhan, an epidemiologist at Brigham and Women's Hospital.

Sound the alarm on harmful medications. Did you know that aspirin, if taken in too high a dose or too often, can harm the nerves in your inner ear?

Fortunately, hearing loss or ringing in the ear caused by over-the-counter medications is usually temporary. Some prescription drugs, however, are more likely to cause permanent damage.

Common drugs that can affect your hearing include Quinidex, which is prescribed for an irregular heartbeat, the painkiller

Vicodin, and antibiotics Garamycin and Amikin. Your best bet? Ask your doctor if alternative drugs will do the trick.

Slip on your sneakers to score benefits between the ears. Who would have thought that walking a little over 15 minutes a day could improve your hearing? But it's true. Scientists in Boston found that women who walked two or more hours a week lowered their chances of hearing loss by 10 to 15 percent, compared to those who walked less than one hour each week.

Why is walking good for your ears? Physical activity boosts blood flow throughout your body, which helps keep your arteries relaxed and flexible. And by controlling your weight with exercise, your blood vessels are less likely to be damaged by inflammation. That's good news because better blood flow to your inner ears and less damage equals a lower risk of hearing loss.

"Hearing loss can impair activities of everyday life, causing frustration, loneliness, social isolation, and dependence," says Dr. Curhan, co-author of the study. "We often think of hearing loss as an inevitable part of the aging process, but these findings provide evidence that potentially modifiable risk factors, such as maintaining a healthy weight and staying physically active, may help in the prevention of hearing loss or delay its progression."

Ring up hearing perks by snubbing your cellphone. In a recent study from India, scientists compared the hearing levels of volunteers who used their cellphones for more than an hour a day, less than an hour a day, and hardly ever.

They discovered that 10 percent of the group using their mobiles more than an hour a day experienced hearing loss. That compares with 2 percent in the group who used their phones less than an hour a day. And those who rarely used a cellphone? None reported hearing loss.

The researchers believe long-term and frequent exposure to your cellphone's electromagnetic field damages cells in your inner ear, leading to high-frequency hearing loss. Once that occurs, it's difficult to hear high-pitched sounds like the microwave beep that signals your food is done.

What can you do? Experts recommend texting and using a speaker phone, landline, or Bluetooth headset. Keep calls short if you have to hold a phone up to your ear.

> Want to connect with other people who live with hearing loss? Get plugged into a support group at *hearing loss.org,* powered by the Hearing Loss Association of America. Poke around the site to find tools on living with hearing loss and news about the latest technological and medical advances.

Lost your appetite for eating out? 3 recipes to shut down restaurant racket

Hard of hearing? If so, activities that used to be enjoyable have probably gone by the wayside. Take for example the simple act of meeting a dear friend for lunch.

In the old days, you'd have jumped at the chance. But now you worry all that background noise — customers chatting, chairs scooting, ice clinking — will prevent you from holding down a conversation. Don't let the thought of eating out give you indigestion. Read on for some simple fixes.

Do some prep work to pick the perfect place. Have a craving for Japanese food? Perhaps you're leaning toward Italian. Either way, you'll want to consider more than the menu when choosing a restaurant.

Picture the eatery's interior. Does it have high ceilings, hardwood floors, and glass tables pushed close together? If so, each sound is going to echo like a bouncing basketball in a gymnasium.

How's the lighting? Dim overhead lights might be romantic, but they sure won't help when it comes to reading lips and facial expressions — key pieces to understanding speech.

Be kind to yourself. Choose a well-lit eatery with sound-absorbing carpeting, cushions, tablecloths, and curtains.

Discover your own happy hour — be at the right place at the right time. If possible, choose a booth. The high, cushioned back will help dampen excess noise.

You'll want to avoid sitting at a table in the center of the room. That's because there won't be any buffers between you and other diners. But if you do have to sit at a table, choose one near a wall and away from the kitchen.

You also might want to pick a less crowded time to meet at the restaurant — say an hour or so before the rush begins. An added bonus? Restaurant staff might be more willing to lower background music if there are fewer diners. Remember, you can always call ahead and request accommodations.

Let your hearing aids work for you. Most new digital hearing aids have directional microphones. If you have one of these gadgets, sit with your back to the noisiest part of the room. And have your dining companion sit with his back to the wall so his voice will be the only sound coming toward you.

That way, your hearing aid will help you pick up the funny story your friend is telling you and not the drink orders from three tables down.

High blood pressure

True or false? These symptoms are all signs of high blood pressure — headaches, blurry vision, and dizziness. The answer? Sort of true, and kind of false. Because some people do have those symptoms, but most people have no signs at all. The only way to know for sure if you have high blood pressure, also known as hypertension, is to let your numbers do the talking.

As your heart pumps blood, sending energy, oxygen, and nutrients all through your body, the blood pushes against the sides of your arteries. The strength of this "pushing" is what's measured when you take your blood pressure.

- The top number — called systolic pressure — represents the pressure in your blood vessels as your heart beats.

- The bottom number, diastolic pressure, is measured when your heart rests between beats.

Experts say to shoot for a reading below 120/80 mmHg. So how high is too high? Recently, the American Heart Association and the American College of Cardiology lowered the definition of high blood pressure from 140/90 mmHg to 130/80 mmHg. That means nearly half of American adults now fall into the high blood pressure category.

And lifestyle choices could be making it worse. Smoking, stress, and excess body fat can cause your blood pressure to get too high, damaging your arteries. And this can lead to some life-altering problems like stroke, vision loss, heart attack, kidney disease — even dementia. Just think about what that could do to your ability to live independently.

Don't worry. You can eat your way to healthier blood pressure. It's simple. Just follow this advice.

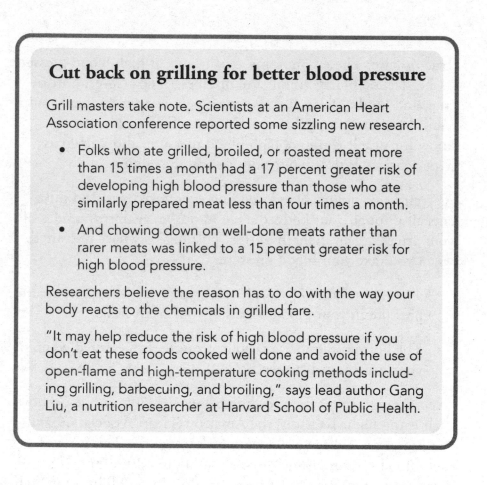

Cut back on grilling for better blood pressure

Grill masters take note. Scientists at an American Heart Association conference reported some sizzling new research.

- Folks who ate grilled, broiled, or roasted meat more than 15 times a month had a 17 percent greater risk of developing high blood pressure than those who ate similarly prepared meat less than four times a month.

- And chowing down on well-done meats rather than rarer meats was linked to a 15 percent greater risk for high blood pressure.

Researchers believe the reason has to do with the way your body reacts to the chemicals in grilled fare.

"It may help reduce the risk of high blood pressure if you don't eat these foods cooked well done and avoid the use of open-flame and high-temperature cooking methods including grilling, barbecuing, and broiling," says lead author Gang Liu, a nutrition researcher at Harvard School of Public Health.

4 easy eats that steady your BP

Go a little nutty at breakfast. In a recent study of more than 2,000 healthy adults, those with the most omega-3 fatty acids in their blood also had the lowest blood pressure readings.

Interesting, perhaps, but what does that mean for you? Researchers think omega-3 fatty acids may help the walls of your blood vessels relax and widen, improving blood flow and helping your blood pressure go down. Got your attention now, right?

To add heart-healthy omega-3 to your diet, just toss some delicious English walnuts on your morning oatmeal. A 1-ounce serving — about 1/4 cup — provides 2,565 milligrams (mg) of omega-3.

You don't have to go nuts. Perk up your breakfast smoothies with a tablespoon of whole flaxseed, which contains 2,338 mg of omega-3. Or taste test a tablespoon of flaxseed oil, which offers a whopping 7,196 mg.

Looking for more delicious foods to lower your BP naturally? Dash to DASH — short for Dietary Approaches to Stop Hypertension. Developed by the National Institutes of Health, the DASH diet focuses on fruits, vegetables, and whole grains with small amounts of low-fat dairy foods. Small servings of meat, poultry, and fish round out your weekly menu.

Snack time calls for berries.
Why are berries so bold? It's because they're packed with pigments called anthocyanins. These antioxidants may work their magic by making your blood vessels more elastic.

Researchers discovered this after looking at data on more than 156,000 participants from the Nurses' Health Study (NHS) I, NHS II, and Health Professionals Follow-up Study. They found that people who ate the most anthocyanins from blueberries and strawberries had an 8 percent drop in their risk for high blood pressure, compared to those who ate the lowest amounts.

And according to experts at Harvard Medical School, it only takes 1 1/2 cups per week — of either berry — to enjoy heart benefits.

Lunch on leafy greens. Found in spinach, kale, cabbage, and other leafy greens, nitrates lower your blood pressure by producing nitric oxide, a gas that helps your blood vessels relax and makes your arteries more flexible.

"We were surprised by how little nitrate was needed to see such a large effect," said Amrita Ahluwalia, lead author of a study published in *Hypertension*. The research shows that the amount of nitrates found in a large bowl of lettuce could lower your blood pressure about 11 points.

And while you're at it, top off your lunch hour with watermelon. This juicy fruit contains L-citrulline, an amino acid that helps your body make the same nitric oxide known to help lower your BP.

Add apricots to the menu for a super supper. You probably know eating less salt goes hand in hand with lower blood pressure. But did you know you need potassium, too? Potassium partners with your kidneys to get rid of extra sodium. And it relaxes your blood vessel walls which lowers your blood pressure, too.

Dr. Alicia McDonough, author of a recent review on the BP-lowering effects of potassium, says lowering your sodium intake is a great place to start, but you can do more. "Evidence suggests that increasing dietary potassium may have an equally important effect on hypertension."

And it's an easy fix. Just 1 cup of dried apricots provides more than 40 percent of your daily requirement of potassium. Not a fan of dishes like savory slow-cooked apricot chicken? Substitute a cup of cooked lentils or a hearty baked potato to your evening meal.

Keep tabs on sodium with a 3-point plan

When the cardiologist explained the seriousness of Bill's congestive heart failure, Rose knew some dietary changes were needed to keep his kidneys working properly and his blood pressure low. Salt was the culprit that had to go.

"We had to lower his daily salt intake to below 1,500 milligrams," says Rose. That's less than 1 teaspoon a day.

So Rose developed a three-point plan.

- First, she talked to her local grocer and the store's dietitian, who helped her select low-salt foods. Rose adds, "The meat department even ordered fresh pork loin that had only 3 percent sodium, compared to the others that were 14 percent and higher." Perfect for Bill's menu.

- Next, Rose kept a record of Bill's daily sodium intake. She was surprised by the amount of sodium in everyday foods like pickle relish, milk, and salad dressings.

- Finally, she learned it's important to stick to the plan. "Bill was doing so well that we relaxed things, thinking we had it licked." But soon Bill started having trouble. Now she advises folks to stay on track with their diet.

So is the plan a success? Bill continues to take his medicine, but Rose is pleased with his progress after almost five years. "With lowering the salt and the blood pressure, I got him from bedridden to wheelchair to walker, and he's using a cane now." Good work, Rose.

Salt shockers — steer clear of sodium hidden in your favorite foods

Experts say you need to keep your sodium intake below 2,300 milligrams (mg) each day, and even lower — a mere 1,500 mg — if you're serious about bringing down your blood pressure.

But how can you get that number down if you don't know where the sodium is lurking? It's like playing a game of hide-and-seek, but with some pretty serious health consequences.

Watch out for these popular foods that contain more sodium than you might think.

Food	Serving size	Amount of sodium
frozen buttermilk pancakes	3 pancakes	815 mg
jarred spaghetti sauce	1/2 cup	525 mg
canned chicken noodle soup	1 cup	474 mg
low-fat cottage cheese	1/2 cup	459 mg
canned mushrooms	1/2 cup	331 mg
kosher dill pickles	1 spear	306 mg
unfrosted chocolate cake	1 slice	299 mg
light Italian salad dressing	2 tbsp	228 mg
rye bread	1 slice	211 mg
ketchup	1 tbsp	167 mg

From the couch to the cuff: 3 simple steps to lower those numbers

You may be able to beat high blood pressure without prescription drugs and their nasty side effects. But you have to turn off the

TV, get up off the couch, and take a few simple steps in the right direction toward a longer, healthier life.

Pull your own weight. Resistance training builds your muscle strength and prevents disabilities by making your muscles work against a force, like hand weights, resistance bands, or even your own body.

And in a recent study, researchers revealed that resistance training is a great way to stave off metabolic syndrome — a group of health conditions that up your chances of heart problems and diabetes. Of more than 7,000 participants, those who did resistance training twice a week had a 17 percent lower risk for developing conditions like high blood pressure, cholesterol, body fat, and blood sugar.

For easy ways to add strength training moves to your daily routine, see *3 brawn-building moves you can do at home* in the *Sarcopenia* chapter. Before you start any new exercise program, clear it with your doctor. Ask him if there are any movements you should avoid.

Flock to friends who go the extra mile. Even simple activities like walking are great for BP, but did you know that grabbing a few friends to tag along could help you score bigger benefits?

According to a review in the *British Journal of Sports Medicine,* people who walked with a group saw their blood pressure drop more than three points — a greater improvement compared to folks who trekked solo. And

Find a walking group in your community by going to *meetup.com/topics/ walkers* and clicking "more local Meetups." No groups right for you? Start your own. Get together with co-workers, neighbors, and friends to plan your dates, times, and routes. It's the friendliest way to tell high BP to take a hike.

experts say walking at a steady pace of 3 to 5 mph counts as moderate-intensity exercise.

"People who walk in groups also tend to have a more positive attitude toward physical activity, a shared experience for wellness, and say they feel less lonely and isolated," said Sarah Hanson, one of the study's lead researchers. "Taking regular walks can also be a catalyst for adopting other healthy behaviors."

Turn up the heat. A new study says both systolic and diastolic blood pressure dropped almost 7 points in folks who indulged in a sauna bath for 30-minute sessions. And during sauna sessions, bathers' heart rates increased just as if they were doing moderate-intensity exercise like walking.

Sauna bathing is a thousand-year-old tradition straight from Finland that takes place in a small room usually heated to a toasty temp between 158 and 212 degrees. Saunas often use dry heat, with a low humidity between 10 and 20 percent.

These conditions may help lower blood pressure by boosting body temp, which allows veins and arteries to expand and contract more easily. Talk with your doctor to find out if a sauna bath is right for you.

Keep your pressure on target with an at-home monitor

Battling high BP? A good home monitor is your first line of defense. But monitors sold at pharmacies and online can range from less than $15 to more than $100, and with dozens of models to choose from, what should you buy?

Experts say arm monitors are more accurate than wrist models. Just make sure the cuff inflates automatically and fits correctly. And look for a digital display that's bright and easy to read. Your doctor should check to make sure you're using your monitor correctly and that your readings are accurate.

Don't stop taking your medication without talking to your doctor — even if your readings are in the normal range. If your numbers are especially high, or if you're experiencing symptoms like chest pain or shortness of breath, contact health care professionals right away.

Perfect timing gives you round-the-clock protection

Timing is everything, even when it comes to taking your blood pressure medicine. If you're like most people, your blood pressure begins to rise when you get out of bed in the morning and hits its highest reading at high noon. It drops down to its lowest point in the wee hours of the night — between midnight and 4 a.m.

But if you have high BP, your pressure may not take that nightly dip. And that's why some experts think taking your medicine at bedtime could improve your numbers — and help prevent heart attacks, which are more likely to happen in the morning.

In one study of more than 600 people with chronic kidney disease and hypertension, a bedtime dose of BP medicine improved blood pressure and lowered the risk of cardiovascular events like heart attack and stroke. But before you change your nightly routine, check with your doctor.

7 steps to measure your pressure the right way

You're checking your BP regularly, but are your readings accurate? To make sure your measurements are on the mark, sit quietly for at least five minutes before you begin. Avoid exercising, eating, or drinking — especially anything with caffeine — for at least 30 minutes before you check your numbers. And follow these simple tips.

Use correct cuff size. One that's too small could add up to **10** points.

Don't chat. Talking can add **15** points.

Put cuff on bare arm. Clothing can add as much as **40** points.

Support back. Slouching can add **10** points.

Empty bladder first. A full bladder can add up to **15** points.

Support arm at heart level. An unsupported arm could add **10** points.

Keep feet flat on floor. Crossing legs can add up to **8** points.

High cholesterol

You might remember Arthur "the Fonz" Fonzarelli of "Happy Days" fame as quite the teenage heartthrob. But it's the star who portrayed Fonzie, Henry Winkler, who's facing real heart trouble these days. Some years ago, he learned his cholesterol levels had soared to 277 milligrams per deciliter (mg/dL). What does that number really mean for heart health?

Cholesterol is carried through your bloodstream by two kinds of lipoproteins. High-density lipoprotein (HDL) cholesterol — the good guy — takes cholesterol straight to your liver where it's removed from your body. But low-density lipoprotein (LDL) cholesterol — the bad guy — can deposit cholesterol in your arteries, forming plaques that could lead to heart attacks.

Cholesterol is not all bad. This waxy fat-like substance has some very important jobs to do — like building cells, digesting food, and making vitamin D. On its own, your body makes all the cholesterol it needs to get these jobs done.

But factors like your diet, your age, a lack of exercise, or even your family history can cause your cholesterol levels to rise to unhealthy levels. Just how much is too much?

	Goal	Borderline	Danger zone
Total cholesterol	less than 200	200-239	240 and above
HDL cholesterol	60 and above	40-59	less than 40
LDL cholesterol	less than 100	100-159	160 and above
Triglycerides	less than 150	150-199	200 and above

Too much cholesterol and triglycerides, fats that contribute to traffic jams in your arteries, have been linked with problems like heart disease, stroke, high blood pressure, and diabetes. And any one of these health issues could rob you of your independence faster than Fonzie jumped that shark.

Henry Winkler's story has had a happy ending so far. At last count, his total cholesterol was down to 137 mg/dL. How'd he do it? The same way you can — by making changes to your diet and exercise plan. Read on to learn about some foods that can help you get your numbers back on track. Exactamundo, Bucko.

Beat back bad cholesterol with 5 everyday foods

Try the miracle seed that does it all. In a study of 50 people with high cholesterol, those who ate 2 tablespoons of roasted flaxseed powder every day for three months had lower LDL and total cholesterol levels — and higher HDL numbers — than those who didn't eat flaxseed.

Researchers think this change for the better is caused by alpha-lipoic acid (ALA), an omega-3 fatty acid known for its heart perks, and polyphenols called lignans.

But the benefits don't stop there. Besides besting high cholesterol, this super seed also fights high blood pressure, heart disease, cancer, and weight gain that can lead to obesity.

For a fitter ticker, go fish. Salmon, sardines, and mackerel are three great catches for folks who want to net more heart-healthy omega-3 and slow atherosclerosis — hardening of the arteries caused by plaque buildup.

How do these plaque-busting polyunsaturated fatty acids (PUFAs) dissolve cholesterol, prevent blood clots, and flush out your arteries? They boost HDL cholesterol, which acts as a garbage disposal to whisk away cholesterol pileups.

Experts recommend two 3.5-ounce servings each week to reel in benefits like a lower risk of heart attack, heart disease, and stroke.

An apple a day to drop LDL? You bet. Here's proof the popular fruit lives up to its hype. In one study, 160 women between the ages of 45 and 65 were divided into two groups. The first group ate 75 grams of dried apples every day for one year, while the second group ate dried prunes instead.

One of the researchers, Florida State University professor Dr. Bahram Arjmandi, was surprised by the results. "Incredible changes in the apple-eating women happened by six months. They experienced a 23 percent decrease in LDL cholesterol."

Not only that, but the apple eaters' HDL numbers climbed 4 percent. Researchers think the benefits come from apples' ample supply of pectin, a soluble fiber that lowers the amount of cholesterol absorbed into your bloodstream.

This sweet treat is cholesterol's kryptonite. Now here's a study near and dear to your heart. Volunteers were asked to eat either 2 grams of dark chocolate or the same amount of milk chocolate every day for six months to see how it affected their cholesterol levels. Sounds great, right?

Don't get too excited. Turns out a 2-gram serving of chocolate is about a quarter of one small Dove chocolate square. But this little serving brought big-time benefits.

Researchers reported a bigger drop in LDL and total cholesterol in the dark chocolate eaters compared to the milk chocolate eaters. Scientists think the healthy cocoa flavonoids, natural antioxidants found in abundance in dark chocolate, are responsible for this happy change. Be sure to choose a dark chocolate that's at least 70 percent cocoa.

Knock out cholesterol with a cup of tea. Chock-full of cholesterol-blocking antioxidants called catechins, green tea may not only lower your LDL cholesterol but also protect you from heart disease. In fact, in one meta-analysis, researchers estimated that the rate of heart attack drops 11 percent among those who drink three cups of tea a day.

To get even more catechin power in your cup, add a splash of citrus juice. Turns out that adding 2 to 3 tablespoons of orange, lemon, or lime juice to 1 cup of green tea boosts the amount of catechins available for your body to absorb by as much as five times.

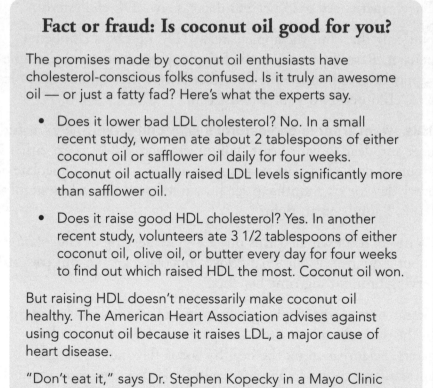

Fact or fraud: Is coconut oil good for you?

The promises made by coconut oil enthusiasts have cholesterol-conscious folks confused. Is it truly an awesome oil — or just a fatty fad? Here's what the experts say.

- Does it lower bad LDL cholesterol? No. In a small recent study, women ate about 2 tablespoons of either coconut oil or safflower oil daily for four weeks. Coconut oil actually raised LDL levels significantly more than safflower oil.

- Does it raise good HDL cholesterol? Yes. In another recent study, volunteers ate 3 1/2 tablespoons of either coconut oil, olive oil, or butter every day for four weeks to find out which raised HDL the most. Coconut oil won.

But raising HDL doesn't necessarily make coconut oil healthy. The American Heart Association advises against using coconut oil because it raises LDL, a major cause of heart disease.

"Don't eat it," says Dr. Stephen Kopecky in a Mayo Clinic Minute feature. "It really does raise your bad cholesterol."

Portfolio diet yields big benefits for heart health

When you invest in a retirement portfolio, you choose a strategic mix of stocks and bonds to raise your benefits while lowering your risks. You wouldn't bet all your retirement savings on one stock, would you?

In his innovative Portfolio diet, nutrition expert Dr. David Jenkins suggests you stock your pantry with the following food groups. Each can lower LDL cholesterol 5 to 10 percent. But no sense putting all your eggs in one basket when a combo of these portfolio picks — in the place of heart-wrecking saturated fat — could drop your cholesterol as much as some statins.

Seal the deal for lower cholesterol with soluble fiber. If you eat just one thing for breakfast, make it oatmeal. The soluble fiber in grains like oats lowers your LDL by stopping cholesterol from being absorbed into your bloodstream through the intestines.

But that's not all. It also eases high blood pressure, cuts diabetes risk, stops weight gain, and lowers the risk of dying from heart attack, pneumonia, and infections.

To treat your ticker, try to include two servings of oatmeal, beans, or lentils and five servings of fruits and veggies in your daily menu. Eggplant, okra, apples, and oranges are all good high-fiber choices.

Bank on nuts to balance your cholesterol. Walnuts, almonds, pistachios, pecans. Just pick your favorite. It's the quantity that matters, not the kind. All it takes to lower cholesterol is 45 grams (g) of nuts daily — that's about a handful.

Researchers say it's the unsaturated fats and plant sterols in nuts that turn the tide on LDL. Just toss some walnuts on your breakfast oatmeal or dinner salad, or enjoy some almonds as an afternoon snack.

Invest in plant protein to drop that number. It might be a struggle to work up an appetite for tofu or veggie burgers — foods that often come to mind when you think of plant protein.

But when it comes to lowering your LDL, it may just be worth the effort. And besides, there are other sources of plant protein that might whet your appetite, like chickpeas, lentils, pinto beans, and soy milk. Give them a try.

Experts recommend eating 50 g of plant protein every day. Sound like too much? Aim for 25 g to start and gradually work your way up.

Reap the benefits of plant sterols to counter your LDL. Plant sterols mimic cholesterol, competing with it for absorption in your intestines which reduces the amount of cholesterol that makes it to your arteries.

You'll find plant sterols in wheat germ, peanuts, and soybeans, but it's easier to get the recommended amount of 2 g every day by eating foods enriched with sterols. You can find added plant sterols in foods like orange juice and yogurt.

Cholesterol counterpunch — Asian superfood KO's LDL

Elephant yam, devil's tongue, and snake palm. Strange nicknames for the heart-healthy plant called konjac (pronounced cognac), a cholesterol-fighting superfood popular in Asian dishes.

It's the fiber extract — glucomannan — found in konjac root that has the power to lower your LDL up to 10 percent by reducing the amount of cholesterol your gut absorbs. And just 3 grams of the fiber every day is enough to do the trick.

Glucomannan is available as a supplement in capsule or powder form. Just be sure to follow the directions on the package. Or if you're feeling adventurous, you can enjoy konjac root in more traditional ways — in konnyaku cake, which is similar to tofu, or in shirataki noodles, also known as "miracle" noodles.

Sidestep ticker troubles with these exercise tips

Does your retirement plan look something like this? A warm summer afternoon, dozing in a cozy chair on a sunny front porch, an icy beverage in your hand. A little nap seems like a great idea.

But wait. What about your high cholesterol? A nap surely won't help that, but some exercise certainly could.

In a recent study, retirement was associated with a 10 percent drop in moderate to vigorous physical activity. In other words, too many folks are napping on their front porches.

And that's bad because the American Heart Association recommends you get 40 minutes of moderate to vigorous aerobic exercise three or four times each week to lower your risk for heart attack and stroke.

Slow and steady wins this race. You don't have to be a marathon runner to reap exercise benefits. Over the course of six years, researchers kept up with 33,060 runners in the National Runners' Health Study and 15,945 walkers in the National Walkers' Health Study. And who do you suppose fared better when it came to heart health?

- The risk for high cholesterol was reduced more than 4 percent by running, but a whopping 7 percent by walking.

- The risk for heart disease was lowered 4.5 percent for the runners, but a little more than twice that for the walkers.

Pick a perfect plan to lower your cholesterol. Not a fan of the open road? There are other ways to get your exercise. Water aerobics, tai chi, and yoga have all been shown to have cholesterol-lowering benefits.

"Proper physical activity should be a lifelong commitment," says Dr. Gerald Fletcher, professor of medicine and cardiovascular disease at the Mayo Clinic in Florida. "The most active individuals have an approximate 40 percent lower risk of developing heart disease than those who do not exercise at all."

" Battle artery gridlock with diet, exercise, and your doctor's sound advice

At the young age of 32, Shelley was shocked to discover her cholesterol was over 300 — a dangerously high number. "I was surprised to learn I had high cholesterol," she says, "especially since I ate a relatively healthy diet, didn't smoke or drink, and exercised regularly."

Shelley's weapons in her battle against inherited high cholesterol included healthy food, exercise, and a low-dose statin. Fried foods, beef, and eggs were immediately dropped from her diet and replaced with lots of colorful fruits and veggies. For nine years, her efforts seemed to be paying off.

But then Shelley had a heart event that sent her to the hospital. Doctors inserted a stent in her coronary artery to open up a 95 percent blockage. How does she describe clogged arteries?

"It's like a kitchen sink drain," she says. "You can continue pouring grease in the drain until one day when you can't. There's a complete blockage that makes a huge mess."

Since then, Shelley has done everything she can to clean up her huge mess. She exercises regularly. She eats mostly vegetables, beans, legumes, fish, and fruit. She avoids processed foods because they can contain hidden fats, cholesterol, and sodium. And she takes the medicine her doctor prescribes.

Her advice to folks battling high cholesterol?

"Heart disease is silent and can go completely undetected — until it's too late," says Shelley. "So be proactive. Know your numbers. Know your family's medical history. Improve life habits like diet and exercise, manage your stress, and create supportive relationships with family and friends." "

Mythbusters: Don't let cholesterol lore break your heart

Confused by all the differing opinions you hear about the best ways to manage your cholesterol? How can you decide what advice is based on old wives' tales and what's straight from brand-new medical research? Here are some common cholesterol myths along with the facts you need to know to protect your heart.

Myth: High cholesterol is something only old folks need to worry about. You can have high cholesterol and not even know it. That's because it usually doesn't cause any symptoms. So to be on the safe side, the American Heart Association says you should have your numbers checked beginning at age 20.

And then, depending on your risk factors for developing heart disease, you should have your cholesterol rechecked at least every four to six years after that.

Myth: If you have enough HDL, you don't have to worry about lowering your LDL. Researchers used to think high levels of good HDL cholesterol would balance out the bad LDL, but recent studies show that's not true. Although high HDL can be a sign of good heart health, your body may still be depositing cholesterol in your arteries, which can lead to heart troubles.

Myth: All fats are bad for your heart. Four different kinds of fats are found in foods. Some are unhealthy, but some are actually good for you.

On the bad list? Trans fats, found in lots of processed foods and baked goods, are known to raise LDL levels. Saturated fats, which come from animal products like red meat and butter, can also up your bad cholesterol. Stay away from those.

Instead stick to healthy monounsaturated fats (MUFAs) — the kind in nuts and olive oil — and polyunsaturated fats (PUFAs), like those found in salmon.

Myth: If you take cholesterol medicine, you don't have to make lifestyle changes. If your doctor has ordered cholesterol-lowering medication for you, it's important that you take it just as prescribed. But don't rely on your meds alone. There are some things you can do to get your numbers back under control. The best ways? First, make sure you eat a heart-healthy diet. And second? Get plenty of exercise.

Ask your doctor if statins are still right for you

"Old age is no place for sissies," joked actress Bette Davis. But when it comes to cholesterol-lowering medications like Lipitor and Crestor, old age may give you an unexpected advantage.

Are you a healthy adult over the age of 75? No type 2 diabetes or history of heart disease? Then you may want to talk with your doctor about stopping your statin.

When researchers studied healthy folks age 75 and up, they found that statins were not associated with a drop in heart attack and stroke rates. This has experts questioning the use of statins among older adults, who are more likely to experience serious side effects.

Your doctor might prescribe a statin if you have other risk factors like being overweight or having high blood pressure. So don't make any changes to your medications without talking to him.

Insomnia

The sheep were running wild in the meadow, and the cow was gorging herself on corn. But where was Little Boy Blue and his trusty horn? Sacked out under the haystack, of course. Seems like Blue got his recommended seven to nine hours of sleep without batting an eye. So why can't you?

There are lots of reasons. Health conditions like allergies, arthritis, and sleep apnea can make it tough to catch your z's. Meds for high blood pressure, depression, and even the common cold can cause sleepless nights, too. Are you worried about your future? Anxiety and stress can be real eye-openers in the wee small hours of the morning.

But at least you're not alone in your midnight misery. Each year, about 1 in 4 Americans spend numerous nights wide awake counting sheep, just like you. That's cold comfort when you consider what those sleepless nights can cause. Insomnia has been linked to health problems like high blood pressure, heart disease, and stroke. And poor sleep reduces your alertness, your decision-making ability, and your safety in general.

Take a look at this checklist to determine if the late night enemy you're battling is insomnia.

- You have daytime symptoms like sleepiness, moodiness, or fatigue.

- It takes you more than 30 minutes to fall asleep.

- You wake up during the night and have trouble going back to sleep.

- You go to bed in a quiet, dark room that should provide a perfect sleep environment, but you just can't nod off.

- You've been struggling with sleeplessness three nights a week for at least two weeks, and perhaps up to three months or longer.

Do these symptoms describe you to a T? Read on for some tips that will have you sleeping like a baby — or even better. Because to stay independent, you need a good night's sleep.

10 simple tips for sound and restful sleep every night

A novel idea for super slumber. Try a little writing before you turn in for the night. In one study, researchers asked folks to make lists for five minutes before they went to sleep.

- The people in one group listed things they needed to do the next day.

- Members of the other group wrote down tasks they had finished in the past few days.

The idea was to see which strategy helped lower stress levels before bedtime. Guess who fell asleep faster? The group who made tomorrow's to-do list conked out significantly faster than the group who wrote about completed activities.

You'll sleep better if you let sleeping dogs lie — in your room. You may think having Fido in your bedroom will disrupt your sleep, but that's not necessarily true, says new research.

"We found that many people actually find more comfort and a sense of security from sleeping with their pets," says Lois Krahn, M.D., a sleep medicine specialist at the Mayo Clinic in Arizona.

Keep Fido off the bed, though. According to the study, folks who allowed their canine under the covers had poorer quality sleep than those who encouraged him to sleep on his own bed.

Close the book on sleepless nights. If you want better sleep, turn off your e-reader. One study showed that people who read e-books before bedtime took 10 minutes longer to fall asleep than when they read paper books. Readers of e-books also felt less alert the following morning.

Scientists say the trouble is caused by blue light — emitted from devices like your e-reader, tablet, cellphone, and computer — which throws off your sleep cycle. So limit screen time before snooze time.

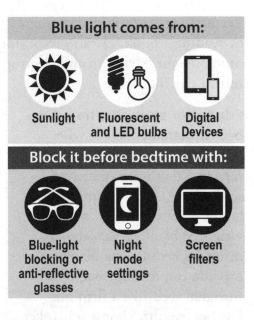

Block the blues for a better snooze. What if you can't avoid your gadgets at night? Researchers recently discovered that when people wore blue-light blocking glasses for three hours before bedtime for two weeks, their nighttime levels of the sleep-regulating chemical melatonin increased by 58 percent. That's even better than the results you might get by taking over-the-counter melatonin supplements.

Nod off quicker in warm socks. Fall asleep more than eight minutes faster, and stay asleep a half hour longer, with this simple trick. Wear your socks to bed. Researchers think warming your feet makes your blood vessels expand, a process called vasodilation. This helps body heat escape through your skin, which lowers your core body temp. And that's a signal to your brain that it's time to sleep.

Wind down from your day before hitting the hay. "Having a one- or two-hour routine at night where you're starting to wind down is very helpful in getting the mind ready to sleep," says Dr. Nitun Verma, a spokesperson for the American Academy of Sleep Medicine.

Verma suggests relaxing evening activities like looking at photos or reading a book. He also recommends turning down the volume on your television and electronic devices to promote a quiet, restful environment.

For better shut-eye, try a better blanket. People who participated in one study reported that it was easier to settle down — and experience better quality sleep — with a weighted blanket. Researchers think it's because the blankets provide comforting touch pressure that feels like a firm hug. For best results, choose a blanket that equals about 10 percent of your body weight.

You thought it was the sandman who made you sleepy? Nope. Actually a brain-produced hormone, melatonin, brings on sweet slumber. During daylight hours, your brain keeps melatonin levels low. But around 9:00 p.m., melatonin levels rise and stay high for about 12 hours — helping you get a solid snooze.

To drift off faster, find your happy place. Counting sheep used to be the cure-all for sleepless nights, but scientists have a new way to drift off faster. They call it imagery distraction. Just imagine a relaxing scene — like a mountain stream or a sunny beach — and concentrate on that instead of your everyday worries and concerns. Research shows you could fall asleep 20 minutes faster.

Sail off to dreamland in your freshly made bed. A recent study by the National Sleep Foundation showed that folks who make their beds every day — or almost every day — are 19 percent more likely to say they get a good night's sleep than those who make their beds less often or not at all.

Train your brain to sleep like a rock. A consistent schedule during the day makes for better sleep at night. Even eating your meals on time can help.

"Having meals at regular times and waking up at the same time every day helps to train the brain to know the difference between the time to go to sleep and the time to stay awake," says Verma.

Try this 11-minute fix for sleepless nights

Emily Bronte of "Wuthering Heights" fame had a unique technique for beating insomnia. She walked in circles around her dining room until she finally dropped off. A novel method for sure, but wouldn't you rather improve your sleep, energy, mood, and memory — in just 11 minutes? With no worries about face-planting on your dining room floor, either.

Tai chi is a graceful form of gentle, low-impact exercise so simple, anyone can do it. The series of stretching movements are performed slowly, allowing each position to flow into the next without interruption so your body stays in constant motion.

Researchers found that older adults with sleep complaints who participated in tai chi reported better quality sleep than those who took part in health education classes or general exercise sessions.

You can do tai chi anywhere — inside or out, alone or as part of a class. And since it requires no special equipment, tai chi appeals to budget-minded seniors. With practice, you can work through tai chi's 18 fundamental moves in under 11 minutes.

Apnea: Don't lose sleep over breathless nights

Oh, the snoring. You've poked and prodded, tickled and tapped. You've tried earplugs. You're even thinking about making a move to the guest room for just one night of peaceful, uninterrupted shut-eye.

The problem? Your spouse has obstructive sleep apnea (OSA).

"Sleep apnea is worse than just snoring," says Dr. Nitun Verma, spokesperson for the American Academy of Sleep Medicine. "When a person's airway closes down completely, no air is moving, and oxygen levels start to drop." And that's when OSA puts you at risk for developing serious conditions like high blood pressure and diabetes.

Two to three times as many men as women have OSA, but sometimes women slip through the gap because they have different symptoms. While men usually show signs like loud snoring and gasping for air, women are more likely to complain about depression, fatigue, and restless legs.

But men and women share the same health risks if the condition goes untreated, says Verma.

While sleep apnea can be controlled with lifestyle changes, like maintaining a healthy weight and limiting alcohol, doctors continue to recommend a CPAP machine — short for continuous positive airway pressure.

"CPAP is a successful treatment," says Verma. "However, it's not always a love-at-first-sight solution. On average it takes people two to six weeks to adjust."

If your mask is uncomfortable, Verma recommends talking to your doctor. "A better mask can make a world of difference," he says.

Sip these teas to catch some z's

"If you are cold, tea will warm you; if you are too heated, it will cool you; if you are depressed, it will cheer you; if you are excited, it will calm you." As you can see, William Gladstone, a 19th-century British statesman, was a fan of England's iconic beverage.

But as much as he seemed to enjoy a steaming cuppa, there's something Gladstone forgot to include in his tribute to tea. He could have added, "If you are restless, it will bring you sleep." In other words, a good night's sleep is in the bag. The tea bag, that is — but only if it's one of these herbal, decaffeinated teas.

Cozy up with chamomile to bring on sweet dreams. Scientists believe chamomile tea gets its soothing powers from an antioxidant called apigenin that works in your brain to make you sleepy. Here's what research says.

- In one study of 80 new moms who were having trouble sleeping, researchers found that drinking chamomile tea for two weeks helped relieve symptoms related to sleep problems and depression.

- In another study, a group of insomniacs that took chamomile extract twice a day for 28 days fell asleep 15 minutes faster and woke up less during the night, compared to the group who did not take the extract.

Valerian gets to the root of the problem. The cure for your sleepless nights might just be valerian, an herb that's been used for centuries to treat nervousness and headaches. And recent studies show valerian helps promote deep sleep, too. Researchers think valerian root may help by increasing levels of the brain neurotransmitter GABA, a chemical messenger that promotes relaxation and sleep.

To make a soothing valerian tea, pour a cup of boiling water over 1 teaspoon of the dried root and steep for five to 10 minutes. For best results, drink your tea two to three hours before bedtime. And be patient. It may take up to a month before you notice results.

Fragrant lavender soothes you to sleep. As far back as ancient Greece, folks knew lavender's soothing fragrance could help relax and settle frayed nerves. And who better to test the calming effects of lavender than that same group of sleep-deprived new moms? After drinking a cup of lavender tea every day for two weeks, the women reported less tiredness and depression.

And for some people, just breathing in the scent of lavender did the trick. One study found that women between the ages of 45 and 55 who received 20 minutes of lavender aromatherapy twice per week for 12 weeks reported a significant improvement in their sleep quality.

For a good night's sleep, tart cherry juice is tops

Did you know Michigan is the nation's leading producer of tart cherries? About 224 million pounds are harvested there each year. A dream come true for folks suffering from insomnia, because experts think these ruby-red gems can bring you the sweet slumber you crave.

In a recent study, two small groups of senior adults who suffered from insomnia were asked to drink 8 ounces of either Montmorency tart cherry juice or a placebo. Folks drank their assigned liquid in the morning and one to two hours before bedtime. After two weeks, researchers found that those who drank the tart cherry juice increased their sleep time by 84 minutes.

What's the secret? It may be that tart cherries are chock-full of melatonin, the sleep-producing hormone. This new research also says the insomnia-fighting power could be the work of a polyphenol called procyanidin B-2.

Wake-up call: Think twice before you take sleeping pills

Popping a pill before you hit the hay may seem like an easy way to head off your sleep troubles. But the nighttime fix that seems so simple may bring on serious consequences in the light of day.

"Although sleep problems can happen at any age and for many reasons, they can't be cured by taking a pill, either prescription, over-the-counter, or herbal, no matter what the ads on TV claim," says Preeti Malani, M.D., a University of Michigan physician trained in geriatric medicine. "Some of these medications can create big concerns for older adults, from falls and memory issues to confusion and constipation."

Over-the-counter sleep aids can cause a nightmare of side effects. Blurred vision, low blood pressure upon standing, dizziness, and heart palpitations. Just a few of the serious side effects linked to the antihistamines found in sleep medicines like Benadryl, Aleve PM, and Unisom SleepTabs.

These drugs sold over the counter at your local pharmacy may also interact with other medications you're taking. Check with your doctor or pharmacist for more information.

Don't fall for these prescription pills. Some prescription sleeping aids — like Xanax, Valium, and Restoril — contain benzodiazepines, man-made medications that help you get to sleep by upping the effects of GABA neurotransmitters that slow down brain activity.

But the use of benzodiazepines has been linked with an increased risk of falls. Other side effects of benzodiazepines can include lightheadedness, confusion, nausea, and memory loss.

Try the natural alternative. The American Academy of Sleep Medicine recommends cognitive behavioral therapy (CBT) for folks suffering from chronic insomnia. CBT involves regular visits with a clinician who will give you a series of sleep assessments. He will ask you to keep track of your sleep in a special diary. And he'll help you find ways to improve your sleep habits.

A recent study released by the Agency for Healthcare Research and Quality shows that even after therapy ends, CBT might keep those sleepless nights at bay longer than sleeping meds — with no scary side effects to worry about.

Simple snacks sure to send you straight to slumberland

So you want to get a good night's sleep without popping pills. Try these delicious snacks. They're loaded with tryptophan, melatonin, and serotonin — substances that encourage a night of sweet dreams.

- Bowl of oatmeal. Eat this breakfast favorite for dinner, and you'll sleep better at night. It even calms restless legs syndrome and painful leg cramps. That's because oatmeal is a rich source of magnesium, a mineral that relaxes restless legs. Oatmeal is also chock-full of melatonin.

- Rice pudding. Warm up your leftover rice with milk, a little sugar, and a splash of vanilla. Rice promotes good sleep, say Japanese researchers. And milk is a tryptophan treat. Put them together and kiss restless nights goodbye.

- Kiwi and banana fruit cup. Sleepless nights? Studies show that people who eat two kiwi one hour before bedtime fall asleep faster, sleep longer, and sleep better. Researchers believe the serotonin in kiwi triggers good shut-eye. Add bananas and yogurt to the mix for their tryptophan boost, and you may nod off in no time.

Memory loss

"I have a two-story house and a bad memory, so I'm up and down those stairs all the time. That's my exercise," quips Betty White, a popular celebrity who's well into her 90s. You know just what she means. You get up off the couch and walk into the kitchen to get — something — and suddenly you can't remember why you got up.

But research says brief memory lapses like Betty's may be brought on by something as simple as going through a kitchen door.

University of Notre Dame psychology professor Gabriel Radvansky discovered that people forgot more after passing through a door than when they walked the same distance across a room. "Entering or exiting through a doorway serves as an 'event boundary' in the mind," he explains, "which separates episodes of activity and files them away."

But what about that time you lost your keys or you couldn't find your glasses? Can't blame a doorway. So what are some of the other reasons you feel like you're in a fog?

Stress, lack of sleep, and some medications are just a few factors that can contribute to memory loss. And while Betty White used her forgetfulness to get a laugh, there's nothing funny about the serious consequences memory loss can have on your ability to live independently. Will you remember to take your medicine? Pay your bills? And suppose you forget to turn off the stove?

The following tips can help you protect your memory — and your independence.

Bump up your memory bank with 4 mind-blowing tricks

Jog your memory with a walk around the block. Exercise drops your chances for developing brain-busters like high blood sugar and inflammation. And scientists think it boosts blood flow to the brain, which keeps your noggin working at its best. It may even help people who are already struggling with dementia.

A little exercise also helps your brain grow. Turns out bigger is better when it comes to your brain's hippocampus, the part responsible for learning and memory formation.

In a six-month study, researchers followed 86 women between the ages of 70 and 80 who were living independently with mild memory problems. The hippocampus often shrinks with age, but the researchers discovered that regular aerobic exercise — brisk walking twice a week for an hour — was all it took to boost the size of the hippocampus.

And a new study suggests a larger hippocampus is linked to improved visual recall in older adults. So lace up your walking shoes and get ready to fight memory loss — with your feet.

Don't forget that water bottle. Researchers tested the memory, planning, and multitasking skills of two groups of cyclists — average age 55 — before and after exercise. The hydrated cyclists significantly improved the completion time of the second test while their under-hydrated peers didn't. Want to up your brain game? Sip a little H2O as you go.

Spend quality time with friends. Social interaction stimulates your brain and helps you fight off dementia. So maybe getting social is how superagers get their superpowers.

Superagers are people over age 80 who have the memory skills of folks decades younger. In a recent study, researchers found that the group as a whole was more socially active than their non-superaging peers. Scientists think spending time with friends and family contributed to their elite performance remembering experiences and specific events.

Try building up your social network by forming new friendships through hobbies or healthy lifestyles like exercise groups and social clubs. If you're more of a homebody, make sure you spend time with some special friends or favorite family members.

For a brilliant brain, just chill out. Living with too much stress raises your body's level of cortisol, aka the stress hormone. And studies say too much cortisol can lead to weight gain, high blood pressure, and — you guessed it — memory problems.

How does it happen? Synapses are connections between nerve cells that help you do things like store and recall information. As you get older, repeated and long-term exposure to cortisol can cause the synapses in the part of your brain responsible for short-term memory to shrink and even disappear.

Don't let stress steal your memory. It's time to take action if you're experiencing depression, difficulty sleeping, or low energy — all signs of stress. Exercising or practicing relaxation techniques, like deep breathing or tai chi, can help you feel more like yourself. Or connect with family and friends who can give you the emotional support you may need.

Sleep your way to the brain of your dreams. To make your memories stay put, your noggin needs to get a good night's sleep. How much? The National Sleep Foundation recommends seven to nine hours of snooze time.

Every night, your brain strengthens and organizes your memories, both old and new. While you sleep, the hippocampus — your brain's memory maker — sends information to other parts of your brain for sorting and storage. Getting enough shut-eye is more important than you thought, right?

But wait. There's more. Sleep may also protect you from developing Alzheimer's disease (AD), says a brand-new study. Among folks with higher levels of beta-amyloid in their brains — a substance well-known for its role in AD — researchers found that quality sleep was associated with better memory recall. For more information about getting the best sleep possible, see the *Insomnia* chapter.

Eat away memory woes with these power foods

Best friends Shirley and Jenny shared a joyful reunion after a 23-year separation. Sweet, but not unheard of. So what makes their relationship so special? Jenny and Shirley are elephants. Guess it's true. Elephants really never do forget.

If your memory makes you feel a little "dumbo," try adding these three power foods to your menu. They're guaranteed to send you — and your super brain — right to the front of the herd.

To hook a better brain, think like Dr. Seuss. Remember reading the popular children's book "One Fish, Two Fish, Red Fish, Blue Fish" when you were a youngster? Bet you didn't know there's more to this title than meets the eye. Turns out both the redfish

— aka the sockeye salmon — and the bluefish — a popular game fish found along the eastern seaboard — contain generous amounts of memory-boosting omega-3 fatty acids. These powerful nutrients defend your health in two delicious ways.

- Just one 3.5-ounce serving of fish — that's about the size of your checkbook — each week can protect you from dementia and mental decline. Even Alzheimer's disease (AD). Fatty fish like salmon, sardines, herring, and tuna are rich in the omega-3 fatty acids that protect your brain by getting rid of harmful beta-amyloid, a protein linked to Alzheimer's.

- Treat yourself to two delish fish feasts a week to fend off heart disease and high blood pressure. Omega-3 fatty acids to the rescue again. By keeping your blood from becoming sticky and forming clots, these little powerhouses can help stop a stroke in the making.

And there you have it — one fish, two fish, red fish, blue fish. The perfect recipe for a healthy brain.

Memory blurry? Try some curry. Dig into this delicious, spicy dish to protect your brain from Alzheimer's disease. Turmeric, the bright yellow spice that gives curry powder its appealing color, contains curcumin. This compound helps stop one of the hallmarks of AD — plaque buildup in the brain.

And researchers think curcumin improves your memory in more ways than one. "It may be due to its ability to reduce brain inflammation, which has been linked to both Alzheimer's disease and major depression," says Dr. Gary Small, director of geriatric psychiatry at the University of California, Los Angeles, and author of a recent study that shows curcumin supplementation boosts brainpower.

You can buy curcumin supplements, but the jar of turmeric spice you see at the grocery store may work just as well. Add 1/4 teaspoon of turmeric to your favorite recipes every day. And since your body doesn't absorb curcumin very well, help it out by pairing the turmeric with a little black pepper. Piperine, a substance found in black pepper, helps your body absorb more of the brain-booster.

MIND-ful eating cuts dementia risk

The MIND diet, short for Mediterranean-DASH Intervention for Neurodegenerative Delay, is the brainchild of Dr. Martha Clare Morris and colleagues at Chicago's Rush University Medical Center.

Their study shows that the MIND diet — a mashup of the brain-boosting Mediterranean and DASH diets — reduces the risk of Alzheimer's disease better than the other two plans. And you may see results even if you don't follow the MIND diet to the letter.

But who wouldn't want to? This food plan features tasty good-for-your-brain favorites like vegetables, nuts, berries, beans, whole grains, fish, poultry, olive oil — even a little wine. You'll still need to limit unhealthy choices like fried foods, butter, red meat, and cheese. Check with your doctor to see if the MIND diet can help you eat your way to a healthier brain.

Blueberries juice up your brain. This "must drink" juice is shown to improve brain function and mood even in people with early memory problems.

In one three-month study, healthy adults age 65 and older were separated into two groups. One group drank a cup of juice made with 2 tablespoons of blueberry concentrate mixed with water.

The other group was served a look-alike placebo.

And guess what? Researchers saw more activity in areas of the brain associated with memory in the blueberry drinkers compared to the placebo group. They think blueberries help increase blood flow to the brain, which allows the memory-making areas to work better.

Want another reason to go blue? Blueberries also pack a powerful antioxidant punch. That's why researchers think this tiny fruit lowers the risk for diseases of aging, like Alzheimer's and Parkinson's. Antioxidants boost communication between neurons in your brain, improving movement-related skills and perking up your memory.

So you choose — a cup of blueberries on your morning oatmeal or a cup of blueberry juice for a cool, refreshing treat. Two delicious ways to protect your memory every day.

Score a better brain with this healthy hat trick

One sharp cookie. Doesn't miss a trick. Quick on the uptake. Do these phrases still describe you, or do you feel like your brain has taken a little tumble off memory lane? It's not too late to get back on track. Pay close attention to the numbers below and you can help prevent memory loss and keep your brain sharp for life.

Don't let high blood pressure do a number on your brain.
Dementia and mild cognitive impairment (MCI) — a condition marked by memory loss that can eventually lead to Alzheimer's disease — can be caused by blocked blood flow to the brain. Just the sort of thing that happens when high blood pressure damages your arteries.

New findings from the SPRINT MIND study, reported at a recent Alzheimer's Association International Conference, suggest that keeping your blood pressure under control may lower your risk of developing MCI and dementia.

"This is something doctors and the majority of their patients with elevated blood pressure should be doing now to keep their hearts — and brains — healthier," said Dr. Jeff D. Williamson, chief and professor of Geriatrics and Gerontology at Wake Forest School of Medicine. "These new results for maintaining cognitive health provide another strong rationale for starting and maintaining healthy lifestyle changes in mid-life."

Protect your brain and your heart by getting your systolic blood pressure below 120 mmHg. For more information about easy ways to lower your BP, check out the *High blood pressure* chapter.

Zero in on your HbA1c. If you have type 2 diabetes, keep an eye on this number. Your hemoglobin A1c, also known as HbA1c, tells your average blood sugar level over the past two to three months by showing the amount of glucose attached to the molecules in your red blood cells. The thicker the coat of sugar, the higher your HbA1c.

Having high blood sugar over time can harm the blood vessels that carry important nutrients to your brain, like oxygen and glucose. Getting your HbA1c below 6.5 percent — and keeping it there — can guard your memory, concentrating, and learning abilities and protect you from dementia.

Scale back the extra pounds. If you want to keep your memory sharp, watch your waistline. Scientists discovered that having a high body mass index (BMI) — a measurement that uses your height and weight to determine body fat — may put you at risk for developing memory problems.

Chronic inflammation is your body's response to unhealthy lifestyles — living with too much stress, too little exercise, or too much fluff around your middle, for example. And now experts know that people with certain markers of inflammation at middle age are more likely to experience brain shrinkage and poor memory as they get older.

How do you help your brain bounce back? Drop a few pounds. One study showed that memory performance significantly improved after overweight women lost an average of 17 pounds. For tips on managing your middle, see the *Weight control* chapter.

Face the music for razor-sharp recall

Doctors are prescribing a natural treatment for Alzheimer's, Parkinson's, stroke, and depression. And it's not a drug. Just take a few minutes every day to enjoy some beautiful music, and you can cross over from bumbling brain to memory maestro.

In one study, a small group of volunteers sat with their eyes closed for 12 minutes daily as they listened to masterpieces by composers like Bach and Beethoven. After three months, researchers saw marked improvements in their mood and memory.

Experts think listening to music improves blood flow to your brain so the parts in charge of memory get more of the oxygen and energy they need to work efficiently. Music also ups your brain's production of dopamine, the feel-good chemical that helps regulate your memory and mood.

Ready to score a sharper brain? Plug into a daily dose of Debussy. It's just what the doctor ordered.

Keep your mind on track with helpful phone apps

"Let's face it," says Patty. "My memory just isn't what it used to be." But rather than dodging the problem, 58-year-old Patty tackled it head on — with the help of her cellphone.

Patty uses these four apps to stay on track.

- **Calendar.** "I didn't start out using my calendar app often," Patty says. "But then I realized how much it could help." She logs her appointments and sets up reminders as soon as she leaves the doctor's office. She even enters household appointments — when is that exterminator coming? — and she won't ever forget to change the filter on the air conditioner.

- **Alarm.** Don't miss your appointments. Set your cellphone alarm so you'll be ready to go in plenty of time. Schedule an alarm for your medication times, too, so you won't miss another dose.

- **Calculator.** Patty was discouraged when her failing memory wouldn't let her do even simple math. The numbers just wouldn't stay in her head. So she turned to her phone's calculator for help, and now she always gets the right answer.

- **Notes.** Who can remember all their passwords? Patty can, now that she stores them in her phone's notes app, protected by a single security code. She also stores addresses, lists of errands, and important reminders.

Patty admits to being a little overwhelmed by the new technology at first. "Older people get intimidated by their phones," she says. "But don't be. Just take some time to figure it out."

Total recall: Unforgettable tricks rev up your memory

At a recent World Memory Championship, "memory athlete" Alex Mullen memorized 1,626 playing cards — more than 31 decks — in an hour, setting a new world record. That's less than two minutes per deck. The following tips may not put you in the same league as Alex, but they may help you remember your new neighbor's name or where you left your car keys.

Repetition is the name of the game. When you meet someone for the first time, say his or her name out loud and repeat it several times in the conversation. Experts say repetition will help you retrieve the information later on.

You can also try to think of words that rhyme with the name, or hum a tune that locks it into your memory bank. Remember "The Name Game," that popular song from the 1960s? "Shirley, Shirley, bo-ber-ley, bo-na-na fanna, fo-fer-ley, fee fi mo-mer-ley, Shirley!" Who could forget a name after that?

All in favor of a great memory? Say eye! Studies show moving your eyes from side to side for 30 seconds may actually improve your episodic memory — the who, what, when, where, and why of your past experiences.

Researchers think side-to-side eye movement makes the left and right halves of your brain work together more to better recall your memories. Although more research is needed, this trick might be worth a shot when you can't remember where you parked your car in a crowded lot.

Remember bygone days with old-fashioned, handwritten notes. No cellphones or laptops allowed. Actually pull out a tablet — the paper kind — and use your beautiful penmanship to help you remember important info. Researchers say writing by hand makes it easier for you to learn and remember new information.

- Through the act of writing, touching the paper, and holding the pencil, your brain gets feedback that helps strengthen the memory process.

- When you type on a keyboard, you don't get the same brain-boosting results.

Rev up your memory even more by choosing red ink to make your notes. Studies show that warm colors like red, yellow, and orange are more likely to help you pay attention than cooler hues like brown and gray. And better attention yields a stronger memory.

Reject negative beliefs about aging. Believing that your memory will get worse with age may actually make it happen. Negative stereotypes like this about aging can worsen your ability to remember things.

Researchers tested the memories of seniors from 60 to 82 years old and suggested to some of them that older people have worse memories than younger people. Those who heard this, especially the younger seniors, tended to do worse on memory tests than the others. So the next time someone tells you memory fades with age, tell them "you're only as old, or as young, as you think."

Osteoarthritis

Does every morning start with a snap, crackle, and pop? No, not from your breakfast cereal, but from your chatty joints. Those chronic noisy knees could be an early warning that you have a higher risk for osteoarthritis (OA), says a new study. But what exactly is OA?

Your skeleton has a natural cushion, called cartilage, that keeps your bones from rubbing and scraping together. Over time, this cartilage can wear away. And without that protection, your joints suffer from painful swelling and stiffness.

That's why this damage, better known as osteoarthritis, is often called a wear-and-tear disease. Age is a major risk factor, though old injuries and genetics also play a role.

OA serves up more than aching joints. It's one of the leading causes of disability in America. If symptoms are severe, you may struggle with simple daily tasks. Activities like brushing your teeth, walking your dogs, or just cooking dinner could become painful and difficult. And worse-case scenario, you might need expensive surgeries — which don't guarantee you'll stay independent.

But if you make a few simple lifestyle tweaks, you can manage the pain and help keep this disease at bay. Read on to find out how.

4 natural ways to relieve your arthritis pain

Fish up some protection for your aching joints. Doctors in the 18th century used to prescribe trips to the beach. Believe it or not, they thought simply soaking in the salty waters could cure all sorts of ailments. A dip in the sea won't heal your joints, but what comes out of it might be just what you need.

In the largest, most up-to-date study of its kind, British experts reviewed dozens of studies that looked at how omega-3 fatty acids in fish oil affect osteoarthritis pain. They found that these powerful nutrients could hold the key to soothing your joints.

Omega-3 works by blocking chemicals called eicosanoids and cytokines, both of which trigger inflammation — a source of the pain, swelling, and stiffness associated with arthritis.

Researchers say low doses of fish oil supplements — around 0.45 grams of omega-3 a day — are better than high doses at improving pain and function in folks with knee OA. But if you want to get the nutrients the natural way, you can score even more omega-3 in a single ounce of Atlantic salmon.

> Knee pain keeping you up at night? Put a pillow between your knees if you sleep on your side. Or slip a pillow under your knees if you sleep on your back — unless you've had a knee replacement. That's because the pillow will keep your knee from fully extending, which may hinder your recovery.

Fight fire with flavor — this spicy treat could soothe your soreness. When you're looking for relief and relaxation, fiery foods usually don't top the list. But you might want to reconsider, especially because scientists think ginger could be a great natural way to fight back against your inflamed joints.

Researchers reviewed five studies that tested ginger's painkilling power in a recent meta-analysis published in *Osteoarthritis and Cartilage*. They found that taking 500 to 1,000 milligrams (mg) of ginger extract daily blunts osteoarthritis pain and reduces disability better than a placebo.

Experts think that this remedy was so effective because ginger acts just like over-the-counter NSAIDs such as aspirin and ibuprofen. It blocks chemicals called leukotrienes and cyclooxyge-nase that cause inflammation and pain.

You can find ginger extracts online or at your local markets. If you're taking blood thinners, talk to your doctor before starting supplements.

Turmeric can tone down your pain. Are you sick of spending your golden years dealing with the aches of arthritis? You might want to call on the golden spice that can help you get the upper hand.

Researchers conducted a systematic review of studies on turmeric extract and its role in preventing OA pain. They found that taking about a gram of curcumin — the powerful, naturally occurring chemical in turmeric — every day for eight to 12 weeks offered the same pain relief results as over-the-counter drugs. How? Curcumin helps fend off oxidative stress and inflam-mation that causes swelling and discomfort.

While turmeric doesn't have major side effects, it can still cause stomach aches and digestive discomfort in large doses. You should talk to your doctor before taking supplements or eating large amounts of this spice.

Go "ananas" with pineapple to fight arthritis. After Christopher Columbus brought the *Ananas comosus* — or pineapple as English-speakers called it — back to Europe, the tasty treat was so sought after that it could cost thousands of dollars. In fact, people would rent the fruit from vendors and return it uneaten, just so they could show off.

But as exotic as pineapples look, it's what's inside that makes them priceless. Bromelain, a naturally occurring enzyme in pineapple may fight inflammation and swelling in your joints to ward off pain.

To see if this natural remedy could keep up with popular painkillers, scientists recently put it to the test. In a small study, 40 people with knee OA took either 500 mg of bromelain or 100 mg of the NSAID diclofenac. After four weeks, both treatments were equally effective at improving three measurements — pain, stiffness, and ability to perform daily activities like taking the stairs and getting out of a car.

If you want to test out this remedy at home, you can find bromelain supplements at health food stores or online retailers. Just make sure to see your doctor before trying supplements, though. They might interact with certain blood-thinning medications.

Mythbuster: Do nightshades fire up symptoms?

Tomatoes always get the short end of the stick. In the 1700s, Europeans dubbed them "poison apples" because so many people got sick after eating them. In reality, the sickness was caused by the pewter plates aristocrats used.

Now, hundreds of years later, tomatoes and other nightshade vegetables still get a bad rap. Some people actively avoid them because they think these foods will worsen their arthritis symptoms. But how could veggies lead to throbbing knuckles and knees?

Nightshade plants contain solanine. Some people believe this chemical causes inflammation and arthritis pain. But research doesn't support this link. Experts say eating tomatoes, eggplants, bell peppers, and white potatoes shouldn't be a problem unless you have a food sensitivity.

Instead, most recommend adding more nightshades to your diet. These veggies are loaded with antioxidants and other nutrients that can help your fight against osteoarthritis.

Leap over these exercise hurdles to keep your aches at bay

It's easy to find excuses to avoid exercising, especially when you're suffering from arthritis. But if you want to maintain your ability to perform everyday tasks, getting up and getting some exercise should be at the top of your to-do list. Still need some motivation to break out your old workout gear? Here are a few ways you can get moving without tearing up your joints.

Try low-impact exercises to loosen up. You might worry that a workout will pile more pressure onto your already aching joints, but there are plenty of low-impact options. Biking, swimming, or even walking could help soothe your joints and beat back the pain.

Exercise works by fighting the inflammation-causing chemicals that lead to nasty swelling and aches. Plus experts think working out helps keep your cartilage healthy and strong so your joints stay protected and pain-free.

Talk to your doctor to see if he can help you find a routine that works for you. Some gyms, hospitals, and clinics offer special exercise programs for folks with joint pain.

> Plan on spending your retirement hitting the links? Experts warn not to cruise the course in a cart. New research has found, for the first time, that walking the golf course is better for your body. And it's not associated with increased knee pain, cartilage breakdown, or inflammation.

Push through the pain — but don't ignore red flags. You may feel some discomfort when you start a workout, and that's normal. Exercise can actually help loosen up your joints, and in a few minutes you'll usually feel a lot better.

You need to know when to take a break, too. If you overdo it, you could make your arthritis pain worse. Here are a few signs you need to give yourself some down time.

- Your workout causes severe pain. Mild pain is often nothing to worry about. But if exercise causes sharp or worsening pain, it's time to ease up. Talk to your doctor about a gentler, low-impact exercise routine.

- Your joints ache after exercise. A little post-gym soreness is fine, but consistent pain following your workouts could be a signal your sessions are too intense. Rest until you feel better, then dial back the intensity on your next workouts.

Knee pain? Shedding extra pounds can take the pressure off

For every pound you lose, you take 4 pounds of pressure off your knees. But losing weight can help your joints in more ways than one.

When you're overweight, your body produces chemicals that cause inflammation. That means all your joints suffer, not just your weight-bearing knees and hips.

Fortunately, slimming down can help tame those out-of-control chemicals. For a few tips and tricks on dropping the pounds, head over to the *Weight control* chapter.

Stay limber to soothe your joints. There is one simple movement you can add to your exercise routine to keep your joints flexible and decrease your risk of falls — stretching. And it's so easy you can do it right in your living room.

In a recent study, Japanese researchers assigned seniors with knee osteoarthritis to one of two home exercise programs.

- The first program focused on strengthening the quadriceps, muscles that play a major role in knee extension.

- The other included exercises for strengthening multiple muscles, including quad and hip muscles, and stretches for improving joint flexibility.

After four weeks, the people in the second group experienced less knee pain. Plus they saw improvements in their ability to perform daily activities.

The researchers say it's important to take up an exercise plan that works different muscle groups and increases joint flexibility. Want to try out the stretches used in the study? You can perform these easy moves from the comfort of your own home.

Seated hamstring stretch

1. Sit in a chair and extend one leg with your heel on the floor.

2. Lean forward slowly and hold stretch.

3. Repeat with the other leg.

Side-lying quad stretch

1. Lie on your right side with your knees flexed.

2. Slowly pull your left foot behind you and hold stretch.

3. Change sides and repeat with the other leg.

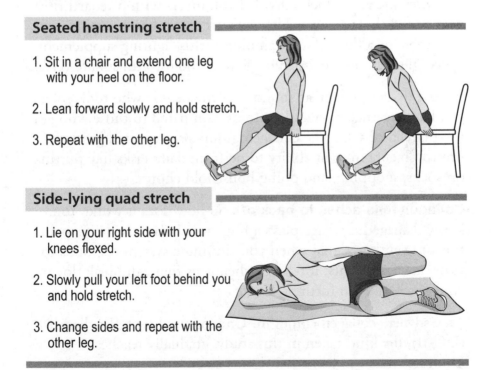

Call on collagen to cool your joints

People first tapped into collagen's powers thousands of years ago when ancient civilizations boiled animal bones to create glue. It was such a common practice that the protein responsible for the binding action was eventually named collagen, after the Greek word for glue.

An appropriate namesake, even in the medical world, because collagen gives your body structure and holds it together. It's even found in connective tissues like cartilage which helps support and cushion your joints. Now, scientists think collagen could change the way you fight off joint pain.

Stay independent with daily tasks. In a study published in *Nutrition Journal,* experts divided volunteers with osteoarthritis into one of three groups. They either got a collagen supplement, a placebo, or a dose of a common arthritis-fighting supplement called glucosamine hydrochloride plus chondroitin sulfate (GC).

After 180 days, scientists found that the people who took collagen had less knee pain and stiffness, compared to those who got the placebo or GC. The collagen group also reported greater improvements in their ability to perform daily tasks like putting on socks, shopping, and doing household chores.

Collagen tells aches to back off. So how does it work? You know damaged cartilage plays a huge role in osteoarthritis pain. But did you know that when your immune system responds to your damaged joints, it releases chemicals that can break down your cartilage even further?

That's where collagen comes in. Undenatured type II collagen (UC-II), the kind taken in this study, gradually teaches your immune system to leave your joints alone.

If you want to try this remedy at home, look for a 40-milligram daily supplement of UC-II. You can find it at health food stores or even online.

Household hacks: Curb OA pain with soothing home solutions

"Warm joints are happy joints," says Ruth, 83 and longtime OA sufferer. That's why, after experiencing her first Missouri winter 15 years ago, a hot water bottle became her new best friend. "My knees and fingers seemed to cramp up in the cold and become even stiffer than usual."

Since then, her joint-warming arsenal has grown to include a rice sock she pops in the microwave and snuggles around her feet, a small heating pad for her neck and shoulders, and a dual zone heated mattress pad.

"My hips, especially, would ache whenever I crawled into a cold bed at night," she remembers. "So the kids got me the mattress pad for Christmas. Best present ever!"

Now she turns the pad on, gets ready for bed, and enjoys the toastiness. "I don't even have to keep it on throughout the night," she explains. "But I sleep so much better and have less pain in the morning when my joints are relaxed."

Looking for more tricks to keep your arthritis pain in check? Choose gadgets designed to take away some of the work.

- Use cleaning tools with long handles and abrasive surfaces so you don't have to stoop over or scrub as hard.

- Opening up your scissors after you cut something puts unnecessary pressure on your hands, so get a pair of spring-loaded scissors to do the job for you.

- Trash cans with foot pedals — or even better, motion sensors — are designed to open with less effort on your part.

Osteoporosis

Termites are easy to overlook. These tiny bugs will munch away at the frame of your house for months before you notice any damage. Let it go on for too long and your house will crumble and fall apart. Believe it or not, your bones aren't too different.

Every day, cells called osteoclasts eat away at your bones just like termites in wood. Normally, it's not a problem. Your body breaks down your bones to release minerals it needs — like calcium and phosphorus — into your bloodstream. Then it repairs the damage with a crew of rebuilding cells called osteoblasts.

Osteoblasts use the nutrients you eat to rebuild your skeleton as quickly as possible. Unfortunately, this process slows down as you get older, and you lose more bone than you make. If you don't get enough of the nutrients you need for rebuilding, like calcium and vitamin D, your bones become weak and brittle. This severe bone loss is called osteoporosis.

The worst part is you can't even feel it happening. Everything seems fine until one day you fall and break a bone. And this isn't an uncommon problem — experts say osteoporosis causes about 2 million bone fractures every year.

If you have osteoporosis, living alone is a dangerous proposition. A missed step or a loose rug is more than a minor mishap — it's a trip to the emergency room and an injury that makes day-to-day tasks impossible. If you want to stay independent, you need to keep your skeleton in tiptop shape. Here's how.

4 bone-building foods that bolster your foundation

Bone up on this legen-dairy snack. Yogurt is one of the most important foods you can keep in your fridge. That's because it's loaded with calcium. Your body uses this common mineral to fight high blood pressure, forgetfulness, and — you guessed it — weak bones.

In fact, calcium is one of the best nutrients you can enlist in your war against osteoporosis. About 99 percent of your body's calcium is stored in your bones where it supports and strengthens your frame. But your body will steal the mineral from your skeleton if you start running low.

Experts say you need to eat plenty of calcium to keep your bones strong, especially as you get older. You can get almost half of your daily needs in an 8-ounce container of low-fat yogurt.

Reel in this superfood to double down on your skeleton.
Fish swim in schools because they understand the value of sticking together. And just like them, the nutrients in your body can't work alone.

Calcium may be one of the most important bone builders in your body, but it needs help. That's where the sunshine vitamin comes in. Vitamin D helps your body absorb calcium.

Your body can make vitamin D all by itself, just by soaking up sunlight. But as you get older, this process slows down, so you need to get more of the nutrient from your diet. Fortunately, there's a tasty treat loaded with the stuff — salmon. One can of sockeye salmon with the bones delivers well over 100 percent of your daily recommended dose.

But that's not all this fatty fish has to offer. That same salmon is packed with omega-3 fatty acids — another osteoporosis fighter for your arsenal. Here's the lowdown.

- In a recent study, experts looked at the diets of 1,865 women in Spain. They found that those who ate the most omega-3 also had the strongest bones in their hips and lower backs.

- The scientists think omega-3 curbs chronic inflammation that contributes to the development of osteoporosis.

Probiotic power can save your skeleton

Your gut bacteria do everything from improving digestion to fighting off ailments. And a brand-new study shows that they can protect your frame, too.

German researchers split 70 older women with low bone mineral density into two groups. Half took a placebo, while the others got a powder packed with a probiotic supplement of *Lactobacillus reuteri*.

Among the women who took probiotics for a year, bone loss was slashed in half compared to women who received placebos. Experts think these friendly bacteria help your body keep inflammation in check. Plus, they may block the overproduction of bone-eating cells.

People in the study took 10 billion colony-forming units (CFUs) of *L. reuteri* a day. If you want to try the same at home, track down probiotic supplements or yogurts with the same strain. If they aren't at your local grocery store, you can always head online.

Leaf those brittle bones behind. Studies show that a shortage of vitamin K1, which is found in leafy greens like spinach and cabbage, is linked to a higher risk for fractures.

Experts noticed something interesting, though. When people with brittle bones bulked up on this vitamin, they were a lot less likely to suffer a broken bone even though their bone density didn't improve. Researchers think it might have something to do with the way this nutrient improves the overall quality of your skeleton.

It's pretty easy to get, too. A cup of cooked spinach is packed with more than seven times your daily recommended dose. As an added bonus, you'll also get a quarter of your calcium needs.

This fantastic fruit helps you maintain strong bones — even in old age. Even the most adamant prune haters will change their tunes once they find out how well this snack treats your framework. In a small study, older women with weak bones ate five to six prunes a day for six months. At the end of the study, a total-body scan revealed that the prunes prevented bone density loss.

A review published in the scientific journal *Nutrients* says prunes may get their superpowers from natural compounds, called phenolics and flavonoids, that slow bone breakdown and boost bone formation. Plus this sweet snack is also loaded with vitamin K1.

Brew up a cup of tea to crack down on fractures

Feeling down in the dumps? A piping hot cup of tea is the perfect pick-me-up, but this old remedy can do more than help you feel better on a blustery day. Your tea leaves actually offer some serious protection for brittle bones.

In a recent meta-analysis, scientists pored over 13 studies that revealed just how powerful tea can be. The studies revealed people who drink tea tend to have stronger bones in their necks, lower backs, and hips than their non tea-drinking counterparts.

The secret lies with a naturally occurring plant chemical in tea called epigallocatechin gallate (EGCG). It works by increasing the activity of osteoblasts, which are the cells your body uses to repair broken-down bones. And it helps the osteoblasts already in your body live longer and work harder.

The studies don't recommend a single type of brew, but green teas tend have the highest levels of EGCG, followed by white, oolong, and black teas. If better bone health is your cup of tea, start sipping today.

Should you get screened for weak bones? The answer might surprise you

Do you know when to get your bone density tested? New guidelines from the U.S. Preventive Services Task Force (USP-STF) might shake up your thinking.

Bone density scans are quick, painless tests that can clue you in if you have weak bones or osteoporosis — before you break a bone. And if you've already been diagnosed with a fragile frame, they can let you know if your medicine is doing its job.

The USPSTF has long recommended that women over 65 get a bone density test. Now they say women under 65 should be screened, too, if they are at high risk for osteoporosis. Risk factors include smoking, drinking too much alcohol, being underweight, and having a family history of fractures.

Though the USPSTF only has official recommendations for women, men aren't off the hook. Experts say high-risk men over 70 should consider getting tested.

The less you snooze, the more you lose: Sweeter slumber shuts down brittle bones

BEEP. BEEP. BEEP. Few sounds are worse than a blaring alarm clock, especially if you spent all night tossing and turning. Restless nights set you up for a rough day, but they can do more than leave you feeling groggy. Skimping on shut-eye can actually cause your bones to start breaking down faster, leaving you at risk for a dangerous fall.

Get a great night's sleep to stave off bone loss. A recent study published in *Sleep Medicine* examined the sleep patterns of more than 1,000 men and women. Researchers found that those who generally slept poorly were also the most likely to have osteoporosis.

The reason lies with how sleep influences your sympathetic nervous system. That's the part of your nervous system that responds to stress by bumping up your heart rate and increasing blood flow. New theories suggest sleep disturbances may cause a jump in sympathetic nervous activity, which could egg on osteoporosis in two ways.

- By boosting bone resorption. This is the process where osteoclasts break down old bone.

- By slowing bone formation. In this remodeling process, osteoblasts lay down new bone to reinforce your skeleton.

This bone-chilling combo leaves you at risk for fractures. And that's nothing to yawn at.

Clock more shut-eye to keep your skeleton strong. Shoddy sleep isn't the only thing that could hamper your bone growth. Not spending enough time in slumberland can also spur on osteoporosis. A study of more than 5,000 adults ages 50 and older found that getting less than six hours of sleep increases your risk of brittle bones.

Experts recommend seven to nine hours of quality sleep each night. Unfortunately, about 40 percent of American adults say they don't meet that standard snooze time. For some tips that will have you sleeping like a stone, check out the *Insomnia* chapter.

> ## Ditch dangerous drugs with a diet and exercise combo
>
> Four years ago Kathy's doctor noticed she had lost half an inch of height. A bone density scan showed her spine had a t-score of -2.3 — a sign of low bone density.
>
> Two years later, another scan revealed her worst fears had come true — her spine t-score was -2.8, which meant she had full-blown osteoporosis. Kathy's doctor wanted her to see a specialist, but she kept putting it off.
>
> "I stopped eating fast food and frozen meals at lunch," says Kathy. "Every day I started bringing a spinach salad loaded with nutrient-packed fresh vegetables." And she made an effort to get more exercise. "I started walking regularly, trying to do a couple miles at a time."
>
> By the time Kathy made it to the specialist, another 1 1/2 years had passed. "I went to see an endocrinologist, and she really wanted to put me on drugs," she says. "Because my spine t-score had been so low, the risk of fracture was a little more alarming."
>
> Kathy started taking daily injections and scheduled a baseline bone density scan for the next month. When the results came back, she couldn't believe her eyes. Her spine t-score was at -2.4, almost exactly where it was four years prior, and her doctor green-lit her decision to stop taking drugs.
>
> "I really think it was the diet and exercise combo," Kathy says.

Skipping out on soy could be a bone-breaking mistake

Osteoporosis likes to play favorites. Unfortunately, women are more likely to wind up with brittle bones than men. There are a few reasons — women live longer so the disease has more time to set in, plus their bones tend to be smaller and lighter. But most of the blame lies with a hormone called estrogen.

Once menopause sets in, your body doesn't make as much estrogen — which is a big problem. This hormone plays a huge part in slowing bone breakdown and helping your body hang on to calcium.

That's where soy comes in. It's loaded with natural chemicals called isoflavones that look a lot like estrogen. They are so similar your body has trouble telling them apart, which means they can help your bones absorb calcium, just like naturally occurring estrogen does.

In a small study published in the *American Journal of Clinical Nutrition*, researchers pitted soy isoflavones against one of the top-rated osteoporosis drugs on the market.

While the soy supplements didn't quite match the results of the drugs, the most effective dose — 105 milligrams (mg) of soy isoflavones — was still considered a success in helping bones hold on to calcium. And it worked without the dangerous side effects that come with medications.

Experts say 50 to 100 mg of soy isoflavones every day may be enough to improve your bone health. You can get 56 mg in a half cup of boiled soybeans. Mix up your menu with other high-isoflavone foods like edamame, tofu, tempeh, and miso.

Breaking bad — weigh the risks of a drug holiday

Bisphosphonates? It sounds like a noise you might make when you sneeze. But they're actually drugs commonly prescribed for osteoporosis because they change the way your body breaks down and reshapes your bones.

Normally they keep your skeleton from breaking down too quickly, but there's a bit of a catch. These drugs also block your body from repairing teeny-tiny cracks in your bones. If you take them for too long, you're at risk for fractures.

The fix is really quite simple — after several years of use, stop taking the drugs for a while. Doctors weren't so sure how long you should be away from your prescriptions. But now new research says drug holidays shouldn't last more than two years.

Don't stop or start taking drugs willy-nilly, though. Talk to your doctor to develop a personalized treatment plan.

This spice will curry favor with your bones

By the time turmeric made it to America, people thought it was little more than a way to add some color and flavor to exotic curries. But scientists have begun to delve into the healing powers of this golden spice.

Now new research has discovered that the active ingredient in turmeric — a naturally occurring chemical called curcumin — could hold the key to beating brittle bones.

In a recent Italian study, researchers split 57 people with low bone density into two groups. Half were told to exercise a few times a week and eat a diet with plenty of calcium, vitamin D, and vitamin C, while the others got the same instructions plus a daily curcumin supplement of 1,000 milligrams.

At the end of the six-month study, people who took the supplement saw improvements in the bone density measurements of their fingers, heels, and upper jaws. The control group, on the other hand, didn't see significant changes. Scientists think it's because curcumin can actually slow down your body's production of bone-breaking osteoclasts.

The turmeric powder you'll find at the grocery store is about 3 percent curcumin, so to get the same amount measured in the study you'd need to wolf down about 11 teaspoons of the stuff daily. Eating that much turmeric every day could cause stomach aches or other digestive discomfort.

But you can track down supplements at your local market or online. Curcumin doesn't mix well with some medications like blood thinners, so talk to your doctor before taking supplements.

Sarcopenia

Does your staircase look as daunting as a steep mountain? Does your shoulder ache after carrying a bag of groceries? If so, you may be one of the many adults who suffer from sarcopenia, or muscle loss.

You may not think weakening muscles are a big deal. They're a natural part of aging, right? But they don't have to be. While you do lose about 3 percent of muscle mass each decade after your 30s, you'll drop even more if you don't stay active. Lounging around on the couch day after day will definitely make your biceps shrink.

The number of candles on your birthday cake also play a big part. As you age, your body produces fewer muscle-building hormones like testosterone and the growth hormone IGF-1. Plus your body has to work even harder to convert protein and other food into energy — if you're even getting enough of it. More often than not, older adults struggle to eat a diet that provides all the nutrients they need.

So if you're not careful, your strength and balance will start to go before you realize it. Walking around the house or taking out the trash becomes a dangerous game as you struggle to avoid slips, trips, and falls. You may even reach a point where you can't lift yourself out of a chair. That's why sarcopenia is one of the biggest reasons seniors are put into nursing homes.

All of this is preventable if you look after yourself. Read on to find out how to fight back against this crippling condition.

4 muscle-building nutrients keep you feeling young

Pack on the protein to pump up your muscles. You can't build a house without walls, and you can't build muscles without protein. It's the most important nutrient in your fight against sarcopenia. But there's a good chance you're not getting enough of it. Experts think 1 out of every 5 seniors aren't eating their fill. Between decreasing appetites and changing tastes, you could be literally wasting away.

How much protein do you really need? It varies based on your body type and activity level, but the general rule is 0.8 grams for every 2.2 pounds you weigh. So a 175-pound man should try to eat at least 64 grams of protein each day.

Fortunately, protein isn't too hard to come by. Half a roasted chicken breast will get you about half of your daily dose. And if you're not a meat eater, don't worry. Lentils, beans, nuts, and tofu are all excellent sources of protein, too.

Go fishing to stay strong — omega-3 keeps muscle loss at bay. Fish are loaded with protein, but some have another secret to staving off sarcopenia. Omega-3 fatty acids are a powerful way to fight back against waning strength.

In a recent review of 36 scientific studies, experts found that pairing omega-3 with resistance exercise is the best way to stay strong. These nutrients appear to speed up your body's natural process for building new muscle in response to strength training.

The scientists recommend that older adults get at least 1,650 milligrams each day. That may sound like a lot, but it's actually less than you'll find in a 3-ounce serving of Atlantic salmon. You can also get omega-3 from other fatty fish as well as foods like chia seeds, walnuts, and flaxseeds.

Soak up some sunshine to stay mobile and independent in your golden years. Spending all day on your couch could come back to haunt you in more ways than you think. If you're staying out of the sun, you're putting yourself at risk for falling. New research claims low levels of vitamin D may increase your risk for muscle weakness.

A new study published in the *Journal of Physical Therapy Science* examined the vitamin D levels of 200 women over the age of 60. Researchers found that people with the lowest levels were also at the highest risk of dangerous falls.

Scientists aren't exactly sure how vitamin D affects balance, but research has shown it has a positive action on muscles and the central nervous system. It appears to bind to a specific receptor in muscle tissue, which leads to protein synthesis and muscle cell growth.

When you're young, you don't have to worry about scanning nutrition labels for your vitamin D. Your body can make its own — all you need is a little sunlight. When ultraviolet rays hit your skin, your body starts producing this essential nutrient.

But your body does have to work harder to make vitamin D as you age, so it's a good idea to seek out vitamin D-rich foods like salmon and tuna. You can also talk to your doctor about adding supplements to your diet.

Don't "B" afraid of sarcopenia — strike back with this vital vitamin. In a recent study, scientists looked for classic signs of sarcopenia — low walking speed, grip strength, and muscle mass — in 400 older adults. The people who scored the lowest on those measurements also came up low in vitamin B12.

Scientists think vitamin B12 may play a role in preventing sarcopenia because it helps reduce blood levels of homocysteine. Studies have shown that high levels of this amino acid are related to lower muscle strength and walking speed.

The recommended daily allowance for vitamin B12 is 2.4 micrograms. It's readily available in fortified cereals, dairy, meat, and fatty fish. And if your taste runs to the unusual, good news — a single serving of liver contains 29 times your daily needs, and clams, a whopping 35.

Work out to work away your age-related woes

You can't stick a bike in your garage and then expect to take it out for a ride a decade later. Time will flatten the tires, gum up the chain, and rust away the frame. In a similar fashion, your muscles will fall into disrepair if you neglect them.

Low physical activity is the No. 1 cause of disability in old age — even worse than smoking or drinking or a bad diet. It ramps up your risk of disability by a whopping 72 percent. But for most people, it's entirely preventable. Pump up your routine by adding in a few smooth moves.

Flex your muscles to fend off sarcopenia. You need your muscles for everything from playing with the grandkids to keeping yourself upright while you walk. But if you don't use them, you'll lose them. Luckily, staying strong and healthy is easier than you think. Just start a simple strength training program.

That doesn't mean you have to start pumping iron at the gym — all you need to do is find a few exercises that use resistance to work your muscles. You can start with resistance bands or even use your own body weight. You'll be amazed by the results.

In one small study, men ages 60 to 71 performed whole-body resistance training exercises three times a week. After 22 weeks, researchers found that their muscle size and strength had increased to levels similar to active young men in their 20s. Who knew exercise could help you be as strong as someone half your age.

Crank up the intensity to turn back the clock. If you're up for it, experts say high-intensity interval training (HIIT) is one of the best ways to stave off old age. In a recent study, two groups of participants rode on exercise bikes in low- and high-intensity intervals three times a week and exercised on treadmills twice a week.

After three months, researchers found that this HIIT routine led to benefits on a cellular level — especially for the older group, made up of volunteers who were 65 to 80 years old. In some cases, it actually seemed to reverse the age-related decline in mitochondrial function — your body's ability to generate energy — and proteins needed for muscle building.

Sarcopenic obesity, or being "skinny fat" — thin-looking with high body fat and low muscle mass — has been linked to dementia. The good news is your Medicare plan might cover a gym membership through the SilverSneakers program to help you fight both conditions. Visit *silversneakers.com* or call 866-584-7389 to see if you're eligible.

Fortifying your frame with exercise is the best way to fight off frailty and make daily activities easier — like getting up from your favorite recliner and lifting your blender out of the kitchen cabinet. And as an added bonus, you'll fight diabetes, lower your blood pressure, ease arthritis pain, and improve your memory.

3 brawn-building moves you can do at home

How many times have you told yourself you're too old, too tired, or too far from a gym to work out? Well in one study, 90-year-olds hit the weights twice a week, and in just 12 weeks they regained balance, built muscle, and felt younger. All it took was strength and balance training, including three easy exercises — bench presses, leg extensions, and knee extensions. Can't join a gym? Use these living room revisions.

Wall pushups

1. Stand facing wall at arm's length and place hands against wall at shoulder height.

2. Bend elbows to lower chest toward wall and push back up to complete rep.

Seated squats

1. Sit on chair, holding hands on hips to balance.

2. Stand, leaning forward to keep body weight centered over feet. Lower yourself back into chair to complete rep.

Knee extenders

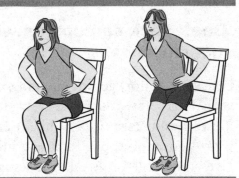

1. Sit in chair with both feet flat on floor.

2. Straighten one leg and hold for five seconds. Lower leg back to floor and repeat with other leg.

Meat of the matter: Protect muscles by avoiding acid-forming fare

You might be tempted to load up your plate with hunks of protein-packed meats to fight off sarcopenia, but experts warn that might not be the best move. Eating too many acid-producing foods, like meat and cereal grains, can actually do more harm than good.

A buildup of acid in your tissues and blood can cause your muscles to start breaking down. In addition to making you weaker, this puts extra stress on your liver and kidneys because they have to work overtime to clean out your system.

But experts say you can keep your muscles from wasting away by eating a balanced diet that includes plenty of fruits and vegetables.

'Beet' back sarcopenia with this surprising superfood

Believe it or not, getting up and exercising could save you $900 a year. That's how much the average person with sarcopenia shells out in health care costs. While it can be tough to get that extra bit of motivation, one food you probably never think of can help give you a little push. All it takes is a plate of beets to raise your energy level and improve your muscle function.

In a small study, scientists looked at the average time it took runners to complete a 5K — first after eating 200 grams of baked beets, which equals about 1 1/2 cups, and then again after eating cranberry relish. Surprisingly, people ran much faster after bolting down the beet meal. And even though they were running faster, people actually reported that they weren't working nearly as hard.

Scientists think the improvements in muscle performance are the result of nutrients in beets known as nitrates. These nutrients work by opening up your blood vessels to increase blood flow. This boosts oxygen delivery, powering up your muscles and taking some of the work out of your workout.

And don't worry, beets aren't the only power-packed foods. You can go for nitrate-rich options like kale, spinach, chard, or other leafy greens. However, scientists aren't quick to recommend nitrates found in processed meats like sausage and bacon. Because these foods have been linked to serious health issues, experts advise getting all your nitrates from plants.

Prescription panic — statins could be zapping your strength

You've started exercising and eating healthier, but carrying a heavy bag still leaves your arm sore. And those trips up the stairs aren't getting any easier. Your tired muscles might have a surprising source — your medicine cabinet.

Some experts think statins, which are used to treat high cholesterol, could cause fatigue and muscle weakness. One reason may be that these medicines interfere with the work of proteins vital for muscle growth.

Scientists also think statins could lower the amount of a substance in your body called coenzyme Q10. This nutrient plays a big role in giving your muscles energy, so if you don't get enough you may feel weak and tired.

If you're suffering from muscle weakness, it might have something to do with your prescription. But don't stop taking your medicine without talking to your doctor and discussing your options first.

Enlist these mighty minerals to maintain your muscle mass

It's easy to get wrapped up in calories, fats, and vitamins when you're reading a nutrition label, but you need to make sure you're not missing one important little section tucked at the bottom — the minerals. These essential nutrients could be the difference between staying in your own house and ending up in a nursing home. Check out three muscle-savers that can aid in your fight against sarcopenia.

Maximize your might with magnesium. Did you know one of your best bets for preventing muscle loss is found in delicious dark chocolate? In a recent study published in *Nutrients*, researchers looked at more than 156,000 men and women and found that eating more magnesium-packed foods was associated with better grip strength and muscle mass.

How does it work? Scientists think magnesium plays a vital role in muscle function and performance. Plus the nutrient is involved in building and repairing your muscles.

Experts say you should try to get around 420 milligrams (mg) of magnesium every day. Mix up your menu by eating high-magnesium foods like dark chocolate, almonds, and cooked spinach.

Seek out selenium to stay strong. Want to rev up muscle power? Make sure you get enough selenium. Researchers think this mineral helps your body create substances called selenoprotiens, which work to build and maintain strong, healthy muscles.

In a recent review, scientists examined 10 studies that looked at the link between diet and muscle size and strength in folks over 64. Experts found that people who didn't eat much selenium were much more likely to suffer from sarcopenia.

But getting this nutrient doesn't need to be difficult — a single Brazil nut contains a little bit more than your entire recommended daily dose. You can also find it in cod, tuna, and sunflower seeds. Just shoot for 55 micrograms of selenium every day.

Cut your sarcopenia risk by chowing down on calcium.
Vitamin D deficiencies often go hand in hand with calcium shortages, so some people blame the sunshine vitamin without giving calcium a second thought. But the latest research says skimping on calcium can eat away at your muscles, even if you get enough vitamin D.

More studies are needed to work out how calcium helps build muscles, but for now make sure you get at least 1,200 mg each day. Step up your calcium game with foods like mozzarella cheese, yogurt, and sardines.

Get a grip on muscle loss with these handy exercises

Experts use two measurements to determine if your muscles have weakened — grip strength and decrease in muscle mass. Losing your ability to pinch, hold, or grab things can affect your ability to live independently. Make sure you include isometric hand exercises in your strength training routine. A soft "stress" ball or a tennis ball is perfect for toughening your grip.

Vision loss

When you were young, you felt like you could read the fine print of a newspaper from across the room. Now you're stuck ordering the same thing every time you take a trip to your local diner because you can't read the menu.

Like it or not, your eyesight will lose some of its edge as you get older. There's a fancy word for this — presbyopia. It means that over time changes in your peepers make it more difficult for you to focus on things closer to your eyes, like the tiny print on your latest recipe.

Other eye conditions connected to Father Time aren't normal and can interfere with your active lifestyle and even cause permanent damage if you don't address them early. That's the case with the four leading eye diseases among older Americans — age-related macular degeneration (AMD), diabetic retinopathy, cataracts, and glaucoma.

Two out of every 3 legally blind people are seniors who lost their sight as a result of eye diseases linked to age. And losing your vision means you'll need more than a pair of extra-strong glasses and large print books. Your sight helps you navigate your house, drive your car, and take care of daily chores. Without it, you might find yourself in a nursing home.

> Age-related macular degeneration (AMD) causes damage to the macula, a small spot at the back of your eye that collects light so everything you see is sharp and clear. This damage often distorts the center of your field of view, making it difficult to watch TV or fix things around the house.

You don't have to fall victim to age-related eye diseases, though. Make a few lifestyle changes and you'll see your life in a whole new light.

> ## Color scheme: Set your sights on safety and comfort
>
> Vision loss makes you feel like a stranger in your own home. Even if you've spent decades living in your house, fumbling around with low vision can make you afraid to just move around. "If you're always looking for lost things, bumping into furniture, and afraid to go up the stairs, the home isn't a happy place anymore," says Audrey Demmitt.
>
> Demmitt is a peer advisor for VisionAware, an organization dedicated to helping adults with vision loss stay independent. And as a senior with a degenerative eye disease, she understands the struggles better than anybody.
>
> But you can make your home feel like a fortress again by taking advantage of bright colors and contrast. Here are two simple tips Demmitt recommends.
>
> - If you bump into furniture or doorways often, mark them with bright, contrasting colors. Have a light-colored couch and a nice dark throw? "Toss the blanket over the back of the chair," she says. That way it's easier to spot.
>
> - Is your fork always missing your meal? Try putting white plates on a dark place mat. Or swap out your dishes to suit your dinner. "I use different colored plates, too, so I can find my food easier," she says. "If I'm eating mashed potatoes, I put them on my red plate."
>
> A few simple splashes of color — on doorknobs, switch plates, stairs, and more — could help you finally feel at home again.

6 must-have nutrients to revitalize your aging eyes

Cut your risk of eye disease nearly in half with these fishy delights. They say you are what you eat, and your eyes are no exception. The retina, the light-sensitive layer at the back of your eyeball, is chock-full of omega-3 fatty acids. And studies have found that eating omega-3 foods is linked to a lower risk of cataracts and age-related macular degeneration (AMD). How?

> Like a camera, your eye uses a lens to focus. But this lens is made of clear proteins instead of glass. As you get older these proteins can clump together, leading to the cloudy spots better known as cataracts. People with this disease say it's like looking through a foggy windshield.

- Omega-3 clobbers inflammation that can harm your retinas, contributing to AMD.

- These nutrients also pump up your good cholesterol, which ferries powerful antioxidants — like vitamin E — to your eyes, where they fight off damage associated with cataracts.

But you can keep your vision sharp into your 90s by snacking on the right foods. In fact, one study shows that eating two or more servings of fatty fish each week — like salmon, sardines, and albacore tuna — can slash your risk of AMD by almost 50 percent.

Double down on your protection with this powerful pair. Great things come in pairs. Just think of salt and pepper, peanut butter and jelly, and lutein and zeaxanthin. That last one may not be as famous, but if you're looking for eye protection, it's hard to top this dynamic duo.

These naturally occurring plant chemicals lower the amount of blue light that reaches the inner workings of your eyes, which helps protect your orbs from light-induced damage. Large studies revealed that eating foods rich in these nutrients can help slash your risk of developing cataracts and AMD.

Experts suggest around 12 milligrams (mg) of lutein and zeaxanthin combined, which is about how much you'll get in a half cup of chopped kale. You can also get them in other leafy greens such as spinach and collard greens.

Beta carotene protects your eyes from hidden havoc. You may have heard that eating carrots can help you see better at night. Believe it or not, that was a myth created by the British air force during WWII to hide the fact that they could pick out German bombers at night with radar.

So what's the truth? Carrots — along with other orange foods like sweet potatoes and cantaloupe — are rich in beta carotene, which is a vital nutrient for healthy eyes. A recent study conducted by New Zealand-based researchers discovered that a diet rich in beta carotene may help ward off glaucoma, cataracts, and AMD.

That's because all three of these diseases are linked to damage caused by oxidative stress, which occurs when your body has an imbalance between harmful free radicals and protective antioxidants. But experts say beta carotene acts as a powerful antioxidant, meaning it neutralizes this damage to keep your eyes healthy.

Help out your headlights with this mighty mineral. A large trial, known as the Age-Related Eye Disease Study (AREDS), found a combo of nutrients that could lower your odds of developing advanced AMD. Zinc was one of the powerful ingredients singled out by researchers.

But it doesn't work alone. That's why the American Optometric Association calls it the "helper molecule." It ferries vitamin A to your eyes where it helps create pigments that protect your peepers.

Experts recommend about 11 mg of zinc each day. Get your fill by eating high-zinc foods like oysters, fortified breakfast cereals, beef, and crab.

Vitamin E looks after your lenses to keep your sight sharp. Beefing up your vision could be as simple as getting more vitamin E in your diet. A recent meta-analysis of more than 15,000 people found that those who got more of this nutrient were also the least likely to develop age-related cataracts.

A high-dose helping of this vitamin is also a part of the nutrient cocktail used in the AREDS supplement. Experts think it's so effective because it attacks free radicals before they get the chance to damage the lens of your eye.

> The landmark Age-Related Eye Disease Study (AREDS) proved vision may be linked to your dinner plate. The study on more than 3,600 seniors showed that a supplement of vitamin E, beta carotene, vitamin C, and zinc could slow down AMD by up to 25 percent in people at high risk for the disease.

Shoot for the daily recommendation of 15 mg each day. Foods high in vitamin E include fortified cereals, almonds, avocados, and spinach.

Call on this vitamin to "C" better. You might reach for some extra vitamin C when you're fighting off a common cold, but your eyes could use a little bit of this power-packed nutrient, too.

A study published in the *International Journal of Ophthalmology* found that people with diets rich in vitamin C were less likely to get cataracts than people who didn't eat a lot of foods high in vitamin C. This nutrient helps fight off oxidative damage that can cause proteins to clump in the lens of your eye, contributing to cloudy vision and cataracts.

Boost your baby blues by making sure you get the recommended 90 mg of vitamin C a day — that's less than the amount you'll find in a cup of orange juice. You can also get loads of vitamin C from red peppers, broccoli, and grapefruit.

Wipe out dry eye with these simple tips

An engine without oil isn't going to do its job well. And your eyes aren't so different. Your body relies on your tear ducts to keep your eyes lubricated so you can see clearly.

If you suffer from dry eye symptoms, you know just how painful and irritating it is when that well runs low. Not to mention this disease can keep you from reading, writing, and driving your car. Fortunately, affordable relief could come from some surprising places.

Strap on your swim gear to wash away your dry eyes. Breaking out your old scuba gear for bedtime might seem odd, but it could be the key to fighting off dry eye. In a small study, experts asked 100 people with dry eye to wear swim goggles for 20 minutes. Ninety-nine percent of them reported a drop in dry eye symptoms. And some continued to see benefits 15 minutes after they took the goggles off.

Goggles and dry eye glasses — spectacles that have a special lining around the frames — work by creating a small, sealed chamber of humidity that helps your eyes stay moisturized.

You wouldn't dare spend a day lounging in the sun without slathering on sunscreen. But are you giving the same protection to your peepers? Ultraviolet rays from the sun slowly damage your eyes and increase your risk of developing cataracts or AMD. So slip on sunglasses that offer 100 percent UVA and UVB protection.

You can pop on your goggles whenever you need a bit of relief, or if you have trouble in the morning try sleeping in your goggles. Just make sure to get a pair with a good seal around your eyes.

Fight fire with fire — a little heat can drive your symptoms away. When your muscles ache, a nice hot bath or warm compress can soothe your pain. So why not try the same thing for your eyes?

In a study published in *Optometry and Vision Science*, researchers found that sitting with a warming mask or eye bag on for 10 minutes improved lipid layer thickness and tear film stability in people with dry eye symptoms. These factors influence how fast your tears evaporate.

The researchers used eye masks like the ones you can pick up at your local drugstore, but you can try it at home, too. Just soak a clean washcloth in warm water and place it on your eyelids. Be careful — if the water is too hot, you could harm your eyes.

Walk your way to healthy sight

Your eyes may be doing more than just taking in the beautiful scenery on your morning march. As you work out your body, you're also keeping your eyes in tiptop shape.

Can't believe simply taking a brisk stroll through the park can fight aging eyes? Check out the results of a study recently published in the journal *Ophthalmology*. For 20 years, researchers monitored the eye health of nearly 5,000 adults. In the end, they learned active folks had a 58 percent lower risk of vision loss compared to couch potatoes.

Other studies agree. Pulling on your tennis shoes may protect against the worst eye offenders — cataracts, glaucoma, and AMD.

Weight control

Do you weigh more now than you did, say, 10 years ago? If so, you're not alone. Lots of seniors find themselves in the same boat. The numbers on the scale creep up each passing year for no apparent reason. Where, then, does the extra weight come from?

Older people tend to be less active, so calories get converted into fat instead of being burned off as energy. To make matters worse, age-related muscle loss causes your metabolism to slow. The critical combo means you can eat exactly what you did at 40 — not a bite more — and still pack on the pounds.

All that extra weight does more than make your pants tight. It puts you at a higher risk for heart disease, breathing problems, and diabetes.

Of course, being underweight is no laughing matter either. It weakens your immune system and increases the risk of osteoporosis and bone fractures.

Bottom line? Weighing too much or too little threatens your mobility and independence.

Does laughing or sneezing put pressure on your bladder? Researchers found that overweight women in their 70s who lowered their body mass index by at least 5 percent were significantly less likely to experience urinary stress incontinence than those who lost less weight. For a 5-foot-4-inch woman who weighs 163 pounds, that means dropping at least 8 pounds.

Maintaining a proper weight isn't easy. But remember, every journey begins with a first step. You can start by staying active. As for your diet, stick to a variety of fruits, vegetables, lean protein, whole grains, and healthy fats.

Read on for some small tricks to help you balance the scale. Don't forget to check with your doctor before making any lifestyle changes.

3 tricks for cutting calories and dropping the extra pounds

Eat legumes to fill up the easy, peas-y way. Protein is a big deal — your body needs it to build and repair tissue and maintain a strong immune system. But instead of tucking into a steak, why not turn to vegetables for your protein fix? Not only are they healthy, but they might just shrink your waistline.

That's according to Danish researchers who compared the fullness factor of 43 men who ate high-protein breakfasts consisting of either beans and peas or veal and pork. The men reported feeling fuller after eating the vegetables than after having the meat. What's more, the vegetable group later ate 12 percent fewer calories at lunch.

The researchers say the high fiber content of the beans and peas — four times that of the meat — probably satisfied the men's hunger for longer. Looking for protein-packed, high-fiber foods? Try lentils, kidney beans, and chickpeas.

Time your meals to take the pressure off losing. Looking to drop weight and lower your blood pressure without having to count calories? The 16:8 plan might fit the bill.

Researchers at the University of Illinois at Chicago recently tested the diet on 23 obese adults over three months. Volunteers could eat any type and quantity of food they desired between 10 a.m. and 6 p.m. Sound too good to be true? Well, there was a catch — the participants could not eat anything and could only drink zero-calorie beverages during the next 16 hours.

Compared with a control group that ate normally and didn't see any weight change, the volunteers ate about 340 fewer calories per day. They also lost an average of 3 percent of their body weight and saw a 7-point drop in their systolic blood pressure.

Krista Varady, one of the researchers, says the results of the study are similar to previous research on fasting. "But one of the benefits of the 16:8 diet may be that it is easier for people to maintain," she says, adding that fewer participants dropped out compared to studies on other fasting diets.

Focus on your food to avoid overeating. Gobbling up your dinner in front of the television or computer screen can seem like a harmless guilty pleasure. Not so, according to a British review of studies on distracted eating.

The researchers found that people tend to eat more when they're not paying attention to what's on their plates. Focusing on a meal, meanwhile, is linked to eating less later on in the day.

So what's the solution in this age of nonstop multitasking? Mindful eating, according to North Carolina State University researchers who launched a 15-week series of online classes to help people become more aware of their eating habits. Those who completed the program lost more weight than a control group wait-listed for the program.

Want to start eating mindfully? Follow these tips.

- Set aside 20 minutes to do nothing but eat your food.

- Think about how hungry you are before sitting down to eat.

- Notice the color, texture, and smell of your food.

- Put your fork down between bites, chew well, and savor the flavor of your meal.

Winning after losing:
Keep the weight off with proven tips

Don't want to regain the weight you worked so hard to shed? Then follow the lead of the "successful losers" enrolled in the National Weight Control Registry, an organization that tracks the habits of people who've dropped at least 30 pounds and kept it off.

"One of the key things for weight gain prevention is a regular pattern of physical activity," says Graham Thomas, Ph.D., an associate professor of psychiatry and human behavior at the Medical School of Brown University and a co-investigator at the Registry. "Our members, on average, do about an hour a day of brisk walking."

Thomas says exercise works double duty in helping you maintain a healthy weight. It burns calories and prevents some of the metabolic slowdown that accompanies aging and weight loss.

Of course, Thomas advises, it's important to eat a healthy, low-calorie diet. You should also keep track of what you eat and weigh yourself at least once a week.

"It gives you an opportunity to catch weight gain early before it becomes a major problem that's harder to reverse."

Any other secrets to successful weight maintenance? Most people on the Registry have breakfast, Thomas says, which likely helps them control hunger and avoid excessive eating later in the day.

They also tend to watch less TV than the average American. "It appears to be one way in which they have time to be physically active," Thomas says, adding that TV time also often leads to snacking.

Wise ways to whittle your middle

A slowing metabolism. Physical inactivity. A poor diet. Add 'em up and you're looking at a recipe for middle-age spread. Call it what you will — Buddha belly, muffin top, or spare tire — there's no escaping the fact that extra weight tends to collect in the midsection after a certain age.

For men, the stomach area is typically the first place the pounds pile on. Not so, though, for women. But hormonal changes after menopause cause fat cells to shift from the hips and thighs to the midriff.

Unfortunately, the extra padding is a problem for more than just your wardrobe. Abdominal fat — along with high blood pressure and too much sugar and fat in the blood — puts you at risk for metabolic syndrome. That means you're more likely to experience a heart attack, stroke, or diabetes.

Fortunately, your doctor can help you slam the brakes on a problematic paunch. Here's some advice to keep in mind.

Banish belly bulge with non-sugary drinks. That's according to researchers who examined the drinking habits of some 1,000 participants in the Framingham Heart Study. The middle-aged volunteers had their abdominal fat measured once at the beginning of the study and again six years later.

The results? The participants who had at least one sugar-sweetened drink a day gained 27 percent more deep belly fat than those who rarely, if ever, drank sugary refreshments like soda and fruit drinks. The researchers say the excess sugar may trigger insulin resistance and increase the amount of fat stored in your abdomen.

Find a flatter tummy with healthy habits. Have you packed more pounds around the middle than you'd like to admit? You've probably taken in more calories than you've burned off. Keep tabs on how much you eat each day with free meal-tracking apps or old-fashioned pen and paper. And follow these tips to shed that spare tire.

- Get a good night's rest and relax during the day. Studies suggest that too little sleep and the stress hormone cortisol contribute to weight gain around your waist.

- Read labels carefully and prep foods in advance. That way you can limit fare with too many calories and belly-bulging saturated fat. Plus you'll have healthy meals within easy reach.

- Fit an exercise routine into your day. Both cardio activity and weight resistance training are linked to trimmer waistlines.

Unexplained weight loss? How to tip the scales in your favor.

Are you shedding pounds without even trying? Don't do a happy dance just yet. Unexplained weight loss — losing 5 percent of your normal body weight in six months to a year without trying — could point to a health problem and jeopardize your independence. So see your doctor if you're losing inches and don't know why. Meanwhile, you can boost your calorie count with these healthy tips.

- Try eating five or six small meals instead of three large meals.

- Eat starchy vegetables like corn and potatoes and dense fruits like bananas and raisins.

- Add shredded cheese to salads, soups, and casseroles.

- Drizzle olive oil over vegetables to boost flavor and calories.

- Prepare cream soups and hot cereals with whole milk instead of water.

Index

E

S

T

U

V